# TAKING COMMAND

**This is a story of the challenges of "military command"**
***as they can and do emerge.***
**This is a story that is keyed to the environment of Korea**
**and especially to that of Kunsan Air Base**
**otherwise known as K-8 or "The Kun"**
***but there have been parallels.***
**This is a story that is not necessarily savory**
***but it arises from fact.***

**If this story is upsetting, perhaps it has been well told.**

John O. Moench 1997.

**John O. Moench**
**Major General, USAF (Ret)**

**Malia Enterprises, Inc.**
**Longwood, Florida**
**1996**

# DEDICATED

To all the men and women who have served in military forces
and to all those who still come to serve.
Upon these individuals rests the future.

Most importantly, the future rests in the hands of our children and
I especially dedicate this work to our grandchildren:
Rachel Kirby, Christina Kirby and Rex Broughton Kirby III.

FIRST EDITION
FIRST PRINTING



Library of Congress Catalog Card Number 95-80665
International Standard Book Number 1-877597-05-8

Comments or questions regarding the content of this book should be addressed to:

Reader Inquiry
Malia Enterprises, Inc.
905 Sweetwater Blvd. South
Longwood, FL 32779-3430

Initial jacket design by Michele Moench Kirby with final design and color separation by Denis K. Lange.

Printing and binding by Bookmasters, Inc. of Ashland, Ohio and Bookcrafters, Inc. of Chelsea, Michigan.

# CONTENTS

*By: Title (Page)*

# FOREWORD

**I have always viewed myself as an educator and it is in this sense that this illustrative account was written.**

**Of all the assignments I had during a long and interesting military career, *Taking Command* of Kunsan Air Base in Korea was the most challenging and frustrating. Almost four decades after that event, some of the elements of that experience remain unnerving and many times, as I reflect on the recalled scenario, it seems unreal.**

**That the situation underlying this illustrative account actually existed would probably be rejected by many who now read this story. And the details set forth herein or otherwise alluded to may well be denied by those survivors "who were there" at the time. That "the best equipped and supported" military forces in the world would be placed on frontier duty to serve the defense of the United States and the Free World, virtually on the doorstep of its major Communist enemies, without adequate personnel, communications, equipment and logistic support is virtually unthinkable. That there would exist a circumstance in which men of the United States Air Force would plan the execution of their own commander is probably beyond conventional acceptance. That the United States would place nuclear weapons in such a position of vulnerability as will here be described is well beyond rational understanding. Perhaps it never happened?**

**But, before reaching such conclusions, recall some of the early history of the Korean War. Remember especially the first confrontation of the North Korean People's Army by Task Force Smith north of Osan. Four hundred and six men whose average age was under twenty and backed up by 131 men manning six 105 MM guns, for which only six rounds of HEAT* were available, were sent to block an enemy advance lead by 33 T-34 tanks and followed by a snaking infantry column six miles long. Lacking necessary strength, armed with inadequate weapons, having rounds that were unfit or duds, about 185 men would be killed, wounded, captured or missing in a demoralizing engagement. *Americans sent to fight are not always the best equipped in the world.***

**The underlying story that will be illustrated here was relayed to some close friends during the years following the event and then compared to their own experiences -- which reinforced the total. But, due to security and other aspects of the situation, any broader presentation, and especially any public presentation, was considered unwise. Now, due to changes in the world's political environment, such restriction is no longer valid.**

---

* *Abbreviations, acronyms and military slang*, along with definitions, are contained in Appendix A.

**Some three decades after the events illustrated herein, I had the opportunity to meet the Division Commander under whom I operated at the time of this account and I asked him to what degree he was aware of my special problems at Kunsan Air Base. To my surprise, he indicated that he had no knowledge of the elements of the situation I described to him. This is not intended as a criticism of him. After the events described in this account, I served on this senior officer's staff as his Director of Plans and Programs and, together, some major defense problems would be successfully addressed -- the situation at Kunsan Air Base, having been significantly altered prior to such assignment and with the command passed on to a very capable officer who was dedicated to carry on with improvements beyond those cited herein, was no longer a matter of primary personal concern.**

**At the time of this account, both this Division Commander and I were new to the existing environment, each having just been assigned to Korea. Neither of us had met before and we had no idea of each others capabilities and limitations. Further, Kunsan Air Base was but a small part of the Division Commander's worries as he served concurrently as the Commander of the air force element of the United Nations Command with primarily United States and Korean Air Forces under his actual and projected operational jurisdiction; as Commander of Air Forces Korea with command lines running through United States Air Force and unified command channels to the Joint Chiefs of Staff -- this especially for nuclear operations and certain intelligence work; as Commander of the Korean Air Defense Sector with the command line running to Fifth Air Force in Japan. Additionally, he served as the senior operational Air Force officer in Korea -- the only other Air Force General Officer being assigned to the CINCUNC/COMUSKOREA staff as Deputy for Air -- and periodically did duty at Panmunjom. As the senior operational Air Force officer, he was burdened with support duties involving the U.S. Ambassador and more and the focal point for U.S. and foreign VIP visitors. He was one of the few Air Force persons accompanied with family and the only one having a wife and children living on Osan Air Base. His two children went to school in Seoul. When in Osan, their primary contacts, outside of their father and mother, were the officers and men on the base. Overall, it was a difficult and trying situation.**

**[*Later, when I was assigned to the staff of the Division Commander and an uprising broke out in Korea with the Division Commander's children isolated in Seoul, I and others urged the Commander to allow us to take a helicopter into Seoul and extract his children. Our view was that his children needed to be with their parents at such a time. He refused stating that such an act would amount to preferential treatment for his children who, he believed, should share in the same dangers as the other American children in Seoul.*]***

* Hereinafter, bracketed comments inserted in this text, presented in italics, are the personal views, observations and expressions of the author as they relate to the presented text but not

**Certainly, just as I expected to find a base operating at a professional level, the new Division Commander would rightly expect that his command, something vital not only to the defense of Korea and the Far East but to the United States, would be turned over to him with proper forces, equipment, in-place procedures and more. Both of us would be surprised and challenged. But this is not a story about the problems of the Division Commander or the overall Korean defense posture and its command and control -- it is a story about *Taking Command* of Kunsan Air Base.**

**In the military system, command is typically a matter of assignment. And, in that system, it is expected that loyalty and support will flow upward to the assigned commander and downward from senior echelons. In the case of Kunsan Air Base, these elements literally had to be carved out of the surrounding woodwork and the fighting up and down the chain of command became most traumatic. This "fighting" to achieve a correct military equation respecting both Kunsan Air Base and Korea extended beyond the period covered by this account -- it extended for the full of the time spent by this author in Korea and beyond -- but that outside the specifics of Kunsan Air Base and the environment of this illustrative scenario is a much wider story.**

**The most responsible and challenging job in the military forces, from the lowest to the highest echelon, is that of the Commander. From the most minor of units, through intermediate echelons, to the topmost authority, it is the Commander on whose shoulders the weight of all problems ultimately rests. But a Commander, no matter how capable he or she is, is only one person. Staffs and supporting personnel serve the Commander in multiple ways. When the staffs and supporting personnel fail in their support of the Commander, most Commanders will fail. General Eisenhower could not have succeeded without a competent staff; neither could General Washington or General Schwartzkopf, or others, succeed without a competent staff. And, because of this, most Commanders work hard to assemble the best talent possible. For me, as I took command of Kunsan Air Base, I had no such opportunity -- my staff and all other assigned personnel had been placed in position by far-away personnel assignment offices. Fortunately, the system had given me some good men but I was to learn that all-too-many of those who had been sent to Kunsan Air Base were marginally qualified for the job at hand and the rigors of the environment -- some were the discards of other organizations -- persons who, having not done a good job, were moved on. Further, I would quickly learn that there was no hope of my orchestrating replacements during the time of my command. I had to live with what I had and what was in the pipeline -- and that which was in the pipeline was largely a mirror of that which already was in position.**

**Command is a chain event. Those subordinate to a local Commander expect and should receive essential support from him. In turn, those**

---

necessarily reflective of the time of the presented text. Supplementary footnotes, such as this one, will be sparingly used.

**commands and staffs senior to a local Commander must not only provide essential support but must not cause turbulence. Lower command can be made or broken by the actions of higher commands; higher commands can be destroyed by the failure of lower commands. There has to be a mutuality of support and understanding in the command chain. When that mutual support and understanding does not exist, while the senior command has a range of options, the subordinate command is usually doomed to failure. That a subordinate command should be orphaned by the senior command echelons is virtually unthinkable. One can understand the circumstances of World War II that left General Jonathan Wainwright orphaned in the Philippines. One can even be led to understand the Task Force Smith debacle. But it is extremely difficult to conceive that, in peacetime, a unit of United States military forces serving on the defense frontier would be orphaned. But how else could one describe the situation that is herein illustrated?**

**Many, all too many, who came to Korea in the time frame of this account, when faced with the seemingly impossible situation that existed, simply gave up. Confronted with this demoralizing situation, the Division Commander addressed his men on the subject:**

***Have your professional standards changed since you came to Korea? . . . . Have you been perceptive and raised your standards or been unwise and lowered them? . . . .***

***How , then, are you reacting to your tour of duty in Korea? Some of you are motivated to highest quality performance. Some of you cannot see or do not accept the challenge and opportunity to do what needs to be done. Some of you hardly react at all but, instead, appear to accept things as they are. Rather than initiate or join a drive for progress, you are careful not to "rock the boat" or "get your fingers burned."***

***Why is it so important here in Korea that we have the highest standards in the United States Air Force; that we strive knowingly, deliberately, forcefully? Look around! We have a very difficult job with many obstacles, limited resources, and little time in which to do it. . . . As you have already observed, we have much catching up to do. Complicating this task is our environment. We are in an underdeveloped country which has limited technical and industrial resources -- men and materiel. There is also the associated poor transportation and communication network. It is a rugged country with very cold winters and very wet summers which altogether produce hazardous flying and living conditions. We are geographically at the end of the supply pipeline which means fewer available resources. We only have our people for thirteen months. In this time frame, they must often learn and produce on half a dozen jobs in addition to their own. . . . Obviously, our task demands higher standards for efficiency, quality, safety and not a lowering of standards as some seem to believe.***

***What are your standards? Are you marking time, merely awaiting the day of your reassignment? . . . . Or are you out to improve yourself and your surroundings? . . . .***

*Go ahead and change your standards, but make them higher. The more difficult the job, the more obstacles to overcome, the fewer resources available, the higher the standards. React to your environment positively with an objective of leaving Korea with the satisfaction of accomplishment. Only thus will the tour seem short, interesting and profitable.*

The story you will here read, written almost four decades after the event, is based on a series of letters addressed to my wife Mary; many voice tapes sent to her in lieu of letters; a series of after-the-fact voice tapes made almost two decades ago in conjunction with an exploration of a sanitized version of this scenario for possible use for TV or movie purposes; various surviving photography; a review of records on file at the Historical Research Agency (HRA) at Maxwell AFB, Alabama; an extensive review of books published on Korea and the Korean War; and post-event communications with some of the persons who served in Korea before, during and after the time. Regardless of this careful documentation, sources will not normally be cited as this is not intended as an historical writing in the sense of the purist.

This account is also a torturous extraction of personal memories of a rather long-ago experience. As in all such cases, the frailty of memory may show through in the sense of time, personalities, specifics, etc. Perhaps there are things I wanted to do but did not do and now, with the passage of time, I believe that they were accomplished. Perhaps there were things I did do that my mind has erased from memory. And I know that there are some things that transpired that, even at this late date, I am obliged not to reveal.

These latter possibilities set aside, by and large, to what will be for many a disturbing scenario and although written in illustrative terms, what follows is a close reflection of then prevailing circumstances and events.

Those who now read this account may have reacted differently than this writer and some of my decisions may have been much less than brilliant. In hindsight, given a chance to rethink events for which there was little or no "thinking time" available, I know that I would have approached some problems differently. What overshadowed me at the time was the totally unexpected nature, enormity and complexity of the problem. It was a case of almost everything being wrong or going wrong that could possibly be or go wrong. What would surprise many, when the dust settled, I found that, of all the officers and enlisted men who served in my command at that time, I would end up concluding that, at the beginning, only a handful was truly trained and competent -- but most rapidly grew in competence -- not only in their own specialty but in the many jobs that were thrust upon them. In overview, provided half a chance, in the thirty-plus years I have served in uniform and as a product of over a score of years in the civilian environment, I have to conclude that, given essential leadership and support, no assemblage of persons equals that of the military family.

**_Taking Command_ took approximately two months. At the end of those two months, as a result of serious exhaustion resulting not just from the strain of events but from a paucity of sleep, I later came to realize that I was on the verge of collapse. This conclusion surfaced when I reviewed a taped message to my wife in which I heard myself stating that I faced a severe problem as a result of having been restricted from providing fuel to the local "Communist gun boat." The real recipient for the fuel was a rescue boat operated by the Korean Air Force (the ROKAF) and used to cover the waters adjacent to the Kunsan Air Base. As a result of extreme fatigue, my mind was beginning to play tricks on me.**

**Because this illustrative and, hopefully, didactic account might be interpreted as critical of certain persons of the past, all involved names of the time, other than those of a few baseline senior officers and other removed or supportive individuals and the persons named "Mike" and "Annie," have been avoided. Further, while real circumstances underlie this rendition, other than myself, no directly involved individual at Kunsan or Osan is specifically personified while many characters are presented in the form of a composite.*[*]**

**In sum, it is hoped that this account will assist up-coming military persons to appreciate problems they might encounter in their future but it is equally hoped that this account will, in some small way, serve to preclude a repeat of the general situation described. Stated otherwise, this account is not intended "to applaud, hang or degrade" anyone -- all those who served in and survived the described circumstances deserve a "pat on the back." It is to be expected that some who served in this environment and who now read this account may have emerged with totally different recollections. Such divergence in observation and opinion is to be understood for only the single individual can perceive that which surrounds him.**

**To up-coming commanders, I urge that the tactics and track set forth herein not be used as a guideline for their future. The world of today is not the world of yesterday and any attempt to mimic my actions of those earlier times here illustrated could prove most harmful. Nonetheless, there are lessons herein to be learned and I would urge that those who aspire to command study this scenario.**

**To a bottom line, in the interests of history and the gathering of knowledge, all persons should avail themselves of the opportunity to record and preserve a record of their experiences. And, in that process, no one should be critical of the exposure of another person's experiences, observations and conclusions.**

**If this account should offend anyone, it is with reluctance that I apologize for that was not intended. And if this story appears unreal, remember that truth is, after all, stranger than fiction.**

---

* *The Characters*, actual and fictitious, found in this story are listed in Appendix B in general order of appearance in this Foreword and subsequent text.

# ACKNOWLEDGMENT

The writing of this account was assisted especially by my wife Mary; by Mrs. Ann Tipton, wife of Major General James B. Tipton (deceased), Commanding General of the 314th Air Division in Korea; by William F. Ricketts, Jr., of the 13th Bombardment Squadron (Light, Night Intruder), a B-26 (A-26) Invader unit stationed at Kunsan Air Base during the Korean War; by Colonel William T. Douthwaite who attended the Air War College with me and then served in Korea as the Director of Operations of the 314th Air Division; by my long-time friend, Ernest J. White who served at Kunsan Air Base; by my very close friend and supporting staff officer, Colonel William P. Jacobs; by Colonel George H. Chase of the U.S. Army who worked on the construction of the original runway at Kunsan Air Base; by Major Paul E. Mulrenin, historian and author, who served with me in the 323rd Bombardment Group (M) and, later, in the B-26 Marauder Historical Society; by CMS Lucien I. Thomas who is one of the most outstanding Airmen of the USAF with service that includes the RAF; by the 8th Fighter Wing, the current organization stationed at Kunsan Air Base, and there were even more who added photos and recollections to this story.

No writer of USAF history can proceed without giving credit to the Historical Research Agency (HRA), a facility at Maxwell AFB, Alabama, which grew out of the need to have an Air Force archival point for the unit and other historical data of WW II and beyond. Without the accumulated record housed in this facility, the portrayal of USAF and related history would be limited if not impossible. The records resident in the HRA, some of which came from my own pen, served to refresh my memory on many points and validate important events.

To all of the above persons and organizations, to all the many persons who were under my command or tenants at Kunsan Air Base, to the many loyal and dedicated Koreans who supported the operation at Kunsan Air Base, and to those persons in Korea, Japan, Hawaii and Washington, D.C. who assisted me in the attack of the many problems that clouded the operation of Kunsan Air Base -- thanks!

To the Air University at Maxwell AFB for the extensive education and insight provided to me in the Air Command and Staff School and the Air War College and especially for the critique on the draft of this writing, I am indebted.

To the ROKAF and ROK Army personnel who worked with me not only at Kunsan Air Base but later, my eternal gratitude.

To "Mike," with whom I have lost all contact, there is no limit to the thanks that can be set forth. Few understand the contributions of the many dedicated secretaries and others who, absent any military uniform, have served on the military frontiers and shared in the trials and tribulations of the military forces of our Nation.

There is herein no listed bibliography in support of this portrayal of military history but mention must be made of *Air Base Defense in the Republic of Vietnam, 1961-1973* by Roger P. Fox, Office of Air Force History, USAF, Washington, D.C. 1979. Fox's detailed and well documented coverage of a very complex subject served to refresh my memory on many points -- in Korea and beyond.

Military lyrics repeated in this book are derived from memory or from the *314th Air Division Song Book*. Cross-reference with the compilation of lyrics assembled in *The Wild Blue Yonder, Songs of the Air Force*, by C. W. "Bill" Getz, The Redwood Press, 1981, was made. As with all such lyrics, there have been local variations.

AIR UNIVERSITY
UNITED STATES AIR FORCE
MAXWELL AIR FORCE BASE, ALABAMA

OFFICE OF THE COMMANDER

TO THE AIR WAR COLLEGE CLASS OF 1959

You, the Class of 1959, will always have a special niche in my memories since you are the first to graduate from the Air War College during my tour as Commander, Air University.

During the past year we have shared many classroom hours, so your curriculum is well known to me. I appreciate the intellectual challenge which you have faced—and met with originality, vigor and enthusiasm.

If you leave Air University with a broadened vision, our mission has been accomplished. I hope that in the years ahead you will reflect with pleasure on this period in your career and will feel that some of the knowledge gained here has helped you to do a better job for the Air Force.

To each of you I extend my heartiest congratulations.

Sincerely,

Walter E. Todd

WALTER E. TODD
Lieutenant General, USAF
Commander

# THE ASSIGNMENT ORDERS

While life in the United States Air Force had its good and its bad days, on the whole things had moved along better than one could expect.

Promotions had come rapidly during World War II; while my Martin B-26 Marauder bomber had taken many hits, my air crew and I had emerged from the months of combat without a single wound; subsequently, senior officers had moved me into ever more responsible positions; and now, having been selected for promotion to Colonel well ahead of my contemporaries and assigned to the Air War College, I was riding high.

The 1960s were approaching and, as the bar room conversation would go, I had not only "done good" but I had collected a lot of "Brownie Points" along the way. In addition, and most important for what was about to transpire, there were many officers, some of them quite senior, who, according to conventional wisdom, owed me a lot for things I had undertaken on their behalf. Eventually, I would have to cash in on those outstanding chits but, for the moment, that possibility seemed remote.

Now, with graduation from the Air War College at Maxwell Air Force Base about to take place, I had the assurance of an assignment to a key "flying" slot in the Strategic Air Command. Having been in headquarters assignments since the close of World War II, I looked forward to getting back in the cockpit.

The nine months at the Air War College had been a great experience. And, with the conclusion of that assignment, not only would I be joining an outstanding group of graduates but, in my spare time, I had managed to complete a Masters Degree.

Living on base in the old Aviation Cadet quarters, now converted into family housing but with exposed heating pipes and rusted Sears & Roebuck showers, had its challenges -- particularly for the wives who sought in many ways to make the barracks look like home. But there was an advantage that would not be present in later classes at the Air War College -- all the students lived on the base and shared equally in the surroundings. The result was the growth of a great camaraderie. Little did I know that soon, very soon, I would be calling on some of these newly-acquired friends for life and death support.

**The student body, most of them Colonels and some of them quite senior (the Class President was Chesley G. Peterson of the American Eagle Squadron who was promoted to Colonel at the ripe age of twenty-one), were all products of World War II. In overview, the student body simply over-flowed with diverse and superior talent. As a group, the sense was that we were "the cream of the crop" and there were few who did not believe that we were all headed for a substantial future.**

**Now, much of the talent in the student body was turned to the task of making the on-coming "Orders Party" an event to be remembered.**

**Except for the Class President and a few close confidants, there was hardly a soul in the student body who had an inkling of what was in store for the coming Orders Party. With all information on assignments carefully kept secret, anticipation and excitement were running at fever pitch. Assignments determined a lot of things for everyone -- career, living situation, family separation -- few subjects could arouse more concern and interest.**

**The coming process of revelation was to take place during an evening social affair and by way of a periodic projection of segments of the orders on a large screen in the vaulted main ball room of the Maxwell Air Force Base Officers Club. To one side of the main ball room a "Happy Bar" had been erected for those who received the better orders; on the opposite side of the main ball room a "Sad Bar" had been erected for those who would find their orders a disappointment.**

**With everyone in formal military attire, the party began in a festive mood. For my part, there was no concern about the future for I had been assured by Major General Paul S. "Stan" Emrick as to where I was headed -- and it was to the Strategic Air Command.**

**Early in my military career, I had learned to leave nothing to chance if there was another way to do it. Thus, with the coming graduation from the Air War College, I had contacted General Emrick, for whom I had worked both in Air Force Headquarters and in Europe, and was assured that, now that he was assigned to the Strategic Air Command, he wanted me in that organization. And the job he proposed would put me in line to become a Wing Commander of a heavy bomber unit. I could not ask for more.**

***[At the time, I had many options open to me through which I believed I could insure obtaining what I viewed as a proper career***

*assignment. As example, the Commander of the Air University was Lieutenant General Walter E. Todd for whom I had worked in the Pentagon. Then, as Commandant of the Air War College, there was Major General Robert F. Tate for whom I had worked in USAFE. My selection of General Emrick as a "sponsor" was that I saw the Strategic Air Command as the prime Air Force operational unit at the time and I wanted to be in the center of things.*]

**As Mary and I went to the Orders Party, there was no sense of foreboding -- only the sense of attending a great event during which there would be a confirmation of a well-planned scenario. But we were going to be surprised and thoroughly shocked. And, along with us, many persons that evening would be shocked.**

**However, this is not a story about all the surprises that took place on that eventful *Friday the 13th* -- this is the story of my own surprise and what then followed.**

**The room stilled as another segment of the class orders was projected on the screen. Mary and I were already situated at the Happy Bar for we were certain of our future home.**

**Finally, the segment of orders bearing my name flashed on the screen. But the assignment was not to the Strategic Air Command! In disbelief, I looked at it several times. It had to be a mistake! Stunned, I reread the destination: Kunsan Air Base, Korea. The job was "Commander" but Commander of what? The unit designation did not make any sense for it read "6175th Air Base Squadron" *and, as far as I knew, no Colonel was assigned to a squadron -- that was, at best, the job of a Lt. Colonel*!**

**I had spent all of my overseas time in Europe -- two tours covering about seven years -- one during World War II and one following with the latter in the headquarters of USAFE and U.S. EUCOM. Except for some study of Chinese history, my in-depth knowledge of the Far East was minimal. I had tried to get a combat command assignment to that area during the Korean War -- as then a Major, my target assignment was to command a B-26 Invader Squadron. I sensed that this would be an easy transition considering my World War II experience with the B-26 Marauder. As my reassignment from the Director of Programs in Air Force Headquarters approached, Major General Walter E. Todd, my boss,**

**assured me that, as a reward for outstanding achievement in his office and prior with Major General Frederick H. Smith, Jr., I could literally have any assignment I wanted. But, then, General Todd and General Lauris Norstad had a private lunch. Following that lunch, I learned that General Norstad, who was headed for Europe as CINCUSAFE as well as to serve in NATO, wanted me to go to Europe to work on the organization, program and more of USAFE, NATO and, later, that of the planned U.S. EUCOM. As to the Far East, the closest I had ever been was to Hawaii.**

***Korea!*** **General news regarding Korea that had crossed my desk had been minimal following the 1953 Armistice. Following that Armistice, Korea had become a confrontation on the ground -- a stand-off at the DMZ with two U.S. Army divisions entrenched north of the capital city of Seoul. Debate raged on at Panmunjom but few other than the exasperated participants gave it much attention.**

**While USAF tactical air units such as the 3rd, 18th and 58th Wings exercised in Korea, by the later 1950s the Air Force had other things to do. Isolated events such as the hijacking of a Korean National Airlines plane by suspected North Korean agents did make news -- especially since the co-pilot was an Air Force Lt. Colonel. And then there was the virtual concurrent shooting down of an F-86 of the 58th Fighter Bomber Wing that had blundered across the DMZ. On the whole, however, the U.S. and world attention was on the Soviet Union, NATO, Formosa, the Middle East and an emerging confrontation in Southeast Asia.**

**With, in violation of the Armistice, the North Korean forces significantly improving their military posture, in June 1957 the Senior Delegate of the United Nations had informed his opposites that the member nations of the United Nations Command would no longer curtail deployments of modern weapons to South Korea.* This action did make news but no one really knew what it meant. I did recall that the 58th Tactical Missile Group, equipped with nuclear-capable**

---

* By the time of the June 1957 meeting at Panmunjom, a roll back/extraction of USAF personnel and materiel from Korea was well under way. As an example, in 1956 plans were made to close out the Kunsan Air Base supply. Progressively, air bases and materiel were turned over to the ROKAF -- materiel not suitable for return to Japan or turnover to the ROKAF was destroyed or salvaged in Korea. Reflecting the step back from direct participation in the defense of Korea, the AC&W turnover schedule was as follows:

| | |
|---|---|
| Paengyong Do (K-53) by March 1958 | Kunsan Air Base (K-8) by February 1960 |
| Cheju Do (K-39) by February 1959 | Kimpo Air Base (K-14) by March 1960 |
| Pyong Taek (K-6) by January 1960 | Osan Air Base (K-55) by January 1961 |

Matador missiles, was to deploy to South Korea but I did not know the status of that action.

And now I faced *Kunsan*! For a moment I reflected on the location of the airfield -- at the extreme end of a peninsula extending into the Yellow Sea. But why me? And why Kunsan instead of the Strategic Air Command? I couldn't even say "hello" in Korean nor did I recognize a single character in the Korean language.

*Kunsan*! *Shit*! I had prepared for and sought an assignment "at the center of things" but Kunsan was somewhere at the far periphery -- *somewhere near the end of the world*! I could think of no assignment short of possibly Tibet or Outer Mongolia that would be much worse.

Then, I was aware of Mary tugging at my arm.

"I thought we were headed for the Strategic Air Command?"

I had no answer -- only a lot of questions. Was it a mistake? Could it be real? Was I being farmed out to pasture -- literally "being sent to Siberia?" Had I made an enemy about whom I did not know?

Suddenly, I realized that friends were looking at us and then turning away. Everyone sensed our disappointment.

Unsure of whether to stay at the Happy Bar or proceed to the Sad Bar, I turned to the nearest friend I could find and asked if he knew what the Air Force had at Kunsan Air Base -- what the mission of the base was? All I got back was a shrug and a half-hearted smile. And the same response came from friend after friend. I decided that the Sad Bar would be the next stop for Mary and me.

Joining a growing number of disappointed classmates at the Sad Bar, I found that a couple of them were also assigned to Korea -- their assignments being to the 314th Air Division at Osan and the Military Assistance Advisory Group at Seoul -- the latter an exception to the unaccompanied Korean assignment. Remarkably, the same as I, these officers had only one intervening Stateside assignment prior to this posting to Korea. Somehow, things did not seem right as there were many in the Air War College class who had never had a single overseas assignment and now they were headed for plush jobs in the United States. And those from the class who were going overseas were headed for accompanied tours in some of the better spots of the world. For those now headed to Korea, the assignment news made no sense -- it was a totally unexplained and unanticipated bombshell! It was as if the assignment system had singled us out for punishment rather than reward for past service and achievement and certainly not being treated as anything like "the cream of the crop."

**When more questions produced no knowledge about the Kunsan assignment, Mary and I decided to spend the remainder of the evening at the Sad Bar surrounded by others who were disappointed in their assignments. Many couples receiving "bad assignments," unable to deal with the shocking news, simply left the party -- a few wives, overcome by the assignment news, cried. On the opposite side of the ball room, at the Happy Bar, laughter and joyous comment filled the air. Somehow, some way, things had gotten terribly messed up. Somehow, personally, I felt like "Casey at the bat" and it looked as if I had just struck out.**

**Suddenly, Maxwell Air Force Base loomed as a dark cloud hanging over me. This was my third assignment to Maxwell Air Force Base. On my first assignment, as an Aviation Cadet, I had contracted pneumonia and fell back by one class -- from 43G to 43H. During the second assignment, this to the Air Command and Staff College, our first son died. Now, on this third assignment, *on this Friday the 13th*, I was being ordered to Korea and to be separated from Mary and our two young children. For Mary, this had to be especially hard as she had only one intervening tour, that at the Pentagon, since we had been married in Wiesbaden, Germany in 1952.**

**I had to do something but I knew that nothing could be done until the next day.**

**The primary direction of the Air War College class had been world strategy, space and strategic operations. In keeping with that focus, the class year book carried a futuristic theme throughout. But, reflective of the vagaries of life and prophetic regarding the uncertain future, in the orders section of the class book under the title of "SOME GLAD! SOME SAD!" there had been dutifully printed:**

***One day as I sat musing***
***Sad and lonely and without a friend***
***A voice came to me***
***From out of the gloom, saying***
***"Cheer up! Things could be worse."***
***So I cheered up and, sure enough,***
***Things got worse.***

# A RESTLESS NIGHT

**As I lie in bed, I could tell that Mary was only half sleeping. Me -- I had more than enough Scotch and I was not sleeping. *Kunsan*! *Korea*! I stared into the blackness at where the ceiling was supposed to be. I needed answers -- information.**

**Dimly, my mind began to march forward from the end of World War II -- the crippling budget cuts that all but destroyed the military capability of the United States as the country plunged forward into demobilization -- in just one year, the combat ready groups in the USAF had been reduced from 243 to 2; the reorganization of the U.S. military services in 1947 which created an endless array of responsibility questions; President Truman's mistrust of the military hierarchy; General of the Army Eisenhower's appointment to preside over the JCS and his shock at learning about the deplorable state of military affairs; the appointment of Louis A. Johnson to succeed James V. Forrestal to head the Department of Defense and the hatchet he used on military programs; General Hoyt S. Vandenberg leading the fight for a seventy group Air Force -- damn but I recalled the days and nights spent trying to help get some meat into the USAF.**

**And then General Omar N. Bradley took on the job of Chairman of the JCS. General Bradley's problems centered not only in the Joint arena and with the President but with his own Army senior officers. In the Army, a view grew that the future was being controlled by the Generals of the European Theater. In the Air Force, although General Vandenberg of the World War II Ninth Air Force was now Chief of Staff, the prevailing mood was that the assignments, promotions and future in that Service were controlled by those who had flown the heavy, strategic bombers. Between such things and the impact of terrible military budgets, morale in the military services was at the bottom of the barrel.**

**Then, in August 1949, the Soviet Union detonated a nuclear weapon and all hell broke loose with the policy of massive retaliation, the only option then open, becoming a fixture. Anything not keyed to that nuclear strategy held second or no place in budget and other thinking. Adding to the problems of the day, Chiang Kai-shek's Nationalist forces were decisively defeated with the remnants of those forces retreating to Formosa. U.S. foreign policy wavered on all fronts. Soon, a modest rearmament of the United States was undertaken but it**

**would take a long time to correct the shortfalls of the past. Between President Truman and Louis Johnson, by the mid-1950s the military forces of the United States had been all but wrecked.**

**In the meantime, by way of personnel cuts and other actions, the Eighth Army, the occupation army in Japan, had its guts torn out and little attention could be paid to Korea which, in U.S. strategic thinking, held no real significance. General MacArthur, virtually unapproachable and serving almost as an emperor in the Dai Ichi building, was lost in the problems of Japan, Formosa and Communist China -- Korea was something peripheral.**

**Army Major General John R. Hodge had led U.S. forces into Korea at the end of World War II and he had become the trustee of the agricultural southern half of the country -- the Soviet Union the industrial north. There, he faced enormous problems in a country that was a sea of human misery, squalor and stench. Transportation, communications, housing, logistics -- everything was somewhat worse than the dismal and the difficult. Adding to the problems were the residuals of the terrible Japanese occupation and exploitation of the Korean country and its people. Soon, General Hodge, feeling the impact of the Truman military cutback, pleaded for assistance from General MacArthur but none was forth-coming. Korea was on the way to permanent separation of north and south; the north was building a military force and economic strength -- in the south virtually nothing was happening. Burdened with decreasing budgets, the situation worsened when the JCS declared that the then 45,000 U.S. troops in South Korea should be withdrawn as South Korea held no strategic interest for the United States and any U.S. forces in South Korea simply represented a liability. For the men stationed in South Korea, this was "good news" but the implications were enormous.**

**By mid-1948, President Truman had dumped the Korean problem into the lap of his favorite organization -- the United Nations. With the U.S. forces deploying from South Korea, a decision was reached to leave enough light arms and ammunition to equip a 50,000 man constabulary but heavy armaments were withdrawn to preclude President Rhee from taking action to invade North Korea. In contrast, with the Soviet withdrawal from North Korea, there was left the elements of about ten divisions supported with heavy weapons and air.**

**With evidence of a growing North Korean capability and on the strongest urging of President Rhee, the U.S. did agree to support an improvement of the military forces of South Korea and, as the U.S. forces were withdrawn, a Korean Military Assistance Advisory Group**

**(KMAG) was left behind to advise and train the forces of that newly constituted country.**

**Concurrently, the situation in Japan had changed. Now the mood was to enhance the economic situation in Japan, reduce the role of the occupation forces and encourage the development of a Japanese military capability as a bulwark against the advance of Communism -- this latter objective was a full reversal of prior U.S. and Japanese thinking and it was destined not to advance. In short order, with decreasing purpose and responsibility, the U.S. forces in Japan became soft. Most of the men then in Japan were new to service life and this was complicated by a terrible turnover rate.**

**Life in Japan, and it was common military gossip, was a languorous event. The Japanese people were extremely docile and supportive. For the young single men, which accounted for the majority of the men deployed, the attractive Japanese girls were most cooperative. For the married men, even the most junior person could afford two maids and more. Military life in Japan was good.**

**With occupation duty a diminishing task, to give purpose and hardening to the deployed forces in Japan they were pointed toward a theoretical invasion by the Soviet Union against Hokkaido. The defense strategy keyed to a nuclear attack launched from Okinawa against the invading Soviet forces -- the use of nuclear weapons now a necessary element in most military planning. While the resulting maneuvers did some good, on the whole it reinforced the view that the U.S. forces in Japan were far from combat ready.**

**In Korea, the new ROK Army was led mostly by opportunistic men with theft, bribery, blackmail and kickbacks commonplace. The enlisted men were mostly illiterate and, even if they were literate, the language did not support advanced weaponry -- even simple terms such as *headlight* were not found in the Korean lexicon.**

**To the south, the indication was that Communist China planned to invade Formosa but U.S. policy in Washington was moving to separate the United States from that island and Chiang Kai-shek.**

**While the forces of South Korea remained almost casually disposed and poorly equipped, the forces of North Korea were steadily gaining in strength and capability. Concurrently, the Washington administration began to divorce itself from South Korea and KMAG was advised to halve its staff (to about 250) by the end of 1950. South Korea had been written off the U.S. books.**

**Apparently, in response to the bad news of the day, Army Major General Lynn W. Roberts, Commander of KMAG, undertook a**

staged psychological campaign to suggest that the forces in South Korea were far better than they actually were -- terms such as *invincible* emerged. The problem was that the campaign did not convince North Korea but it did convince many in Washington.

Then, on June 25, 1950, the North Korean forces attacked. Within days, the "invincible" ROK forces were beaten back; KMAG had disintegrated; by sea and air, all non-combatant U.S. and friendly foreigners were evacuated. Such U.S. combat forces as were hesitatingly moved in from Japan, and beginning with the initial encounter by Task Force Smith at Osan, were quickly overwhelmed. Chaos prevailed.

I could well remember the time. I was then assigned to the office of the Director of Programs of DCS/Operations -- the key operational point in the Air Staff for overall materiel control. As a Major and with no staff, I had overall program responsibility for all materiel in the U.S. Air Force with the exception of installations, aircraft and electronics -- but I became peripherally involved even in those items. Major General William E. Farthing in DCS/Material, under whom I had initially served in the Pentagon, would allow no significant action in his office to proceed without my approval. This was a tremendous responsibility to place on a 29-year old not educated in the military system.

Work in this nightmarish period often went into 72 hour stretches as supplemental budgets were prepared, priorities shifted, and emergency actions taken. The USAF, which at the outset of the Korean War stood at 48 wings, was jumped to 87 wings within a year -- by 1953, this number would increase to 106 wings but much of the expansion had been realized by calling reserve and national guard units to active duty -- sometimes only to acquire the personnel for reassignment. Airlift, a commodity that along with combat forces had been depleted by the post-World War II military cutbacks, was called on to do things it could not do. Everything seemed to be "priority" but there was so much of a priority demand stacking up at west coast airports that the common joke was that, if you wanted to get to Korea in a hurry, walk!

No matter the amount of energy thrown into the equation, the terrible situation that had been allowed to develop in Korea and within our own military forces was too much and the combined U.S. and ROK forces, with heavy casualties, were beaten back to the Pusan Perimeter. There, with the North Korean ground forces lacking effective air or naval support and with logistics massively stretched, the U.S./ROK defense line finally did hold but not before serious consideration was given to the use of nuclear weapons.

Air support, USAF mostly from Japan and Okinawa and USN mostly from carriers, had been a right arm to the defending ground forces. It was a traumatic situation, however, as I recalled the stories of fliers having breakfast with their families in Japan, going to the flight line, and then the wife along with other wives at the flight line awaiting the return of the aircraft, counting the number of returning aircraft, and wondering if the missing aircraft was a husband and father.

General MacArthur's follow-on planning keyed to an amphibious landing behind the forward North Korean forces. While some perceived this as "brilliant," it was a typical army flanking maneuver and a concept already embodied in early Korea contingency planning in the Joint Staff of the JCS. Two primary amphibious landing sites were the focus: Kunsan and Inchon. General MacArthur promoted the Inchon landing -- almost all others promoted the Kunsan landing. Eventually, General MacArthur, employing an element of deceit and deception in his communications with the JCS, would have his way and Kunsan would fade from history.

Following the Inchon landing, the military mood swung from pessimism to optimism. U.S., ROK and other forces plowed north beyond the 38th parallel and by October of 1950, against a background of wavering politics, were moving to liberate all of North Korea. And then the Chinese Communists entered the fray.

Once more the frenzy of the period of the initial invasion of South Korea by North Korean forces took over -- once again 72 hour work stretches in the Pentagon were a norm -- once again the nuclear option loomed high on the horizon. But, by mid-1951, the front lines had stabilized north of Kangnung on the east coast and north of Seoul to the west.

In the meantime, the Formosa situation worsened and General MacArthur's strong views on overall Asian strategy had bumped into Washington thinking with an irreparable rift between President Truman and his advisors and General MacArthur developing.

And then I was ordered to USAFE Headquarters in Wiesbaden, Germany. While bullets still flew and bombs still fell in Korea, the first priority in the U.S. scheme of things was Europe. No longer would I even have time to think about Korea -- it would not be my war -- the problems in Europe were more than enough.

I tried to think of what transpired in the ensuing years but it was all extremely vague. I was aware of the continuing confrontations between the southern and northern forces in Korea, the well-publicized attacks or defense of this or that hill or ridge, the mounting casualties and the final armistice of 1953 but those had all been far away events.

In 1953, I was ordered back to the States to attend the Air Command and Staff College at Maxwell AFB and from there I would return to the Pentagon to be involved mostly in European matters. Then, once again, I would return to Maxwell AFB to attend the Air War College -- Asia, and especially Korea, would, in the meantime, be distant matters left for others to worry about. Since commissioning in 1943, I had been immersed in the strategy loop for Europe and mostly outside the strategy loop for Asia.

I wondered what had happened in Korea? Had it reverted to the chaotic political/military situation that marked the period before the North Koreans attacked? Had the wartime damage that had leveled almost every village and city of consequence been rebuilt? Was there now in South Korea a viable military structure? How deeply was the United States committed? What was the current U.S. plan for South Korea -- I knew that the USAF, for many reasons, had held little interest in the country? Was the United Nations concept still valid? Was the U.S. aiming to get out of South Korea or dig a deeper hole? Strategically and environmentally, was there any comparison between Korea and the Europe I knew so well?

Photos of the miserable fighting conditions in Korea filled my mind -- destroyed cities and villages, lines of prisoners, the retreat from the Changjin Reservoir, the air battles over the Yalu, the night air attacks and bombings, the cold of winter and the wet of summer, hills denuded by gunfire and bombs, hills that never had trees in the first place, men wading through rice fields, whole men or parts of men destroyed in battle, atrocities of enormous proportion, roads with piled up debris of war that looked like the roads in the Falaise Gap, generals and admirals posing for public relations photos, tired and beaten G.I.s not posing, treacherous mountains, narrow valleys, virtually non-existent transportation and terrible poverty. Korea was fixed in my mind as a land of misery. Was I thinking wrongly? Had South Korea changed in the years since the Armistice?

Viewing priorities, I knew that strategic warfare, the Soviet Union and NATO commanded the topmost positions. Where did the priority for Asia fit? And, within Asian priorities, where did South Korea fit? Finally, where did Kunsan Air Base fit in the big picture?

In the blackness of the bedroom, I had no answers. Eventually some restless sleep engulfed me.

# THE NEXT DAY AND FOLLOWING

**It must have been one minute past eight the next morning when I rang through to the office of Colonel Assignments in the Air Staff at the Pentagon.**

**"What the hell is this assignment to Kunsan?" I demanded of the duty officer.**

**"Couldn't help it," came the answer.**

**"What do you mean *you couldn't help it*? General Emrick gave me his assurance that my assignment to the Strategic Air Command had been approved by the SAC Commander. All you had to do was write up the damn orders."**

**"Things happen," was the response.**

**"What things happen?" I asked, my already ragged mood rising to a boiling point.**

**"Well, it seems that there was an issue about who was running Air Force Personnel and Emrick and a lot of others lost. You ended up with the Kunsan job." Suddenly, I saw the handwriting on the wall -- the Director of Personnel at Air Force Headquarters was out to claim his territory and assert his authority and I was a pawn in the game of upsmanship. But, perhaps, there was still a way out.**

**"And so I'm going back overseas again and with only one intervening Stateside assignment -- and on an unaccompanied tour? What about all those Colonels you're assigning in the U.S. and on foreign accompanied tours -- chaps who got to be Colonel without stepping a foot overseas -- not even during War Two or Korea?"**

**"Sorry, but that's the way the ball bounces. The boss here in Personnel has cognizance of your overseas time and he recognized that you had a bunch of headquarters assignments since War Two. You needed a command job and so he gave you one. Further, it is in the Far East and you need the experience -- you've never been there. He did run it by the Chief. You ought to be happy."**

**"Happy? Shit! What the blazes is the Kunsan job? It's a squadron -- a God damned squadron -- and I can't even find anyone who knows what's out there -- not even a clue."**

**"It's a good command job -- a lot of opportunity and exposure. There is a lot of high-level interest in the Kunsan operation. They call it the *Riviera of Korea*. Kunsan Air Base is on the Yellow Sea and . . ."**

"I know where the hell it is but what is it?"

"I can't give you any details over the telephone. But, trust me, you'll like it."

With a curse, I hung up. Apparently, I had been had. I decided to call General Emrick at the Strategic Air Command and bleed a little -- perhaps the situation could still be reversed.

"General Emrick, this is John. I just got my orders and they aren't to SAC. What happened?"

"Sorry," came the reply, "things just did not work out. I had a fight with Personnel and they won. Where are you headed?"

"They got me pegged for a job at Kunsan Air Base in Korea -- Commander of whatever is out there. Do you have any idea what it is?"

"I've never been there but I have some idea of what it is. I judge that it's an important base but I can't tell you more over the phone. I think you'll like it and it will give you experience in the Far East. That should serve you well in the future. Keep me informed. And give my best to Mary."

[*General Emrick's forecast for the future would be on target. I would end up spending more than ten of the following years in various positions in the Pacific Command, both Air Force and Joint, and would rise to Major General in those posts -- but that would be another story and something certainly not visible at the moment. And, to my later surprise, I would never again be posted to a European assignment.*]

With everyone, including General Emrick, telling me that I'd like the job but no one telling me what it was, I felt trapped.

And then, even before I had lunch, a message arrived from the serving Commanding General of the 314th Air Division at Osan -- from a Brigadier General I would never meet. It read:

> JOHN: I HAVE BEEN INFORMED THAT YOU HAVE BEEN SELECTED AS COMMANDER FOR KUNSAN. PLEASE ADVANCE MOVEMENT AS EXISTING COMMANDER HAS TO DEPART EARLY. WE NEED YOU IMMEDIATELY. LOOK FORWARD TO MEETING YOU. LET ME KNOW IF I CAN HELP EXPEDITE YOUR MOVE TO KUNSAN.

"Shit!"

Not only was I going on an unaccompanied tour but now my new boss wanted me to move up the reporting date. That meant I would have none of the traditional "between assignments" leave. And it meant that I had to find accommodations immediately for Mary and our two children for the next year. In that Mary's family was located in the Washington, D.C. area, the best choice was to locate an apartment in that vicinity.

The next morning I checked out a C-45 and flew to Bolling Air Force Base outside Washington, D.C. On board as passengers were some other unhappy Air War College Colonels who wanted a face-to-face talk with Colonel Assignments. It was hardly a joyful group that was on the aircraft as I flew north.

Unlike the rest of the Pentagon bound passengers, I had given up on the idea of getting my assignment orders changed so my first task on arriving in the Washington, D.C. area was to look for housing. And it was a bitch of a job as housing was short as hell. Eventually, however, I located a modest, two-bedroom apartment in Virginia -- tight on space but enough for Mary and the children to get by. It did have a basement and I planned to do some quick shelf building to take care of the overflow of files, records and other stuff that I had accumulated.

Then I headed for the Pentagon. I had to learn something about Kunsan Air Base. But I was to be disappointed.

In the office of the Director of Manpower, I did learn that the unit on the base was authorized some 1,100 men. But that was still more like a job for a Lt. Colonel.

"Why do you need a Colonel if there are only 1,100 men out there?" was my question. "And what do these 1,100 men do? What's the job?"

"Don't rightly know," was the answer. "I think they have some temporary duty men or units on the base that don't show up in the regular computer documents. Then, there may be some units of the Korean Air Force on the base, maybe some U.S. Army personnel, maybe some other stuff -- who knows? To get the real answer, you are going to have to talk to the people out at PACAF in Hawaii -- more likely the Fifth Air Force out in Japan. As you probably know, the command situation in Korea is all screwed up between what is the United Nations Command, what is the unified command of COMUSKOREA, what is the regional air defense command headed up by Fifth Air Force, and what are the USAF and joint command lines

**running from PACAF and CINCPAC in Hawaii back to the Pentagon. In any event, I'm told that the Kunsan assignment is great -- they call it the *Riviera of Korea.*"**

**Damn! There it was again. The "Riviera of Korea." No real information but I was being told that it was the "Riviera" and that I would like it.**

**As I walked out of the office of the Director of Manpower, I was dimly aware that he told me that, due to personnel shortages, when I arrived at Kunsan Air Base, I should not expect to find a full complement of personnel assigned. I probably should have pursued that issue but I was fed up -- resigned to an unknown and terrible fate.**

**Disgusted, I returned to Operations at Bolling Air Force base and proceeded to fill out the forms for the flight back to Maxwell Air Force Base. However, I soon discovered that none of my fellow classmates was around. Probably an hour later and slowly, one by one, they trickled into Operations. There was not a happy face among them. One did not have to be clairvoyant to know that no one had succeeded in getting his orders changed. A few had some cases of booze from Harry's liquor store and I could sense the reason therefore.**

**I flew back to Maxwell Air Force Base with a deepening, dark cloud hanging over my head. It was an instrument flight and with a lot of thunderstorms banging us around. The C-45 bounced all over the sky and I soon found myself descending with throttles wide open and, in an instant, ascending with power fully cut off.**

**The returning Colonels on board did little talking -- there was no good news for anyone. On arriving at Maxwell Air Force Base, I made an instrument approach and hit the runway dead on but it was followed by a bad landing and I cursed. It all seemed like an omen of what was to come.**

**Adding insult to injury, I tripped as I descended from the aircraft and sprawled on the parking ramp.**

**When I got to our quarters, Mary had a drink waiting for me. She could tell from my face that I was not the bearer of good news of any sort.**

**We spent a few minutes trying to organize our thoughts -- the move to Virginia, how to sort and pack, what the apartment was like that I had acquired, arranging finances and more. And then we hugged each other and went to bed to get ready to tackle the uncertain tomorrows.**

# THE TRAVEL BEGINS

**The following morning I went to the transportation office at Maxwell Air Force base, gave them a copy of my initial orders to Kunsan Air Base, showed them the message from the Commanding General of the 314th Air Division and asked that they issue some new orders to expedite my transfer. Then I told the transportation duty officer that, en route to Korea, I wanted to stop in Hawaii to visit and be briefed at the PACAF Headquarters and, following, in Japan, to visit and be briefed at the Fifth Air Force Headquarters. I suggested that I would need two days at each location.**

**"We can't split a ticket," the duty officer answered. "It's against regulations. You have to travel straight through to Kunsan Air Base."**

**For a moment, I simply stared at the duty officer. Inwardly, I wanted to reach across the counter and choke the S.O.B. Regulations! Regulations were for persons who couldn't think. But I knew that, when a person hid behind regulations, it was pointless to continue the discussion.**

***[In retrospect, I have to recognize how many military persons tended to fall back on "regulations" or "orders" as a form of security blanket. In my own case, I lived by the rule that if I thought something was proper, it was proper. This orientation emerged in combat in Europe where if something made sense I did it and "regulations be damned." By the mid-forties, a few Field Grade Officers and I were, on our own, writing scores of major policy directions and our seniors simply signed the authorizing papers. Just to illustrate the reach of a few junior officers, the conversion of four-wheel drive jeeps to commercial vehicles for normal Air Force base operations was accomplished by a Lt. Colonel and myself over a few drinks -- the next day we wrote and published the USAF authorizing regulation. Operating unilaterally, however, was a dangerous undertaking in that any failure left one high and dry. Fortunately, none of us failed.]***

**"O.K. Then forget about the damned orders -- I don't need them. I'll travel out there as a space available passenger. Just give me some orders that will get me from Japan to Kunsan."**

"I can't do that," the duty officer replied.

"And why not?"

"I just can't. The regulations don't allow me to do such things."

Again I wanted to choke the spineless S.O.B. behind the counter. As so often in the past, I found myself confronted by a person who was dedicated to finding ways not to do something rather than finding ways to do something. Containing my anger, I walked away from the confrontation. Dimly I heard the duty officer asking me what he was to do about the orders and I think I told him to "shove them."

Obviously I would have to solve my own problems and I decided to call one of my friends in the office of the Director of Transportation in the Air Staff in the Pentagon. I needed help and I might as well cash in a chip of two.

"Bill, I have a problem and you owe me a favor."

Ten minutes later, I was assured that a message would be on the wire to the transportation office at Maxwell Air Force Base to amend my orders to allow a stop over in Hawaii to visit PACAF with another stop over in Japan to visit Fifth Air Force.

At least I had won something. Now all I had to do was get some footlockers of my stuff packed and en route to Korea and Mary and the children packed and moved to the apartment in Virginia. With the way my luck was going, I was beginning to feel as if my footlockers would not reach Korea or the moving van would catch fire and burn.

★★★★★★★★★★★★★★★

The MATS flight from Andrews Air Force Base to Hickam Air Force Base in Hawaii was hours upon hours of mind throbbing boredom. For some reason, the pilot could not keep the C-54 props in synchronization and I soon had a headache. There was a refueling stop at Travis Air Force Base which did provide some relief from the in-flight noise but we were hardly off the ground when the out-of-synch props again took over and again, for seemingly endless hours, those on board had to endure the constant ARUMMMM-ARUMMMM-ARUMMMM. The flight, however tiring, did give me time to think. But thinking simply failed to produce answers to the many questions that haunted me. And the more I thought the more questions I had.

To divert my mind from the many unanswered questions that kept popping into it, I had purchased a book on Korean history and another on the Korean War -- officially known as the "Korean

**Conflict." Both books were heavy reading. I had been aware of some of the events that transpired in Korea -- but not enough to satisfy myself. At the tail end of my last European assignment, General Ridgway showed up but he was engrossed in NATO and politics. Unlike his CINC U.S. EUCOM predecessor, he had little time for subordinates and I learned nothing from him regarding the Korean War. Unfortunately, I had not read his memoirs but I doubted if they would shed light on something as insignificant as Kunsan Air Base.**

**It was early morning when the MATS aircraft settled onto the runway at Hickam Air Force Base. Although the flight had been long, I was still unsure as to my next moves. I was, however, dedicated to learning something substantial about Kunsan Air Base before my arrival in Korea. I had always prided myself on knowing a good deal about a job before I took it over. In this case, however, my knowledge was still next to nothing and in a few days I would be at Kunsan Air Base and taking command -- but command of what?**

**There was only the briefest mention of Kunsan Air Base in the Korean War book I had read. According to that book, the Kunsan Air Base had been built by the Japanese as a fighter-interceptor base in 1938. At the end of World War II, the base had become the home of elements of the U.S. Korean Military Advisory Group -- the KMAG. At that date, there was little thought given to a long term U.S. presence in Korea and "KMAG" was quickly termed "Kiss My Ass Goodbye" by the American troops desiring to return to the States and place World War II and Korea behind them. A few years later, in 1949, with the withdrawal of U.S. forces from Korea, Kunsan Air Base was turned over to the fledgling Republic of Korea Air Force -- the ROKAF. Then, within two weeks of the outbreak of the Korean War, The Kum River defense line, which would have been anchored in the west by Kunsan had there been sufficient U.S. and ROK forces, fell to the North Koreans with such U.S. personnel as had been stationed there evacuated in advance of the attacking North Koreans. Finally, on September 30, 1950, the 3rd Battalion, 24th Infantry Division, U.S. Army recaptured Kunsan City and the air base. Immediately, Fifth Air Force took over and the task of runway expansion and rehabilitation began. For that work, the 808th Engineer Aviation Battalion, a SCARWAF unit, was deployed to Kunsan Air Base and in August 1951 the 3rd Bombardment Group with the 8th, 13th and 90th Bombardment Squadrons flying B-26 Invaders, along with some USN and other units, occupied the base. In October 1954, the 3rd Bombardment Group would redeploy to Johnson Air Base in Japan.**

**Notwithstanding this historical information, I had no idea what role the base currently played in the strategy for the area. I could not even recall that, at the Air War College, Kunsan Air Base had surfaced in any discussion or briefing.**

**By the time I checked into the Hickam Air Force Base VOQ and changed into a fresh uniform, my troubled thoughts were beginning to solidify into a course of action. Hopefully, I would succeed in adding to my meager knowledge of Kunsan Air Base and Korea.**

**First, I decided that I would talk to the Director of Plans, then to the Director of Operations, then to the Director of Personnel, then to the Director of Materiel and, finally, to the Chaplain. I thought about presenting myself to the Commander of PACAF or his Deputy but that was a bit presumptuous on my part and I concluded that it was best to stay away from those offices. Certainly, I would learn enough from the persons with whom I planned to meet. But, when the visits were over, I was to have learned next to nothing. I could not believe it!**

**From the Director of Plans, I had the authorized base population figure of 1,100 repeated but little more than that and a cup of coffee. I did examine the contingency war plans for Korea but learned little from them -- they were not much more than outline plans. And, in that they were several years out of date, I had to conclude that most of the information included in them was terribly in error. The plans did call for stock-piling of certain war reserves (such as fuel, bombs and drop tanks) at Kunsan Air Base but if the store of drop tanks was as stated in the plans they would be useless as most of the aircraft designated in the "Friendly Forces" section of the plans were no longer in the active Air Force inventory. As to why the contingency war plans for Korea were so out-of-date, the alleged answer was that basic planning done by CINCPAC was not current and it was suggested that the reason for that was that the planning at USAF Headquarters and the JCS was similarly out-of-date. "So what is my job if we go to war?" I asked. There was no answer.**

**From the Director of Operations, I did learn that Kunsan was a nuclear alert base but either no specifics were held at PACAF or there was reason why information could not be divulged to me. I was beginning to conclude that something was missing in my security clearances. However, I was told that, for administrative purposes, I had a C-47 and an L-20 assigned. "Great," I thought, "I'm a Colonel with all of two aircraft assigned." A full decade and a half prior, as a Major, I lead formations of fifty-four bombers in combat -- now I had one old transport and one old liaison aircraft! Things did not look very**

favorable. Finally, I got the standard "good word" from the Director of Operations.

"You'll love it," he said. "It's a great assignment and far out enough that you won't be bothered by a lot of headquarters staff. You know, it's called the *Riviera of Korea.*"

There it was again -- the "Riviera of Korea." I was beginning to hate the term but the idea of limited interference from higher headquarters appeared as a form of blessing -- so I thought. And then I decided to ask a dumb question of the Director of Operations.

"When was your last visit to Kunsan?"

The Director coughed a bit and replied.

"Actually, John, I have never been there -- but one of these days I will drop in on you."

"Christ," I thought, "I going to command a base that is so unimportant that the Director of Operations of PACAF hasn't given it enough attention to visit it. Yet, the duty officer in Colonel Assignments had stated that there was a lot of high-level interest in the operation at Kunsan. Something did not track."

I was about to add some follow-on questions when the Director of Operations looked at his watch and announced that he had another appointment. He thanked me for stopping by, wished me well, and left. I was thoroughly disgusted.

From the Director of Personnel, I learned that, although the base was authorized some 1,100 men, it had less than 600 assigned. "Manpower shortage" was given as the answer -- and with the added comment that the manning document for the base probably would be reduced more in line with the personnel that were actually assigned. "After all, if Kunsan can operate effectively with half the authorized strength why do we need to state the remainder as a requirement?" What did the Director of Personnel think about Kunsan? The answer paralleled that of the Director of Operations -- he had never been there. What was the court martial rate at the base? He did not know -- it was suggested that I might want to talk to the JAG. Could I rely on support from PACAF Personnel if I got in a jam? "Not much," was the answer. "Assignments to Korea, officer and enlisted, are pretty well controlled out of Washington. Further, the personnel pipeline to Korea is about 12 to 18 months. If it's not in the pipeline now, it probably won't come out the end until your tour in Korea is long over." And that meant that I was going to have to live with about one-half of the level of manpower that was authorized for the job. But what was the job?

**From the Director of Materiel, I learned that the budget was tight but they had nothing in file that indicated any serious materiel problem at Kunsan. I asked for a copy of the budget for Kunsan but it seemed that no one could find it. Had any of the logistic staff visited Kunsan? Apparently not. It seemed that job was left up to the Fifth Air Force Director of Material. The PACAF Director of Materiel did state that a good supply of fuel was maintained at the base to support planned wartime strike efforts. As to what the "planned wartime strike efforts" were, at best, the measurement was vague. When I asked if the storage tanks were revetted, the Director did not know. Apparently Kunsan was a wartime recovery base, possibly for the Strategic Air Command, and a forward base for fighters programmed to attack the Soviet Union, Communist China and North Korea should general or limited war break out -- but data on the type aircraft, flow rates and other planning essentials were absent.**

**From the PACAF Chaplain, I received assurance that there was no problem at Kunsan; that I had two Chaplain officers one of whom was Catholic and one of whom was Protestant; that a Rabbi from Osan visited the base periodically. With noticeable braggadocio and a photo retrieved from his desk to make the point, the Chaplain added that the Kunsan Air Base chapel had been replaced with a new structure. On questioning, he advised me that, while the chapel built during the Korean War had been usable, he had managed to finagle funds for this new chapel. Further discussion revealed that this was apparently the only building on Kunsan that had been replaced -- all other buildings were leftovers from the Korean War but, apparently, viewed as satisfactory. Based on the chapel photo, I felt reassured regarding the remainder of the base. Laughingly, the Chaplain told me that God gave him a construction priority. Asked about his last visit to Kunsan, the Chaplain informed me that he had never been there. "Housing shortage" was his answer. "Hate to impose on people," he said as he gave me a smile and a wink. What that meant, I did not know.**

**With each officer to whom I spoke, I had sought out historical background to the Kunsan Air Base and Korea in general. And, in each instance, I had come up dry. Even for those who had served in Korea there was no real historical knowledge present -- and virtually nothing in relation to the current time frame. Apparently, as limited as my knowledge was, I already knew more about the base and the history of Korea than did those to whom I spoke.**

**Leaving the PACAF headquarters, a building that still had exterior and interior bullet pock marks from the Japanese attack of**

December 7, 1941, I strolled though officer's country. The quarters, many of them dating from before World War II, were substantial. Little did I then realize that, before I would retire from military service, I would spend some nine years in those quarters -- three tours serving both for CINCPACAF and CINCPAC.

That night, I went to the Hickam Officers Club bar that faced the Pearl Harbor Channel and ordered a double Scotch. The tropical surroundings were absolutely delightful but it did not help my mood -- my thoughts were in a terrible jumble. I had spent the day and had learned virtually nothing of substance. I reviewed my conclusion about not seeking to talk to the PACAF Commander and eventually decided to hold fast. The Commander had just taken over his job and the odds were he would not be up to speed and all I would get would be a cup of coffee and some senseless words of encouragement. With another stiff drink, I decided that my best bet was to wait out the visit to Fifth Air Force Headquarters in Japan -- certainly, much closer to Korea, the answers I would obtain there would be more focused. But first I decided that, the next morning, I would extend my visitation in Hawaii to include the PACAF JAG and Flight Surgeon. So the next morning I squeezed in those visits before boarding a scheduled aircraft for Japan.

From the JAG, I learned that the court martial rate at the Kunsan Air Base was very low. But there was some helpful advice that was volunteered. "If you want to learn anything about what has taken place in Korea, look up Mike in Osan." I made a mental note to meet with the all-knowing "Mike" person.

From the Flight Surgeon, I learned that, among other things, the venereal disease rate at Kunsan had been running quite high -- something like an annual rate of 800 per 1,000. "Most of it is curable," the Surgeon stated, "but some of it is hard to fix. Still, don't get excited," he said. "That rate is about on par with all of Korea and most of Japan." In parting, the Surgeon stated that I had a good Flight Surgeon and Dentist at Kunsan and that I had nothing to worry about. Much as others, however, he had never visited the base.

And with those minor additions to my knowledge, I boarded the flight to Japan. Hopefully, the staff at Fifth Air Force would be more informative. If not, I was certainly going to have to look up "Mike" -- and quickly.

The flight to Japan was long -- very long. Four piston engines droning on for hours is nerve-wracking and my nerves were already "wracked."

I tried to make sense out of everything I had learned, such as it was, but no sense was to emerge. I was particularly disturbed that during the two days at Hickam Air Force Base I had not met a single person I knew. Fortunately, I knew that soon some of my Air War College associates would be reporting in at the PACAF headquarters and I would have some "friends in court." But, for the present, I had none.

Finally, I slipped into a fitful sleep. Dimly, I recall that someone placed a blanket over me. And, then, someone came through the cabin with an aerosol spray. I hated those things and doubted that they really did anything but it was an international requirement.

In minutes, we landed but it was too dark to see anything clearly.

Almost drugged with tiredness, I got into a staff car and was whisked off to some quarters -- and then, with some of my clothes still on, I was asleep. I had arrived in Japan but I doubted that anyone really knew that I was there -- or cared.

*The rebuilt Kunsan Air Base chapel. It was the only building on Kunsan Air Base that had been replaced since the Korean War. The PACAF Chaplain advised that other buildings at Kunsan were viewed as satisfactory. I would soon learn otherwise. This photo was taken after arrival at Kunsan Air Base. The road in the foreground was one of the better on-base roads.*

# JAPAN

At the end of World War II, I entered Germany as a part of the occupation and disarmament forces. Then, when again assigned to Germany, we were nearing the end of the occupation period. Now, many years later, I was in Japan and partaking of the remnants of that occupation. But "remnants" they hardly were.

I had heard stories about how the occupation forces lived in Japan but I was hardly prepared for the accommodations.

With the coming of dawn, I realized that the VIP quarters to which I had been assigned at Fuchu Air Station were absolutely magnificent. Outside was a carefully manicured Japanese garden. To meet every personal need, a slightly built, attractive Japanese girl in kimono scurried about. With almost continuous bows, she served me a breakfast in bed, quickly unpacked my clothes, took some for laundering, did some pressing and shined my shoes. On the adjacent driveway, a highly polished sedan with Japanese driver awaited me. Decidedly, the occupation forces in Japan were living "high on the hog."

But there was one thing for which some cultural "adjusting" was needed. While there were a score of private rooms in the VIP quarters, it was served by a common shower room -- a white tiled affair with a half dozen shower heads and no separating walls or other means of privacy. Apparently, men and women used the same facility. I guessed that it was a take-off of the common Japanese bath facility and, finding no alternative, I waited for a moment when the shower was unoccupied and did a fast scrub down and retreat.

Arriving at the Headquarters of the Fifth Air Force, the chrome-helmeted guards snapped to attention. One of the guards opened the entrance door for me. I was impressed and I suddenly had visions of the same reception taking place at Kunsan Air Base. "Perhaps I am really heading for the Riviera," I thought.

After signing in at the entrance post, I soon found myself in the office of the Director of Operations -- a Colonel -- once again, an officer I did not know. The desk, office, everything was sumptuous -- almost over-powering. In size, it was beyond that of most corporate executives. Expensive artworks adorned the walls; a tremendous, highly decorated vase stood by the door. An Oriental rug covered the floor -- obviously an antique.

I introduced myself and stated the reason for my visit. Purposefully, I had not wired ahead to PACAF or to Fifth Air Force that I was arriving and what my desired agenda was.

The Director of Operations seemed annoyed both at my unannounced visit and my questions -- I was not even offered the traditional cup of coffee. I quickly gathered that no other in-coming Colonel had arrived at his office to seek answers relating to an assignment and the Director did not know how to handle the situation. Finally, he suggested that I might wish to receive a command briefing -- to which I agreed.

Much as everything else, the command briefing room was decidedly plush. Deep cushioned chairs made up the front VIP rows. The room lighting was well controlled and soft. At the back of the briefing stage were two large screens on which information was presented from a balcony projection booth. Everything was high class. More than ever, I was convinced that I was nearing the promised "Riviera."

Settling into one of the plush chairs in the front row, the lights were dimmed and the briefing started with the typical intelligence overview. I could see, however, that the briefing was made mostly for non-cleared visitors -- substantive detail was sadly lacking -- but I decided to sit through the thing.

Following an intelligence overview that was not much more than what one could learn by reading TIME magazine, a few organizational charts were presented to show the command lines and the location of various U.S. and friendly forces. Confirming my earlier knowledge, the only USAF combat unit assigned to Korea was the nuclear-capable Matador unit. When I asked questions about the nuclear stockpile in Korea and whether the Matador unit was armed nuclear or conventional, I was informed by the Director of Operations that the level of security of the briefers was insufficient for such a discussion -- and, further, that I would get that information when I got to Korea. I wondered if the answer covered a lack of knowledge on the part of the Director but I knew that pursuit of that thought was without merit.

Then, at the close of the presentation, some charts on logistic readiness were flashed on the screen. True to the PACAF conversation, there was a good supply of fuel at Kunsan -- mostly JP-4. I asked about fuel delivery to the base and was informed that it was primarily by way of a tactical pipeline from the port of Kunsan. I did not raise the issue of fuel storage tank revetments. Finally, a chart covering key commanders and other persons filled the screen.

The briefing was well put together, the graphics were great, and the briefers were polished "presenters." But it answered few of my questions. As a result, when the lights came on and the Director of Operations asked if I was satisfied, my answer was: No! Obviously, the Director was not pleased.

"Well," he asked, "what more do you want to know?"

"What I want to know," I answered, "is what is the mission of Kunsan Air Base; in detail, what is on it or is supposed to be on it; what problems exist and what is being done about those problems; and what do you expect me to do when I arrive at the base in a day or so?"

"We expect you to be the Commander," was the curt reply.

"And, as the Commander, what assistance will I get from you?"

"You'll get the same assistance we give every other Commander."

Seeing that I was getting no where, I thanked the Director of Operations for his time and the briefing, thanked the briefing personnel, and departed. I had intended to talk to other staff sections but the exercise seemed pointless. For a moment, I considered knocking on the door of the Commander of Fifth Air Force but let the idea drop. The world was just not turning the way I wanted and expected it to turn and I could not understand why. Ever since the Orders Party at the Air War College, things had not been going well. Perhaps it was me? Perhaps it was just more of that *Friday the 13th*?

I decided to go back to the VIP quarters and get ready for a departure to Kunsan Air Base the following day.

That evening, I went to the Tachikawa Air Base Officers Club for dinner. It was a sumptuous club (later I would learn that it was recognized as "one of the Air Force's finest") with an outstanding band. For American consumption, the leader went by the name of "Smiley" but his real name was Goro Asahina. His music was fabulous -- on the level of Glen Miller -- and I discovered that, time and again, his band had been named "Best in Japan."

Led to a table by an immaculately dressed Japanese maitre d'hôtel, I settled in for an introspective evening. The menu set before me was elaborate -- better than many one would find in the best of New York or London hotels. I decided on a Kobe steak. The price for the whole dinner was little more than that of a MacDonald's hamburger in the United States. Obviously, life in Japan was of the highest order

**with the very minimum of cost. Again, I had the feeling that I might actually be approaching the much-acclaimed Riviera.**

**I was having a final cup of coffee when I noticed a Colonel seated alone at one of the nearby side tables. He was not part of the regular crowd and, also feeling much alone, I decided to self-invite myself to his table for a final cup of coffee. Circumstance, it seemed, had played into my hands. To my absolute surprise, the Colonel introduced himself as none other than the departing Commander of Kunsan Air Base! And soon I was to be advised of many things.**

**★★★★★★★★★★★★★★★**

**1. Contrary to the message I had received at the Air War College from the Commander of the 314th Air Division, there was no emergency at Kunsan Air Base. Actually, the departing Kunsan Commander had simply asked to be relieved early in order to take an extended home leave prior to reporting to a new assignment. He assured me several times that there was no urgency in my going to Kunsan and he urged me to take a few days off and "have a good time in Tokyo" before getting involved with matters at Kunsan Air Base, the Korean josans and the ROKAF. Frankly, I was stunned and miffed. I had unloaded many problems on Mary and given up the normal family leave to rush to Korea simply because this Colonel had wanted and been given extended leave with his family.**

**2. As to who was now running Kunsan Air Base, the departing Commander stated that he had left a very good Lt. Colonel in charge and, when he had departed for Japan a few days prior, everything was running smoothly. Several times, he assured me that there was no significant problem at the air base although he did comment that the one-year tour had lead to considerable turmoil in personnel as a result of the constant change-over. But, balancing that, he said that some of the men liked it in Korea so well that they had extended their tours to successive years -- some, he said, had been in Korea for over three years and many of them seemed interesting in continuing to extend. "It provides stability," he said.**

**3. Kunsan Air Base, he stated, was, along with Osan Air Base, a forward nuclear strike base for USAF tactical units operating out of Japan and Okinawa -- there was no USAF fighter unit permanently based in Korea. This, he asserted, was to keep the USAF fighter forces from coming under the control of the joint command: U.S. Forces Korea. "Of course," he added, "we can't allow our nuclear**

**forces to come under the command of the United Nations Command even if that post is filled by a U.S. officer and is the same person as commands U.S. Forces Korea." Regarding the nuclear alert aircraft at Kunsan, I was informed that it was not a problem of mine. "They do their own maintenance and are controlled from their home base and from Fifth Air Force. They're not your worry -- all you have to do is feed them and provide some security. And don't worry none about the nukes at Kunsan -- that's a Fifth Air Force responsibility."**

**4. Located on Kunsan Air Base was a radar installation covering the west central sector of Korea and extending outward over the Yellow Sea. This installation had some USAF persons in it but, technically, it was owned by the ROKAF. Also on the base was a ROKAF fighter squadron equipped with F-86 aircraft and a helicopter for air-sea rescue and other purposes. With that statement, he smiled and noted that other purposes for the helicopter might include slicky operations, black market and more. The radar installation and the ROKAF fighters, he stated, were tied into the air defense net covering Korea and were, in some way, subordinate to Fifth Air Force coordination or control. He indicated that part of the problem was the fact that the Koreans would not accept communications from Japanese personnel with the result that all communications between Japanese and Korean parties were via an American. "That's one of the reasons we have Americans in all the radar installations in Korea and Japan." And there was more. No ROKAF aircraft was allowed, even in hot pursuit, to cross into Japanese air space and the reverse was true. Adding to the international complications was the line established by President Rhee defining Korean waters -- a demarcation line rejected by the Japanese. The command situation in Korea was, in his words, "All screwed up -- but," he added, "it's not your worry."**

**5. There was no U.S. Army outfit in or near Kunsan Air Base. However, there was a Korean Army reserve organization in the central area of Korea -- the First Military District Command. But, for all intent, Kunsan Air Base was on its own when it came to defense. "It's not a problem," he stated. "We breezed through the last inspection without a serious question."**

**6. Situated around Kunsan Air Base were a half dozen ROK Army light anti-aircraft guns -- he thought they were 37 or 40 millimeter. How they got their fire orders, he did not know. "You don't have to concern yourself with those things," he stated. While that assertion startled me, I decided not to pursue the issue.**

**7. Relations with the Korean officials at the city of Kunsan were great and they were looking forward to my arrival. To my surprise, he stated that the Mayor and others already had framed photos of me in their offices. He indicated that the Mayor "was on my side" when it came to getting things done and that I would be surprised at the Korean reception when I got to Kunsan -- he did not elaborate and I did not question him.**

**8. As Commander of Kunsan Air Base, I was also commander of a small USAF unit at Taegu in the central part of Korea and had to support the personnel there who were associated with the ROKAF Military Assistance Advisory Group. "For that job, just fly over there once in a while and spend a few hours -- it's not a problem area. There is a Major over there who gets done what needs to be done."**

**9. President Rhee, he stated, was getting quite old and feeble and might be overthrown. At the present, Mrs. Rhee seemed to be running everything. But, he added, that was none of my concern -- all those matters were handled in Seoul.**

**10. In construction at Kunsan Air Base was a new mess hall for the enlisted men, some igloos for nuclear weapons storage and improvements to the water distribution system. The officers lived in refurbished Japanese quarters. The Commander's quarters consisted of a bedroom, a large living room and a bathroom. "Very comfortable and fully furnished -- really a Stateside house. And you will have a staff car awaiting your arrival. Regarding construction," he added, "it's not your worry. It's run out of Fifth Air Force and the Army Corps of Engineers takes care of the management."**

**11. This was the summer rotation of personnel, basically termed the "silly season," when an almost full turnover took place. Most of the senior officers at Osan, to include the Commander, were rotating.**

**12. Yes, he knew "Mike" at Osan. Mike, it turned out, was a girl who had been stationed in Korea before and after the Korean War -- she worked in the Operations Office as a secretary. "One hell of a girl," he added.**

**13. There was good hunting in Korea. "Get down to Cheju Do -- there's a radar site down there and an airfield -- the pheasant and other hunting is great. And, when the ducks and geese start flying south, plan a trip to Kangnung on the east coast. They've got a marsh over there that's a north-south stopping point for the birds -- terrific hunting. You bring a gun?" he asked. "I've got a 12 gauge**

**Browning automatic and a thirty-ought-six with scope in an on-coming shipment," I answered. "You'll get along," he replied with a wink. "You'll enjoy the hell out of Korea."**

**[*A year later, I would leave Korea with no serious pheasant or other hunting done. At one point, the Commander of a ROKAF unit stationed to the south of Kunsan Air Base would present me with a deer carcass from one of their hunts. In turn, I gave the ROKAF Commander a case of Bourbon.*]**

**14. Oh yes, there was a great Officers Club at Kunsan which the men jokingly had termed "The Bottom of the Mark."**

★★★★★★★★★★★★★★★

**"I guess you know there's no military flight out of Japan to Korea until Monday?"**

**I did not. And, this being Friday, it might mean that I was going to have to cool my heels in Japan for two days. The ex-Commander sensed my thoughts and added, "Why don't you move down to the Sanno Hotel in Tokyo and see some of the city before you ship over to Kunsan. You may not be able to get back to Japan for a long while?"**

**The time was getting late and the club was preparing to close for the night. Then, when we shook hands and ended our conversation for the evening, I again heard the familiar words: "You'll like it there; it's the *Riviera of Korea.*" Somehow the words did not ring true but I could not place a finger on what was wrong. In a few days, I would begin to find out. But, for now, I had my first real glimpse of what would greet me at Kunsan Air Base. On the surface, it did not appear to be too bad a situation but I wondered how much of what I heard was true and how much of it was false. I was particularly worried that so much of what I would assume was my command was, somehow, run by others -- tenant units, Fifth Air Force, the Army Corps of Engineers, the ROKAF, the ROK Army -- it just did not seem right. If so much was being run by others, what was my job?**

**Returning to my billet, I decided that I would take the advice given to me and move to the Sanno Hotel. The next morning, after dressing and packing, I called for a staff car.**

**As I waited for the staff car to arrive, I reviewed the events of the prior evening and a strange worry crossed my mind. Had my**

"accidental" meeting with the departing Commander of Kunsan Air Base really been an accident or had it somehow been orchestrated by Fifth Air Force -- or some other party? Was there a game being played that I did not understand? In retrospect, the entire event seemed too pat. How was it that I worked so hard to learn so little and suddenly a world of information was dumped on me? And was the person to whom I talked really the departing Commander of Kunsan Air Base? Based on the message I had received at Maxwell AFB, I would have expected that the Commander would have departed the area some time ago. Things did not add up.

The trip from Fuchu to the Sanno took over an hour. The streets were narrow and, in spite of it being a Saturday morning, crowded bumper to bumper. To occupy myself, I studied the Japanese architecture and admired the neatness and orderliness of the passing surroundings. Soon the disturbing thoughts surrounding my "accidental" meeting with the departing Commander of Kunsan Air Base faded from my mind. For a long time, however, this event would return to concern me but I would never discover if the meeting was planned or truly accidental.

As we drove, my attention was drawn to the Japanese people. In my limited study of history, I had been astounded by the extreme cruelty exhibited by the Japanese not only against occupied populations, especially in China and Korea, but against their own peoples. And then there were the events of World War II the full scope of which I probably did not know but I knew enough to wonder about the social and psychological make-up of the Japanese. Although, at the Tokyo war crimes tribunal, Justice Radhabinod Pal of India suggested that the greatest atrocity act of World War II was the dropping of the nuclear bomb on Hiroshima and Nagasaki, that was a terminal event and contrary to popular opinion, in the short and long term actually benefited Japan. The Japanese, on the other hand, had a history of the most severe of atrocities against prisoners and the general populations from the earliest days right through the end of World War II. Why had they acted as they did -- and had the make-up of the Japanese changed as a result of the terrible defeat inflicted upon them in World War II? Somehow, I felt that it had not -- and would not. And I sensed that Japan would find the means to advance to again be a threat to the world -- especially to the United States. Already, I was aware of how the Japanese had prospered as a result of the Korean War.

Eventually, the driver pulled up to a multi-storied hotel and assured me that it was the Sanno. It was a pre-war hotel taken over by

**the U.S. occupation forces. In outward appearance, it reminded me of hotels in Germany and Austria.**

**I told the driver to wait. I had not made reservations and I wanted to be certain that I could get a room.**

**At the reception desk, I presented a copy of my orders and my ID. There was no problem getting a room and a Japanese busboy quickly retrieved my bags and escorted me to my room. In the elevator, I noticed a sign advertising a hot bath and massage facility on a lower floor. I had heard about the famous Japanese hot baths and decided that, before I proceeded to Korea, I would try out one. I wondered if these baths were similar to the hot mineral baths of Wiesbaden, Baden-Baden and other German resorts? In the meantime, I wanted to stroll through the city and, above all, visit the famed Ginza.**

**Tokyo was a bustling city with much construction on-going. To my surprise, the shops were full to over-flowing with goods. I had obtained a tourist map and laid out a walking plan for myself. By late afternoon, I found that I was far from the Sanno and on the tired side. At the hotel, I had been briefed on the Tokyo taxi system and I hailed one of the smaller taxis -- commonly termed a "Kamikaze." The drive to the Sanno Hotel verified the terminology accorded both the taxicab and the driver.**

**Back at the Sanno, it was time for dinner but I first stopped at the bar. I was surprised that, since my arrival in Japan, as was the case in Hawaii, I had not met a single person I knew. At the bar, it was the same story -- there was present a lot of Americans but no one I knew.**

**Eventually, I struck up a conversation with an American officer -- a fighter pilot on R&R. He told me that he was going to visit a Japanese night club and suggested that I join him -- which I did.**

**I don't recall the name of the club -- it had a very large circular bar that rotated. The bar stools were all occupied by men -- almost exclusively Americans. Bar entertainment was situated on a raised platform in the center of the bar. Standing elbow-to-elbow at the outer wall was a line of young Japanese ladies in skin-tight, revealing silk dresses. As the bar rotated, the men had a chance to observe the qualities of each of the ladies. Now and then, a man would select one of the ladies and disappear out a side door. I noticed that, while the ladies were Japanese, almost all of them had round eyes.**

**"What's with the eyes?" I asked.**

**My pilot friend laughed.**

"The Japanese girls think that the Americans prefer round eyes. It's a simple operation. Most of them get it."

I was being introduced to a new culture.

Sunday was a repeat of Saturday -- a lot of walking and sight-seeing. Returning to the Sanno, I sought out the Japanese bath. I found it strange to be bathed by a scantily dressed young lady. Then, at the bar, it was a repeat of the day prior -- all strangers. I had the sense of being very alone.

Dinner that night was both sumptuous and inexpensive. There was excellent stringed dinner music that reminded me of Germany and no one could ask for better service. By bedtime, I had almost forgotten about Korea and Kunsan Air Base. Before dozing off for the night, however, I did get off a short note to Mary telling her about Tokyo -- I did not mention the hot bath.

The next morning, reality set in and I went to the airfield to continue on to Korea.

I had seen some of Japan and the Japanese people. I was struck by the organization and discipline of everyone. They appeared to have a great work ethic. But I was uncomfortable around them. Frankly, I did not trust them. Soon, I would have to reach conclusions respecting Koreans and I wondered what those conclusions would be. And I wondered if, before this adventure into the Orient was over, whether I would find myself critically assessing the Chinese and other national groups.

In my limited study of history, I had found that of the Far East to be most complicated. Following was that of the Middle East. Central European history was, to me, rather clean cut and understandable. Of one thing I was convinced -- without a knowledge of the history of peoples, one could not make good military or other decisions. And here I was heading for Korea with but a modicum of knowledge of the history of that country. Yet, I had come to believe that none of those with whom I had interfaced in the last few days really gave a hoot about the history of the countries in the Far East. For all too many, the good life was of greater importance.

Perhaps I was "barking up the wrong tree" and worrying about all the wrong things? Perhaps I was failing to understand the real world about me?

# ON TO KUNSAN AIR BASE

The air transport from Japan to Korea was a C-47 "Gooney Bird." On board was a mix of U.S. Army and U.S. Air Force personnel on assignment to Korea or returning to Korea after an R&R trip to Japan. I was the only officer on board.

The C-47 was configured for hauling combat troops and military cargo -- everyone wore a parachute and sat on the metal bucket seats that folded down from each side of the cabin. The cabin was hot and the parachutes were dirty -- the seat belts looked like they had been dragged through a grease pit. I could forecast what my uniform would look like on arriving at Kunsan Air Base and I did not like the prospect.

From front to rear, the center of the aircraft's cabin was stacked high with passenger purchases in Japan plus their travel luggage. There also was a good number of shipping crates. By the markings on the crates, it seemed that most of them contained food -- it was obvious that many contained perishables: fruit and vegetables. I wondered why food was being flown from Japan to Korea? Probably something special, I reasoned -- and let the matter drop from my mind.

I had seated myself so that the wing of the aircraft did not obstruct my downward view and, periodically, I turned and glanced out the small side window next to me. The sky was relatively clear of clouds and visibility was quite good. Flying under 10,000 feet, a lot could be seen and I was eager to see lands that I had never seen before.

As we proceeded from Japan, I suddenly realized that the islands passing below had changed from lush green to yellow clay. Apparently, we had crossed the boundary between Japan and Korea and I was witnessing the ravage of the country-side that had been inflicted on the Koreans by the Japanese. And now, rather than the substantial buildings that I had seen in the Japanese environment, the villages that appeared below were little more than mud huts with straw roofs. Here and there, one could discern meandering foot trails but there appeared to be little in the way of improved roads. Most of the cultivation seemed to be rice fields -- terraced when they came to the sides of the hills and mountains.

The first scheduled stop of the C-47 was to be Kunsan Air Base; then the aircraft was to go on to Kimpo Air Base outside the capital city of Seoul. The final stop was to be the home facility of Osan Air Base. I quickly learned that I was the only in-coming passenger for Kunsan Air Base. While I sought to engage the men sitting beside and across from me in conversation, they were not talkative -- I sensed that they either held resentment toward an officer or were upset at being assigned to or returning to Korea. I was probably correct on both scores.

Soon we left the island dotted sea area and came over solid land. The terrain was rugged and barren. Again. all the cultivation I observed seemed to be rice paddies. Finally, I spotted a railroad track but there was no movement on it and the lack of reflection from the rails suggested that there had been no movement for some time. Now and then, I saw a vehicle on the few roads that came into view but they all appeared to be military rather than civilian. A few of the vehicles looked like busses. All of the roads seemed to be little more than traveled dirt. When I did observe a moving vehicle, it was followed by a cloud of dust. Periodically, I observed an ox or horse drawn cart -- and a good number of A-frame carriers.

Then my ears popped and I knew we were letting down for Kunsan Air Base -- the "Riviera of Korea."

Fortunately, the pilot made a wide circle of the airfield thereby giving me an opportunity to assess my new home. While my view of the facilities below me was limited to the small window at my side, "Riviera" was not what I saw. Now, at about 1,000 feet, it was obvious that most of the buildings were of corrugated metal and apparently well rusted. I could see no painted building other than the new base chapel about which the PACAF Chaplain had briefed me -- it appeared to carry a fresh coat of paint -- white. The chapel, in stark contrast to the surrounding buildings, stood out like a sore thumb. I had to wonder about the logic that apparently placed a higher priority on the chapel over operational and living facilities. But then I recalled the PACAF Chaplain's statement that God gave a construction priority to chapels. I was not amused.

In the distance, I could see that one road led out of the base -- apparently it connected to the distant city of Kunsan. Like the other roads I had viewed, it was obviously dirt and, even from 1,000 feet, I could see that it was in terrible condition.

In the opposite direction, the island-dotted waters of the Yellow Sea stretched forth. These waters came right up to what I assumed was the seaward boundary of Kunsan Air Base. I presumed the tide was in as I knew of the great tides in the Yellow Sea. I wondered how far seaward the waters would go when the tide was out. In the water area,

**the wind filled the sails of several small fishing boats -- I could see nets hanging from the masts of some.**

**On a large concrete hardstand area adjacent to a taxiway that paralleled the longest runway, I noted several parked tactical fighter aircraft -- F-100s -- apparently, these were the nuclear alert birds. There appeared to be no aircraft revetments on the field. At one end of the runway, I observed some F-86 aircraft parked. These, I surmised, were air defense aircraft of the Korean Air Force standing alert. It looked like there was an old hangar at the north end of the airfield -- there were some F-86s parked near it. It was obvious that the hangar had suffered bomb damage during the war -- it had not been repaired. There was a second, shorter runway on the field but it appeared not to be in use. Then the C-47 pilot turned on the final approach and my view of my new home was stolen from me.**

**I felt the flaps being lowered, then the wheels, then there was a bump and we were down.**

**The taxi trip to the off-load area seemed to take forever. Finally, the crew chief came to the rear of the cabin and readied to open the door. At the same time I heard the left engine being shut down; the right one kept turning. We had arrived but, obviously, the pilot was in a hurry to depart.**

**I unbuckled, stood up, picked up my B-4 bag and a navigator case that contained my records, some personal papers, a camera, my pistol and my shaving kit and moved to the door. As I looked out the cabin door, I saw that there was a line-up of some twenty officers and enlisted men waiting to greet me. I had advised no one of my intended arrival so the greeting was a surprise. It must have been the work of the ex-Commander I had met in Japan -- so I thought. Apparently, he was legitimate and had decided to telephone the base to alert them that I was in-bound. My intention had been just "to pop in" on the base as I felt a surprise arrival would serve to tell me more than a staged arrival. But my plan had fallen apart. So what was new?**

**"Oh well," I thought, "make the most of it."**

**At the foot of the stairs, a Sergeant saluted and took by bags; I proceeded to the greeting line. As I did, my eyes took in what I presumed was the Operations building as it was located adjacent to the parking ramp the C-47 had used. It was a decrepit building -- not something with which one would want to live. Weathered and torn sand bags held down the concrete slab tiles that formed a roof. Plywood sections in windows told of missing glass.**

**With my eyes on the Operations building, I stumbled on a hole in the parking ramp macadam. Looking down, I could see that the parking ramp was thoroughly cracked and with potholes everywhere. Clearly, it was not suitable for jet aircraft -- it was hardly suitable for a C-47.**

**As I moved to the first officer in the greeting line, the C-47 behind me had already fired up the left engine and was moving out to the takeoff runway. The blast of air from the props of the C-47 blew pieces of macadam and dirt everywhere. Quickly, the friendly sound of the engines faded away in the distance.**

**Suddenly, I felt alone -- very alone -- almost deserted. Somehow, the departing C-47 seemed to be kissing me off -- stranding me in a new and strange "no man's land."**

**I had arrived at the "Riviera of Korea."**

**The transition from the luxury of Japan to the bleakness of Korea was a professional and cultural shock. But, little did I appreciate how great that shock would grow to be.**

***The Korean villages below were little more than mud huts with straw roofs. Here and there, one could discern meandering foot trails.***

# DAY NUMBER "ONE" BEGINS

I felt tired, defeated -- but I straightened my shoulders and proceeded to the line of officers and enlisted men awaiting my arrival.

The first officer in line saluted. I did not return the salute. Instead, I put out my hand.

"I'm John Moench, your new Commander," I said. I tried to smile but it was not easy.

"Yes sir. Welcome to Kunsan Air Base, *The Riviera of Korea*," the officer replied. "I'm Lt. Colonel Davidson -- Walter Davidson. A short time ago, our old boss called from Japan to say that you were coming in and I decided to have some of our officers and enlisted men here to greet you."

"Thanks," I muttered as I surveyed more closely the line-up of officers and enlisted men. It hardly looked like a military formation. Some stood stiffly; others sort of lounged in the line. Some uniforms were rather neatly pressed; others looked like they had been slept in. Some of the men needed a shave; others needed a hair cut. A few pairs of shoes were shined; most were not. I could see that several of the men were intently surveying me -- others simply looked straight ahead -- they were performing an obligatory duty, no more. Obviously, the group standing before me wondered what their new Commander was going to be like. For my part, other than the quick observations of uniforms and bearing of those in the line-up, I wondered why, even though notice of my arrival might have been a last minute thing, of the approximate five or six hundred men on the base only some twenty were present? If Lt. Colonel Davidson was trying to make an initial impression on me, it wasn't working.

One by one, I went down the line shaking the hand of each person. I tried to memorize the names but the event was mostly a blur by the time I reached the end of the line. One man did capture my special attention -- he leaned to the stout side and the buttons of his blouse seemed to be ready to pop off. Somehow, he struck me as over-weight but still not fat. I poked him in the stomach suggesting that he had been eating too much. His reply was sharp. "I agree, sir." His name was Pastiak, Captain Joseph "Joe" Pastiak -- and he was the JAG. Of all the American men (and women) I encountered at Kunsan Air Base, I never forgot this man. In the years following, he would emerge as a most prominent attorney and we would carry on a life-time

**of communication. When I first shook hands with Joe, unlike most of the others, he looked me straight in the eye, unaffected by the fact that he was a Captain and I was his Colonel boss. I concluded immediately that he was a strong individual on whom I could count -- and I never regretted that conclusion.**

**Parked at the end of the receiving line was a blue sedan -- at least at one point in its life it had been blue. Apparently, this was the staff car the ex-Commander had mentioned.**

**"These are your wheels," Lt. Colonel Davidson proudly advised.**

**I looked at it in disgust. As I neared more closely to it, I could see that it had been repainted so many times that the surface was a series of lumps. The rear bumper was not a sedan bumper -- at one time it apparently had belonged to a jeep. There were dents on all sides of the vehicle. The windshield was cracked and discolored and I noted that there was only one wiper blade. The Sergeant who had picked up my bags had placed them in the trunk. He was now busily tying down the lid with a rope. Apparently, the lock was broken. A glance showed me nearly threadbare tires. The seat cushions were in tatters with here and there a broken spring protruding.**

**"Do you want to drive or do you want me to drive?" Davidson asked.**

**"You drive," I responded as I cautiously crawled into the passenger side of the front seat. Dirt covered the floor and I knew that by just seating myself my already rumpled and soiled uniform would be additionally covered with the filth of Korea. The vehicle was a military disgrace.**

**On the third or fourth try, the engine sputtered to life -- a cloud of blue smoke poured out of the exhaust. Then, with a rumble of miss fire on one cylinder, we were off -- the formation of men saluted and broke rank.**

**"Where to, sir?" Davidson asked.**

**For a minute, I sat quiet. Nothing seemed right. The broken and potholed parking ramp should have been condemned -- no jet could taxi on it without major engine damage from foreign object ingestion and, certainly, we were in the age of jets. The formation of officers and enlisted men seemed almost to come from a comic strip. The wreck of a car we were in should have been salvaged years ago. I tried to get my thoughts together as Davidson maneuvered the staff car down a narrow, potholed macadam road.**

**As we moved, I think the first thing that caught my eye was the grass. In most places, it was knee high.**

**"What's with the grass?" I asked. "Don't you know how to cut it?"**

**"We don't have to cut it, sir. We have permission from Wing to let it grow. We don't have any lawn mowers. Periodically, we let the Koreans come in and cut it for feed and fuel."**

**I was stunned. A peacetime military base with no grass cut was something I had never before encountered. And no lawn mowers? Why?**

**"Where would you like me to go, sir?" It was Davidson asking the question again.**

**"Take me to the headquarters," was my answer.**

**As we continued to wind around potholes in the macadam covered but narrow roadway, past poorly dressed and unsaluting men, past buildings that seemed fit not even for farm animals, I was overcome. So this was the "Riviera of Korea?" I smarted at the often-repeated assessment that I would like it. Already, I hated it!**

**[*Later, I would learn that the roads were once adequate for two-lane traffic but the Koreans had continually "stolen the roads." The original macadam surface of the roadways was about two inches in thickness. What the Koreans did was progressively break off parts of the sides of the roadways and steal them for fuel. Slowly, the two-lane roadways had become single lane and less. One would have to be there to understand that, in the poverty-stricken Korean homes, a broken piece of macadam could serve as precious supplemental fuel.*]**

**"This is your headquarters," Davidson announced as we pulled up to a one story, corrugated sheet metal building -- an old log marked the point at which the tires were to stop. A small, hand-lettered sign in front of the parking space announced that it was reserved for the Commander. As we came to a stop, a cloud of dust engulfed us. Suddenly, breathing became difficult.**

**Stepping from the staff car, I noticed that in front of the headquarters building there had been implanted a crooked tree trunk. An old, rotted rope dangled from a rusted pulley at the top.**

**"Is that supposed to be a flag pole?" I asked.**

**"Yes sir. But we don't have a flag to fly. We had one once but it got all tattered and we burned it up."**

"Didn't you requisition a replacement?" I asked, somewhat stunned.

"Yes sir, we did. But Fifth Air Force supply said that we had used up our budget and had to wait until next year to get one."

I looked at Davidson in disbelief. A United States Air Force facility with no flag! And, seemingly, no one cared! I wanted to hit someone but didn't know who.

Reflectively, I was overcome by the comparison of the pomp of Fifth Air Force in Japan, the shiny chrome helmets of the Air Police guards at the headquarters, the good quarters and gracious living and, here in Korea, a few hundred miles away, the situation I was observing could only be described as primitive squalor

Shaking my head in disbelief, I realized that a sign on the door to my front read "Entrance" and so I did. Unfortunately, my temper was getting to me and, when I opened the door with too hard a pull, the rusted hinges broke and it came off in my hand. Davidson quickly grabbed it. "I'll get it put back," he announced as he stood it against the building.

Entering the headquarters building, I was greeted by a Second Lieutenant and a Master Sergeant. A Korean girl was at a desk to the side. The Lieutenant and the Sergeant rose and saluted. The Korean girl pretended to look at a paper in her typewriter -- I could see that it was blank.

"Sir, your office is over here," the Lieutenant said as he pointed to an open side door.

Without acknowledging, I stepped into what was going to be my center of operations in the days ahead. It was a mess. The furniture looked as if it came from a salvage yard; everything was covered with a deep layer of dust. The screened windows, open for ventilation, were full of holes. There was a sort of conference table to the side of the room with a number of unmatched wooden and metal chairs grouped around it. The top of the table was abundantly marked with cigarette or cigar burns and with numerous sets of initials and dates carved into the wood.

Suddenly, I recalled the World War II movie that depicted an Air Force Commander arriving at an unkempt base in England who, in somewhat similar circumstances, took a fire hose to his office. I wanted to do the same thing but there was no fire hose around. In fact, I didn't even see a fire extinguisher.

"My God," I thought, "what have I inherited?"

**While I had then no way of knowing it, the new Division Commander in Osan would, on his arrival, find equally upsetting circumstances. In later, off-the-record reminiscences of his wife:**

***My husband left Japan for the Korean assignment as a Colonel and landed masquerading as a Brigadier General. What had happened was that the promotion list he was on had been held up by Margaret Chase Smith who did not wish to see Rosie O'Donnell promoted to four stars. Just before takeoff from Japan, the Commanding General of Fifth Air Force pinned a star on my husband! The job in Korea required the grade of Brigadier General.***

***We arrived at Osan Air Base to find a "Tropical Hut" on what was known as Hill One-Eighty as our new home. It was nothing more than a one story tin house that had been used to house senior bachelor officers. The middle of what was supposed to be the living room had four big burgundy plush-covered chairs arranged back-to-back to each other. It looked like some kind of fourth rate hotel lobby. Some prior occupant had installed a "picture window" that overlooked the airfield but it was a two-section affair that had an ugly four inch wide bar across it at eye level. As for the bedrooms, on the door of each was a metal bracket where one put one's calling card to indicate the occupant. The whole thing was more like a transient hotel than a home.***

***The prior senior occupant had left the kitchen stocked with food rations in large military containers -- mostly "Number 8" cans. We found we had two Korean cooks who arrived at 0600 hours and normally left after the noon meal. Their cooking skills were minimal and one had to suspect that their training was associated with campfires more than stoves. There was no base commissary -- for such fundamentals we had to travel to the Army facility at Seoul and what was at Seoul was very limited.***

***As to support for our children, there was no local school, no kid books in a library, no play accouterments, no friends of their age -- only combat oriented officers and enlisted men, guns, airplanes and strange-speaking foreigners.***

***Although a courier flight went daily from Osan to Kimpo, the political situation dictated that I drive to Seoul in a military vehicle. While Seoul was only some 40 miles distant, the drive, terribly dusty in summer and equally muddy in winter, took more than two hours during which we had to pass through several ROK Army check points.***

*Our quarters were in ungodly condition and before they were reworked, during one storm, water actually poured out of the electrical outlets.*

*Then there was the roof. When it was finally repaired, it seemed that they removed two or three feet of thatch, tar and more before covering the place with corrugated metal.*

*Eventually, we managed to get the kitchen refurbished and the Air Force provided us with decent furniture and carpet for the floor. Installed in the living area was a huge fireplace some enterprising person had built years ago. This fireplace was seldom used as we had no need to burn the scarce supply of wood in Korea.*

*To the rear, directly out of my kitchen window, were the dilapidated metal Quonset huts of officers.*

*This was Hill One-Eighty.*

*Our children, having no playmates, periodically, the officers would talk to them but any relationship was strained.*

*It was in these primitive surroundings that I found that I had to put on a happy face and entertain senior Air Force officers, diplomatic persons and foreign dignitaries.*

*Had I not had a strong, supportive husband, I don't think I would have survived the two years in Korea.*

**Based on what I eventually observed when I transferred to Osan Air Base and moved into a billet a few feet directly behind the Commanding General's quarters, the foregoing overview is an understatement. Much as I would not appreciate these problems when I was at Kunsan Air Base, I fear that many of my problems were also far over the Osan horizon. Collectively, however, many persons worked to improve the situation in Korea but improvement did not come easily -- or quickly for the obstacles up-the-line were tremendous.***

---

* Reflecting the priority assigned the rehabilitation of the chapel at Kunsan Air Base, the history of the 314th Air Division covering the time period of this account records that a rehabilitation of the chapel at Osan Air Base made it "the most beautiful and modern building on the base." Additionally, the Staff Chaplain of the Division would record that "all other religious facilities in the command are in good shape." In contrast, this same history would state that "all bases and sites [of the Division] were continuously faced with problems of inadequate troop housing, sanitation and equipment." (Source: HRA files.) <u>God's priority was not mine!</u>

# THE FIRST STEP

**Steaming inside, mad at the world, pissed off at higher headquarters and the folderol to which I had been subjected ever since receiving the orders to Kunsan Air Base, and now confronted with what appeared to be an ungodly mess -- a dump, I had the "urge to kill" but I worked to contain my temper.**

**To give myself some "thinking time" and to simmer down, I walked to a window and pretended to look out. The blast of hot air that flowed in the holed screens of the open windows hardly helped my mood but I knew I had to get my tumultuous thoughts together. Behind me, I sensed that Davidson, the Lieutenant and the Master Sergeant were standing -- waiting for me to do or say something. Finally, I turned to them.**

**"Call a staff meeting of officers immediately -- here in this office. And, Lieutenant, confirm my presence by Special Order with an effective time of now."**

**"Sir, I don't understand?" the puzzled Lieutenant answered as he looked to Davidson for help but there was none there.**

**"Lieutenant, start by thinking. I am taking command of this base as of this minute -- as of 1530 hours today -- and we live by orders. Type up an order relieving Lt. Colonel Davidson of the responsibility and placing me in command -- I will sign it. It may come in handy for the courts-martial that are beginning to cross my mind. And send an arrival message to the Colonel's Group in the Pentagon. Here, let me draft it."**

**I picked up a stubby pencil from the desk along with a half-used, dust-covered yellow tablet and scribbled out the message:**

**TO: HEADQUARTERS USAF**
**WASHINGTON, D.C.**
**DCS/PERSONNEL**
**ATTN: COLONEL'S GROUP**
**PER ORDERS, I ARRIVED KUNSAN AIR BASE, KOREA, THIS DATE AND AT 1530 HOURS ASSUMED COMMAND.**
**COL. JOHN MOENCH**

"Now send a copy of this message to Division, Fifth Air Force and PACAF -- but do it by mail -- not TELEX. Understand -- by mail! And not today -- mail it tomorrow. I need a little breathing and thinking time."

"What about the Wing, sir?"

"What Wing?" I had heard Davidson mention the term *Wing* when he stated that the base had a waiver on grass cutting. But I knew nothing of a Wing. If it had been depicted on the organizational charts at Fifth Air Force, somehow I had missed it.

"We're subordinate to the Wing at Osan, sir."

So insult was added to injury. Although I had a message from the Division Commander to report early, I now was being advised that there was an intervening Wing to which I reported. How low on the totem pole had I come?

"Who's the Wing Commander?"

"It's a Colonel Musgrave, sir. He reported in just recently."

Damn! Another stranger. Why couldn't it have been someone I knew -- someone I had worked with before?

"Well, along with the mail transmission to the others, mail him a copy. As to additional distribution, as soon as you can make copies, post the order on the bulletin boards on this base."

With a "Yes sir," the Lieutenant left the room. Davidson looked at the Sergeant who seemed, in a knowing way, to send a return message. I felt that they were silently amused and laughing at me.

"I think I just asked for a meeting of officers to be called. What are you two standing here for? Get it done."

Davidson and the Sergeant were hastily retreating from my new office home when I found myself bugged additionally by the Korean girl at the outside desk.

"Sergeant, come back in here."

"Yes sir."

"What's your name, Sergeant?"

"It's Paul Young, sir. I'm your First Sergeant."

"All right, Paul. Close the door and let's do some talking."

"Yes sir."

The door shut, I tackled first my next most visible problem.

"Paul, do you know what this is on my desk?" As I spoke, with a finger I wrote my name on the desk top.

"It's dust, sir."

"And do you know how to get dust off a desk?"

"Yes sir. But it comes back almost as fast as you wipe it off."

"Then there is going to have to be a lot of time spent keeping it clean. Isn't that so?"

"Yes sir. I'll get a mama-san in here right away to dust things off."

"Correction, Sergeant Young. You dust it off and keep it dusted off. And, while you're at it, begin to figure out how you are going to get some decent furniture in this office. Then you might figure out how to get these windows fixed. I'm sure you have more mosquitoes here than you can count and screens with holes in them don't serve the purpose for which they were made. Get them fixed."

"But, sir, . . ."

Sergeant Young stopped in the middle of what he was about to say. Then, with a "Yes sir," he turned and started to leave the office.

"And one more thing, Paul. Who is that Korean girl sitting outside?"

"That's Miss Lee, sir. She's your secretary."

"And what is the security clearance of Miss Lee?"

"None, sir. She's Korean -- not American."

"And she may well be a spy for all I know. Move her desk well away from my office and, from now on, you type any correspondence I may have. Is that clear?"

"Yes sir."

I knew that I had stepped on a lot of established procedure and protocol and there would be many rumors flying in short order but I had to start somewhere. And, from experience, I knew that a good First Sergeant, almost any Sergeant, had ways to get things done that officers did not. Soon I would learn if Sergeant Young was or was not a good Sergeant."

With a sigh, I sat down at the desk and opened a drawer. It was stuffed with old papers, half-used pencils, cigarette butts that were partly in and partly out of an ash tray, old rubber bands and paper clips, mostly junk. The second drawer held the same conglomeration of miscellaneous crap. And the third. With rising fury, I pulled out every drawer and emptied the contents on the floor. This time I called for Davidson.

"What the hell is this mess?" I asked Davidson as he entered the office. "You have been acting commander here and I have to believe that you have been sitting at this desk. Why in hell couldn't you clean it up?"

"I'll get the mama-san to clean it up," he replied.

"You will like hell. You left it here, you clean it up."

"But, sir, . . ."

Suddenly, Davidson realized that he was in hot water.

"I'll take care of it, Colonel."

"And damned fast," I answered.

I didn't have a fire hose but I was hosing down the place as best I could.

The step from service in the higher military headquarters in Washington, D.C. and in Europe to now Kunsan Air Base at the extreme line of confrontation with the Communist enemies was the equivalent of moving from Capitol Hill to a front line foxhole.

During the Korean War and later, I had participated in military program and budget work which, by 1952, had resulted in a four-fold growth of military funding -- enough to fight the Korean War, support NATO and counter the growing Soviet threat. Defense had called for a higher plateau of readiness and, as early as 1952, tactical nuclear weapons and related support were being deployed overseas -- especially to Europe but also in the Far East.

Now, I suddenly found myself at the tip of the sword -- a sword that appeared to have a golden handle but a blunt and rusted point. I could not believe that which I was observing.

What had gone wrong? Why was I even here rather than being posted to the Strategic Air Command? Was this all some terrible joke? And who were the individuals who had allowed this situation to develop? The ex-Commander I had talked to in Japan -- was he part of the problem -- or was he a good man who had just gotten hemmed in by higher headquarters and a lack of support? But what about the Wing and the Division -- what about Fifth Air Force -- what about the United Nations Command -- what about U.S. Forces Korea? Was there anyone who had been paying attention?

To say I was sick at heart would be an understatement. I felt as if I was in mid-Pacific with the radios dead, the fuel running out, ice on the wings, fire on board and worse.

Yet, the sobering fact was that I had been appointed as the leader of over half a thousand men. And all of these men could be equally sick at heart -- frustrated, discouraged, defeated. This situation was not of my choosing but circumstance had made me the captain of this ship and, regardless of how rotted the hull and torn the sails, I had to make it function.

# THE STAFF MEETING

It took almost a half hour for a group of officers to assemble for the called staff meeting. Due to the short notice, I expected that the group would not be the whole of my staff but it would suffice. Unfortunately, the time since arriving at Kunsan had worn on me and, with each advancing minute, my frustration was expanding and my temper was growing shorter.

Outside the office, there had been a lot of shuffling and murmured discussion. Miss Lee apparently had been moved well away from the entrance to my office. Davidson had cleaned up the mess from the office drawers and they were now back in place. Obviously, he was thoroughly pissed off at the "clean up" order I had given him and I knew there would be comments flowing down the line. One of two things would be the result of my order -- either I had made a permanent enemy or I had brought him around to a position of subordinate support -- possibly reluctant support but support in any event. Somehow, I didn't care which of the answers was correct. In any event, I was certain that, within the day, I would be looked upon as an S.O.B. and, maybe, that was good.

Finally, Davidson knocked, came in and told me that he had managed to locate most of the key officers and that they were standing by outside the office. By now, Sergeant Young had managed to dust off the desk, table and chairs and was working on what was supposed to be a book case -- what it held, I was not certain.

"Paul, you can leave that for now. Get back to it after I have this meeting with the officers."

"Yes sir." Sergeant Young seemed to be pleased to leave the office. I suspected that, at first opportunity, he was going to get the mama-san on the cleaning job.

As the officers shuffled into the office, some in uniform and some in civilian clothes, I had the sensation that they were not accustomed to a staff meeting. I thought I might as well find out.

"When was your last staff meeting? " I asked.

There was fidgeting as the officers looked from one to another. Finally, Davidson answered.

"Colonel, we didn't have any general staff meetings until just now."

"Then how did you do business before this?"

"Well, the Colonel just talked to people now and then and everyone sort of went about doing what he thought ought to be done," Davidson answered.

I reflected on the situation for a moment. Could this all be a dream? Could a Commander run something without meetings with his officers? Could a base run with each person doing what he "thought he ought to do?" I was totally flabbergasted.

Looking from one face to another, I could see that the assembled officers did not comprehend what was running through my mind. By now, my words about courts-martial had probably reached some of them and I reasoned that they were wondering what was in store. Then I recalled the discussion with the personnel office in PACAF where I had been cautioned that getting new people was a 12 to 18 month task. Undoubtedly, I was stuck with those standing in front of me -- at least most of them.

As I tried to come to grips with the situation at hand, the words of one of my graduate professors came to mind: "As a leader, your job is to get the best out of every person and they all are different." So, "O.K.," I thought, "let's give it a try."

The officers still standing, I invited them to sit down. With not enough chairs for everyone, I suggested that more chairs be found and brought in. Quickly, the door opened and Sergeant Young came in with two chairs. It was obvious that my conversation could be heard in the outer office. Soon there were enough chairs for everyone and I opened the meeting.

Noting that some men had lighted up cigarettes, I issued my first staff order.

"With the windows open and holes in the screens, this room has a good air flow but I don't like to breathe tobacco smoke. There will be no smoking in this office."

Quickly, the lighted cigarettes were squashed out.

As my eyes moved from one officer to another, there was increased fidgeting.

"O.K. So I'm here. And so we can get on with the job of running this base, let's begin with who we are. For starters, I am . . ."

As I recounted my military career, I could see that they were viewing me as some sort of a prima donna. Obviously, my time in Air Force Headquarters and at major command levels was something beyond their appreciation. When I ended up by stating that I had just graduated from the Air War College, I knew we were on different wave lengths. I suspected that none of the officers in the room had served in major headquarters nor had they been to much in the way of military schools.

Finished with my own bio, I asked each of the officers present to tell me who he was, to brief his military career, and to tell me what his job was. Since Davidson was the senior officer in the group, I asked him to lead.

One by one, I learned about the officers who were present:

★★★★★★★★★★★★★★★★

Lt. Colonel Walter Davidson, who served as my Deputy Commander, had a lack luster military career. He had been in Korea about eight months -- he had four months to go and made a significant point of that fact. For some reason, I sensed that Davidson was one of those "lay back" types more inclined to dodge responsibility than to assume it. I noticed that, periodically, his hands shook. I wondered if he had a physical problem. I crossed him off as a weak character -- hardly the outstanding officer the ex-Commander had described to me.

Major Thomas "Tom" Akers was the Operations Officer. He appeared to be the senior Major. He was a happy, rotund individual, somewhat new to Korea and to the Far East. Of all the officers present, he was the only one with graying hair. Prior to this staff job, all his experience had been in flying tactical aircraft. But I wondered how much he really knew about the operations function. On the other hand, I had to reflect on how little I knew about the operations function when, at the ripe age of twenty-three, I was made the Assistant Group Operations Officer of the 323rd Bombardment Group (M) in Europe. The good news was that Akers gave me the impression of really wanting to do a job.

Major Steve Peterson, the Supply and Transportation Officer, came from Texas and spoke with the easy drawl of a Texan. He had been in Korea for about six months. This was his first assignment in this field of work and I could tell that he knew next to nothing about it but he seemed to be trying. He was also a pilot with his experience in transports.

Major Paul Benson was in charge of Communications and Electronics. He was relatively new to Korea -- about three months into his assignment. In addition to handling the base communications systems, he worked with the ROKAF when it came to radar problems.

**He seemed over grade for his job and I suspected he had been put out to pasture. He was not rated.**

**Captain Joseph Pastiak, the JAG who had impressed me at my arrival line-up, had been in Korea some five months. His background was strictly legal. Unlike most of the other officers, he spoke with complete confidence.**

**Captain Peter Wild, another non-rated officer and also about halfway through his Korean assignment, was in charge of Air Police -- to him fell all matters of security. Much like Captain Pastiak, he leaned to the stout side. Prior to this assignment, he had been in administrative work. I wondered if he knew how to use the forty-five he carried.**

**Captain Jesse Polk stated that he was the Engineering Officer. His prior experience was in flying transport aircraft. He was apologetic about the fact that he did not have an engineering degree nor had he ever before performed this type of work. He had only recently arrived in Korea. I asked Polk if his office possessed any of the engineering and lay out documentation covering Kunsan Air Base. He replied that he had discovered nothing like that in his files. He suggested that such information undoubtedly was held at Fifth Air Force.**

**And so it went. One officer after another reciting his background and virtually none of them trained for or experienced in the work which they were charged to perform. About one-third were newly assigned; one-third were approaching or at the mid-point of the 12 month assignment; and one-third were FIGMO! I had to wonder about the personnel system that had orchestrated such mis-matches of people to jobs.***

**Finally, we came to the Dentist, a Lieutenant Able Grossman. His background was typical of many dentists in the military service -- a young dentist educated at government expense and now filling out a**

* Much later I would learn that the personnel situation I was faced with was common to all of Korea. As summarized in one Division history statement, "All Air Force units in Korea [are] handicapped by personnel shortages, turnover, and by personnel with low experience levels. . . . In many cases, personnel assignments [are] made by balancing manpower authorizations with urgent needs and with the particular skill, grade, and experience level available at the time." (Source: HRA files.)

required service obligation. I could tell that his heart was somewhere else -- probably thinking about his up-coming private practice.

My eyes scanned the group. Where was the doctor?

"Don't we have a Flight Surgeon?" I asked. "I seem to recall being briefed that this base had one assigned."

"He's on leave," Davidson answered.

"So who takes care of the sick and wounded while he's gone?" I asked.

"We have some medical Sergeants and, if the case is beyond their capability, as it was with the burn casualties this past week, we air evac the individuals to Osan."

"What burn casualties?" I asked with sudden concern.

"We had a petroleum fire. One of the storage tanks accidentally ignited and we lost a man -- plus three others were pretty badly burned. They were trying to fix some leaks in a tank and probably caused a spark. Lieutenant Grossman and our medical Sergeants, along with the help of some our officers, did what they could. We were delayed in the air evac because of weather but we got the casualties up to Osan the next day and I understand that they have been evacuated to Tripler in Hawaii."

"Has notification gone to the family of the deceased?"

"They take care of that at Osan," Davidson replied.

"And his effects -- have they been packed and shipped?"

"I'll have to check on that, sir. I think Lieutenant Jones, you met him coming in, has that as a job."

"You think!" I stared at Davidson. Apparently my Deputy Commander was no "Commander." "Why is not Lieutenant Jones in here? Is he not part of my staff? From now on, he comes to staff meetings."

Half a thousand men and no doctor on the base? I made a mental note to raise hell about that as soon as I reported to Division Headquarters at Osan -- or was that something that was under the supervision of the Wing Commander, Colonel Musgrave? Then, as an additional annoyance, I noted that none of the officers present was from the fighter unit standing alert.

"How come no one is here who belongs to those tactical fighters out on the line?" I asked.

"They're tenants," Davidson answered. "They don't belong to us."

Again I was stunned. Tenants or not, they needed to be a part of the scenario -- needed to understand and share in the problems of the base. Apparently, I was seeing what the ex-Commander had told me -- the tenants did their own thing. But I was not going to be a fifth wheel. Perhaps I had been too exposed to the Navy concept of the all-powerful ship commander; on the other hand, perhaps, in spite of my considerable exposure to the Air Force way of doing things, I had lost sight of how the system really ran at the lower levels? And, quickly, I realized, but this for the first time, that the tactical fighters on the field were, somehow, also outside even the command line of the Division Commander in Osan. What a screwed up mess! Commanders, commanders and more commanders -- and no one was "commanding!"

"Davidson, they may be tenants but they live here, they eat here, they sleep here, they fly from here. From now on when I have a staff meeting, I want the senior officer of each major tenant unit present -- whatever his title, home base or command line is. And if there is any grumbling about that directive, just tell me and I'll take care of the problem. Is that clear?" I had no idea as to how I would "take care of the problem" if my demands were resisted. But I knew that a good offense was better than any defense. My gut feeling was that no one living on the base was about to offend the new Commander.

"Yes sir." I could tell that Davidson did not like the order.

Finally another thought struck me. Where were the Chaplains that I had been briefed on -- the Catholic and Protestant Chaplains?

"Why don't I see a Chaplain here?" I asked.

"I didn't advise either of them to be here," Davidson answered. "I didn't think you would consider them to be staff officers -- I don't. Perhaps I made a mistake?"

"That you did. Just be certain that at our next staff meeting the senior Chaplain is here."

So much time had transpired that dusk was beginning to fall. One of the officers switched on a light in the office. Overhead, a single, low wattage bulb began to burn -- dim at first and then slowly brightening. In the background, I heard a generator start up.

"All right, I can recognize the time. I presume that we are about at the dinner hour and I'll meet you all for dinner. Is it at the Officers Club or do you eat in a mess shall?"

"At the Mark, sir," a voice answered. Fortunately, I knew what the "Mark" was.

"O.K. At the Officers Club. But before this gathering breaks up, let me discuss tomorrow. Unless there is an emergency of some sort, as the first thing on tomorrow's agenda I want to sit through your base briefing."

"Sir, we don't have one." It was Davidson speaking.

"Then you have from now until tomorrow morning to get one," was my curt reply. I could see Davidson shake his head in wonderment.

"After the base briefing," I continued, "I want Captain Wild to take me on a base tour. I'd ask Colonel Davidson to do this but I sense that he will have some work to do as a result of the base briefing. Anyhow, as a part of the base tour, I especially want to look at some of the security set up and that means Captain Wild needs to be my guide.

"Right after lunch, I want Major Akers, who I assume is qualified, to give me a check ride in the C-47. I have had considerable time in the Gooney Bird so that should not take long. Tom," I purposefully switched to his given name, a practice that I would selectively employ when a person was in good standing, "do brief me on your check out procedure, forms, etc. Then, if all goes well, the following day, I want a check ride in the L-20. I haven't flown a light aircraft since World War Two -- and then it was mostly L-4s and L-5s when I was with a B-26 Marauder unit. I probably have forgotten how a light aircraft feels.

"By the way, I don't think anyone at the 314th Air Division, or that Wing up there at Osan, knows that I am on the ground here and, for the moment, I want it to stay that way. As soon as Major Akers has me checked out in the Gooney Bird, I'll fly up to Division and report in to it and the Wing. I understand that the Division Commander has changed. Who is the Brigadier who now fills the slot? Is he aboard yet?"

"It's a General James Joyce," Davidson answered. "He came in from an assignment in Japan. I understand that he is on the recent Brigadier list and was frocked for the job. I think he took over last week."

"What else do you know about him? Do you have a bio? Do you have his photo?"

"Nothing, sir."

"O.K. Davidson. Add that to the things that need to be done and, while you are at it, get Colonel Musgrave's bio and photo. Now how about you driving me up to where I am supposed to live? I need to unpack and change into a fresh uniform.

"And, by the way, from now on I want to start the day with a staff meeting. Tomorrow, it will be primarily to review the base briefing. Normally, it will be to review where we are and where we want to go. If I am not there, you lead the meeting. If both of us are

**gone, give the lead to the next senior officer assigned to this squadron. The meeting need not be long -- just long enough for us to huddle as a team and get our signals straight before we jump into the line for the day."**

**I knew that Davidson's "yes sir" did not come from the heart. Obviously, I was creating a new and unaccustomed routine.**

**Picking up my hat to leave, I noticed a safe sitting by a side wall. It was a small thing and rather ancient.**

**"Is this the best we can do when it comes to safes?" I asked.**

**"Yes sir," Davidson answered. "We've only got three safes -- yours, a big one in the finance office and one in Operations. They are all civilian jobs that were here when I arrived. According to the markings, I think they originally belonged to the Japanese. Some of the file cabinets do have bar locks."**

**"Does the combination work?**

**"It does."**

**"Well, change the combination. I'll tell you later who can hold it."**

**"Sir, we can't change the combination to your safe or the others. We don't know how. I think it takes a key and we don't have one."**

**Again I was shocked. God knows who knew the combinations to the safes. Possibly even the Japanese!**

**"Well, figure out an answer. I want the combinations to all safes changed immediately and I want to know who holds those combinations."**

**Davidson shook his head. I sensed that he would pass off the job to some other person.**

**"And something else."**

**Davidson cringed. We were about to get into the staff car, he on the driver's side; me on the passenger side. We talked over the top of the car.**

**"Bring to breakfast tomorrow morning a list of the assigned officers together with their dates of rank and security clearances. Add to the list Sergeant Young and any other key EM. And, before tomorrow passes, try to get the same data on the key personnel of our U.S. tenant units."**

**Davidson looked a bit sick. His hands were beginning, once again, to shake. I knew that I was unloading on him but I had to find out what he was made of -- and, already, I was doubting that the finding would be a good one.**

# THE WALDORF ASTORIA

**By the time Davidson and I drove away from the headquarters building, it was dark. And there were few lights on the base -- here and there a small bulb illuminated the door of a building. Overall, all I could see was what the headlights revealed and that was not much. However, it was enough to remind me of the grass situation.**

**"Davidson, do you remember what an *idiot stick* is?"**

**"Yes sir. We used to have them in boot camp. That was before we had powered lawn mowers."**

**"And do we have any idiot sticks here?"**

**"I don't think so, sir. At least I haven't seen any."**

**"Well, as soon as you can, and that means tomorrow morning at the latest, you get word to Captain Polk -- as I recall from our meeting he's the Engineer on this base -- you tell Polk to build a bunch of them. And, if he doesn't know what an idiot stick looks like or how to make one, you explain it to him. By noon tomorrow, I want to see some idiot sticks at work on this grass. Map out the main base area in sections and assign the sections by units, barracks, or by any way that makes sense. And make grass cutting a responsibility of everyone -- officers included. And have one idiot stick delivered to me."**

**"The officers?" Obviously the thought came as a shock to Davidson. For my part, it was a quick decision triggered by the recollection of Colonel John S. Samuel of the 322nd Bombardment Group (M) in World War II calling out everyone, including the officers, to repair runways and taxiways during the Battle of the Bulge and to get the snow removed to allow combat operations. It worked and, years later, every person who had participated, officers and enlisted men, was proud of the achievement. I prayed that I would get a similar result out of grass cutting but I knew it was a long shot.**

**"That's right -- the officers. And you can tell them that I expect the grass in their area to be better trimmed than that in the enlisted and other areas. Is that clear?"**

**"Yes sir. But what about the grass out on the airfield? The Koreans cut that on a contract basis and haul it off for fodder and fuel."**

**"Let that system continue -- I'm talking about the grass in the living and administrative areas."**

**Without looking, I knew there was a scowl on Davidson's face. He did not comment further. The silence was deafening. I wondered what the grass cutting "contract" was -- did we pay the Koreans or did they pay us? That question, however, could wait.**

**Finally, Davidson steered the staff car up a slight hill and approached a small, siding sheeted building. As the headlights illuminated the back entrance, fully a half dozen large black rats scurried away from a rough platform that served as an entrance step. They appeared to run under the house but some tall weeds next to the door obscured my vision. Above the door was a hand-lettered sign that read: *Waldorf Astoria.***

**"Lots of rats here, sir. We put poison out but they seem to thrive on it. After a while, you get used to them."**

**"I'll be damned if I'll get used to them," was my response.**

**Stepping out of the staff car, I realized my billet was one of a series of identical buildings. Some distance from my quarters, a dim outside light bulb burned. To the side of the building I could see a 55 gallon oil drum on wooden two-by-four stilts -- most likely, by a gravity system, it supplied oil to an inside heater. Obviously, it was leaking.**

**"What a fire hazard," I thought. I had seen many a tent go up in flames in World War II with just such a system -- and, often, the men inside went up in flames with it.**

**To the side of the entrance were two outside wooden lawn chairs -- both with well-rotted slats. The roadway we had driven on was located adjacent to the building and it was dirt. Now the cloud of dust that had followed the vehicle descended on us. It made breathing difficult and I began to cough.**

**"Who built these quarters?" I asked as soon as my throat cleared.**

**Confirming what the ex-Commander had told me in Japan, Davidson asnwered.**

**"These are Japanese buildings. From the Koreans, I understand that they were built some time before the end of World War Two. We think the Japanese occupying Korea built them for their officers -- possibly as family quarters although they don't have conventional kitchens. They're better built than the typical Korean stuff -- but not much better. From the outside, they look pretty good -- inside is something else. The siding you see was put on some years ago -- but only on the ones up here -- those down hill are just plain stucco -- it's the original stucco and some of it is pretty bad. Recently, we**

scrounged some gray paint, enough for your billet and a few others, so they don't look too bad."

Davidson went to the rear of the staff car, untied the rope holding the trunk lid down, and took out my B-4 bag and navigator case.

"Door's unlocked, sir. I contacted your mama-san and had her leave it open. You can go right in."

"My mama-san?"

"Your housekeeper, sir. She takes care of the quarters and does your laundry -- or anything else you want done."

"What's she paid?"

"No need to worry, sir. We have a contract covering all mama-sans for the officers -- it's handled by the Officers Club."

The concept bothered me but before I could reach any conclusion a rather short, uniformed person, a Korean, stepped out of the shadows and saluted. I noted that he carried a well-worn American carbine slung over his shoulder. The uniform was neither American nor Korean. Davidson saw my concerned reaction.

"Sir, this is Mister Kim. He is the head of our Korean guards. They protect the officer's housing area at night. It helps to hold down the slicky stuff. He speaks a little English. He used to work for the Japanese -- hates them to beat all hell. He's a good man. He and his men will make sure that nothing happens up here."

I saluted back and "Mister Kim" bowed and retreated into the shadows.

"And who pays for the Korean guards?" I asked.

"The Officers Club, sir."

"And to whom do the guards report -- the club manager?"

"No sir. Captain Wild serves as their supervisor."

Damn! I could sense all sort of problems with this arrangement. What was the liability if these Korean guards shot someone -- the "wrong one?" How were they trained? In what direction was their loyalty? Were they given any sort of security check? What were their instructions -- their orders for the day? In the case of a military engagement, did they fight alongside the Americans? It was mind-boggling. I knew I was going to have to review this arrangement with Captain Wild -- and with Joe Pastiak.

Davidson's words brought me back to reality.

"Careful when you walk in, sir. The bathroom has been giving us a problem -- the water pipes leak most of the time -- and the floor in the entrance way and bathroom is on the rotted side."

Seeing my hesitation, Davidson led the way in -- switching on a single hallway bulb that hung precariously from on old ceiling fixture. As I followed Davidson in, the surroundings overwhelmed me.

"What in the hell happened here?" I asked.

"You mean the food trays?" Davidson answered.

"I mean the food trays, the empty beer cans and liquor bottles, the piles of crap in the corners -- and look at that closet -- the floor is covered with what looks like old blankets, military equipment and just plain junk!"

"The Commander had a party before he left, sir. I guess the place was not cleaned up. I'll get the mama-san to clean it up tomorrow. If I had known ahead of time that you were arriving today, it would have looked a lot better but we only knew of your arrival a short time before your aircraft touched down."

"Davidson, I don't know how this base operated in the past but I get the impression that, since my predecessor left, you haven't done much of anything. Worse, from what I've seen so far, I get the sensation that this base is being run by a bunch of incompetents. To me, it's beginning to look like something out of a comic strip. To hell with changing uniform. I'll find your Officers Club and get a bite to eat. And, after I do that, I'm coming back here at which time I expect to find these quarters cleaned up. And I don't care who does it -- mama-san or someone else. Since you allowed this situation to exist, maybe you ought to clean it up. Now give me the key to that blue pile of junk you call a staff car."

With that, I stormed out of the billet slamming the door behind me, fired up the blue bomb and drove off. I didn't know where the Officers Club was located but calculated that it would not be too hard to find -- it had to be somewhere near.

As I sought out the Officers Club, I had one dominating thought crashing through my mind. "Just what in the hell was it that I had been presented as a base and a command? Could this all be real or was it some sort of a crazy joke? And was Kunsan Air Base a microcosm of all USAF presence in the Republic of Korea or was that which I was observing limited to the K-8 outpost?"

Thank God that, in the darkness, no one wandered in front of the staff car for, in my growing anger, I might have run over the person.

# THE BOTTOM OF THE MARK

**They had named it "The Bottom of the Mark." Certainly, it was the bottom of something.**

**A rambling, ramshackle, one story building, the loud music coming from inside suggested it was a club -- the number of jeeps and other vehicles parked in front signaled that it must be the Officers Club.**

**The headlights of my staff car picked up a sign that read "Base Commander" and I pulled into the open slot, carefully slid out of the seat so as not to get caught by the spring protruding from below, took a deep breath of the night air, and readied myself for what probably was going to be another unhappy surprise.**

**Stepping inside the club, I was greeted by a rush of smoke-filled air, heavy with the odor of stale beer and the smell of greasy, fried foods. A small Korean band was thumping out some all-too-loud music but the rhythm was not bad. Several noisy air conditioners were churning at the side walls but with little effect on the temperature -- the air was hot and virtually unbearable and the air conditioners simply recycled the smoke-filled air.**

**Major Peterson was the first person to spot me and he walked toward me with a greeting.**

**"*Annyong hasipnika* -- welcome to the *Bottom of the Mark*, sir. It's not much but it's all we got. Can I get you a drink and show you around?"***

**"Please, " I answered as I hung my hat on a rack by the entrance door, "but no drink -- not right now." I could have used a double or triple Scotch -- or, with the heat, a great big cold beer -- but decided that it was better not to create a first impression with a drink in my hand. Fortunately, I had already heard the Korean greeting and did not have to ask for a meaning.**

**In seconds, it was obvious that my presence had been telegraphed to those present -- waiters, waitresses, josans and band included. The music stopped and the leader of the band bowed. A deathly silence fell over the room. Everyone seemed to want to look -- to study the new Commander.**

---

* In G.I. slang, the friendly Korean greeting of "annyong hasipnika" became bastardized as "on your horse amigo."

With Peterson leading the way, I was escorted through the main room, to a bar room that had a center fireplace that Peterson said was a good idea that didn't work, to the dining room, and then to the smoke-filled kitchen. En route, there were some mumbled greetings; the Koreans bowed. Then, as soon as we would leave a room, a swirl of American and Korean conversation could be heard.

The tour finished, Peterson asked if I had any questions.

"Indeed," I answered. "The number of officers here suggests a population much larger than was indicated by the number attending my quick staff meeting or by the manning documentation. Do these officers belong to me or are they here on temporary duty, just transients, or what?"

"Most of them are from the alert tactical fighter unit, sir. We do get a few transients in here but not many. We don't have any VOQ facilities and I think everyone in Korea, Japan and Okinawa, possibly even the Philippines, knows this. If we get some over-night transient officers, we have to find a vacant bunk among those already assigned. With the enlisted men, it's not too big a problem -- but it still is a problem. We try to discourage anyone spending the night here."

"And how about all the Korean girls I saw as I passed through the club?"

"You mean the waitresses or the josans?"

"The josans."

"They're from Kunsan City. They're brought in every night for the men. It's pretty tough being assigned out here and, except for the rickety Korean buses that none of us should ride, there is no regular transportation to the city -- so we just use some GI trucks to bring the girls out here."

Suddenly, I felt as if I had inherited a military house of prostitution.

"Steve, tell me more."

"Like what, sir?"

"Like what is going on. I'm no damn fool. Are we running a whorehouse on this base?"

"Well, no sir. Not that. It's just that this must have seemed like a good idea -- and, apparently, it has been going on for a long time -- it was going on when I arrived. Each club, officer and enlisted, just orders up how many truck loads of girls it thinks would fit in for the evening and some vehicles are sent to the city to pick them up. The girls in the city know the routine and they are always ready and eager. We try to clear them all off the base by midnight. Sometimes it's a bit

**tough to gather them all up but they don't seem to cause any problem. Naturally, by one or two o'clock the base is clear. I appreciate that for someone not used to Korea, or the Orient, this may seem a bit odd but it works and it keeps the men happy."**

**I would be a fool not to recognize that I was being viewed as someone not understanding the situation -- someone not familiar with the Orient or Korea. From the rundown of my bio at the staff meeting, Peterson and the others knew that I had no prior service in the Far East. That point had probably already been communicated far and wide. Further, my bio had displayed a weak point -- I had not had prior service as a base commander. I easily recalled how in World War II we were shouldered with senior persons arriving in the middle of combat and attempting to run the operation as if they were running a Stateside training base. I knew the pitfalls and I recognized that the overseas environment often presented problems not found Stateside and allowances had to be made. But this seemed preposterous.**

**"Well, I'll be damned! Would you make a note that I want to talk to you, Davidson, Captain Wild and Captain Pastiak about this tomorrow. I'm going to be on a tight schedule so I'll leave it up to you to work out the time."**

**"Yes sir. But what do you want me to tell them is the purpose of the meeting -- what is it that you want to talk about?"**

**"I think you know what the subject will be -- if not, you haven't been thinking."**

**Peterson looked confused but I thought it best to let the matter stay that way -- exploration and explanation could await tomorrow.**

**"Where are the reefers?" I asked.**

**"They're in the back."**

**"Let's go look."**

**"The Korean cooks have the keys," Peterson advised as he headed back to the kitchen. "I'll go get them just in case you want to look inside."**

**"Hold it," I ordered. "Isn't there a club manager here?"**

**"I guess I'm it," Peterson answered. "We sort of rotate the job and I have it for this month."**

**"And you allow the Korean cooks to run the inventory?"**

**"Yes sir. They are very dependable. Most of them have been here for years. We do an inventory check at the end of each month and it comes out pretty good."**

**The answer was hardly comforting but, for the moment, I saw no need to pursue the subject and I waved Peterson off. In a minute, he was back with a ring of keys.**

**Outside the rear of the club stood two large, portable reefers. A portable generator huffed and puffed to the side.**

**"We're on back up power right now," Peterson explained. "One of the main diesel generators went down some time ago -- a connecting rod broke. We have a spare rod so we should have it back on line by morning."**

**"What would happen if you didn't have a spare rod?"**

**"We'd be in deep kimchi. It would probably take us six months to a year to get a replacement and our back up generator capacity is limited as all hell."***

**"O.K. Let's take a look inside the reefers."**

**There was a rush of cold vapor when the reefers were opened. Inside I saw a reasonable supply of frozen meats and other products. Some of it carried military labels but a good portion carried Japanese printing -- something I had already learned to distinguish but not read.**

**"Why so much Japanese product?" I asked.**

**"It's the only way we can run the club mess," Peterson answered. "The rations we get out of the Army's supply point just don't handle our needs so we supplement our inventory through purchases in Japan. We have tried to make one flight a week to Japan but we recently got an order from that new Wing Commander at Osan to cut out those flights. The Wing Commander stated that there was a fuel shortage. I doubt the fuel argument but he's still the Wing Commander. Unfortunately, if we don't get back to Japan pretty soon, this stock will be used up and what happens then no one knows."**

**"You mean there is a restriction from Wing at Osan on where we fly our Gooney Bird?"**

**"Yes sir. We now have to get approval for any flight outside Korea. In the past, this hasn't been a problem -- we even have flown as far south as Hong Kong and Clark in the Philippines. Now the new Wing Commander at Osan has clamped down on everything. I understand that he's a real son-of-a-bitch!"**

**"Is the problem the Wing Commander or the Division Commander?" I asked.**

---

* A typical statement from recorded history: "There is definite lack of . . . primary power. Most of the power requirements in Korea are met with power units designed to furnish auxiliary power and were not designed to furnish steady primary power." (Source: HRA files.)

"From scuttle, as far as we can determine, it is the Wing Commander. He's pretty well advertised as a real stick-in-the-mud. You'll have to wait until you meet him to make up your own mind -- but the stories that came with him are pretty bad. Frankly, I don't think this new Wing Commander has ever served in the Far East before -- he hasn't a clue as to what makes things tick out here. He's got wings but most of those I have talked to conclude that he still thinks he is riding horses in the cavalry. As the stories go, he's at the end of the line and desperate. The word I get is that he's out to impress the Division Commander and visiting VIPs any way he can. I get stories from Osan that he could care less about anyone other than himself, those senior to him and how he might still get promoted. I understand that he's hogging all the stuff coming from Japan for Hill One-Eighty and the Osan Officers Club."

Hidden in Peterson's words it was there again. I had to wonder how long it took for a person to move from the category of "the new kid on the block" to that of the "old hand." Apparently, this Colonel Musgrave had more than newness to Korea in his saddle bag. I had prior experiences with the type officer Peterson was describing, one of the worst in the Pentagon when I was ordered to stop work as I was creating "too many waves," and I did not look forward to a repeat experience -- but I readied myself for it. I did not know what the "Hill One-Eighty" comment was all about and I did not ask.

"Has this new Wing Commander visited Kunsan?" I asked.

"Not the current one nor the past one -- not in the time I have been here." Added to what I had already learned about people not visiting Kunsan, Peterson's answer told me a lot about the problems I would face.

Returning to the club's interior, Peterson accompanied me to the bar. There I ordered a beer for myself -- Peterson did the same. Peterson took pains to introduce me to everyone he knew but there were a good number of strangers. He explained that, with the rotating of alert air crews and their support personnel, the club was usually populated with a number of strange faces. "With most of the tactical people on a two week rotation schedule, we don't get to know many of them."

When I reached into my pocket for some money to pay for the drinks, the bartender waved me off. Peterson explained.

"Out here, every newcomer's first drink is on the house. It is sort of a welcome to the ravages of Korea."

In the background, the Korean band played on. On the dance floor, many of the officers were paired with the imported josans. Most of the josans were well proportioned with their tight, high slit silk dresses showing off every physical vantage item they possessed. I suspected what would happen before the trucks took them back to the city but that had to await the next day's conversation with Davidson, Peterson, Wild and Pastiak.

Suddenly, I realized that I had not eaten since breakfast and I asked Peterson about the menu. He suggested fried chicken -- he stated that the remainder of the last shipment of steak out of Japan was pretty tough and the Korean cooks were discussing cutting it up for stew.

I didn't like fried chicken but I took his advice. The meal -- heavily coated fried chicken, French fried potatoes and bread -- was filling but I sensed that the absorbed grease content was such that I would suffer by morning. I asked Peterson about salad and vegetables and was informed that most of the salad items, even vegetables, obtained from the Army supply point, particularly if they arrived by rail, were rotted on receipt. Onions, carrots and cabbage seemed to take the trip from the United States to Korea but other items did not fare too well. "Often all we do," he alleged, "is take the stuff out of the freight cars and throw it into garbage cans. Frankly, based on the condition of some foodstuff on arrival," he added, "I think it should never have been shipped. We can blame a lot on refrigeration and the transportation difficulties to and in Korea but I think the problem starts way back in the U.S. purchasing system. Some of the stuff we get must have been over-ripe, even beginning to rot, before it left the west coast."

As to fruit, Peterson stated that, periodically, the base obtained apples or oranges but never pineapples, bananas or soft fruit such as peaches and plums. The base did get in some dried fruit and, at breakfast, they might have stewed prunes. He stated that any flight going south to Taiwan or the Philippines usually brought back as much pineapple, orange and other tropical fruit as could be carried. However, there had been no flight that far south for some time.

The meal over, Peterson picked up the check. He commented that I could pay for the next one. I did not like the idea of someone paying for my drinks or meals but, for the moment, disagreement about who picked up the check seemed a bit clumsy.

Increasingly disturbed and with time running late, I decided to go back to my quarters and get ready for my first full day of whatever was the job the personnel assignment system had unloaded on me.

# THE END OF DAY ONE

**Lt. Colonel Davidson was standing outside my quarters when I arrived. The place, he said, had been cleaned out and swept. I did not ask who had done it.**

**Davidson handed me two padlocks -- one with a red mark on it. He told me that there was a bolt inside the front and back doors and he suggested that I use them. Further, he suggested that, using the padlock with the red mark, I padlock the entrance door when I left in the morning. He assured me that my mama-san had a key to that padlock but not to the other one. The other padlock, he said, was for a large wooden chest in my bedroom. He urged me to put anything of value in that chest and lock it. "For security, it's bolted to the floor from the inside so don't try to move it."**

**"I thought you said that the Korean guards held down the slicky stuff in the officer's billeting area?"**

**"They do," answered Davidson, "but we still have some problems."**

**"How bad?" I asked.**

**"Pretty bad," was the response.**

**I decided to leave it at that -- slicky problems were hardly a priority at the moment.**

**"What time does the Officers Club open for breakfast?"**

**"It's open at 0630," Davidson answered, "but, if you get down there before that time, they will fix you up." Then he added, "Operations at Headquarters begins at 0800. Is that O.K.?"**

**I declined to answer the question.**

**"I'll see you at the club at 0700. Are my bags inside?"**

**"They're in the bedroom next to your bed."**

**Davidson saluted and began walking down the dirt road behind the quarters.**

**"Well, here I am," I thought as I opened the door and stepped inside. Having been cautioned about the rotting floor, I proceeded warily, testing as I walked. The give in the floor suggested that it needed early replacement. In one area, a sheet of plywood had been placed over the original flooring. I could guess the condition of the underlying boards.**

**The lights on, I surveyed my new home: the *Waldorf Astoria*.**

There was a living room of sorts. On one wall a stone fireplace had been constructed by some enterprising person. I wondered if, like the one in the Officers Club, it would fail to work when the cold of a Korean winter descended on me. I gathered that it did not work very well as there was a G.I. pot belly stove in the center of the room -- a rusted pipe reached up to the ceiling. A small copper pipe ran from the outer wall, across the floor and to the stove -- apparently there was another 55 gallon oil drum on the side of the billet away from the entrance and the one I had observed earlier. Four brownish, rather threadbare lounge chairs, a small coffee table, and a small table with four beat-up office type chairs constituted the primary furniture. Goodwill would probably have refused to take any of the items. I hit a lounge chair with my hand and a cloud of dust immediately filled the air.

The bedroom consisted of a bed, a bedside stand on which there was a small lamp, an old four-drawer dresser of sorts -- one drawer was missing -- it stood against the wall -- broken -- and the large wooden box that Davidson had described. To the side of the bed was another G.I. stove -- this one was a regular oil burner. The bed had two mattresses -- one stacked on top of the other. "RHIP," I thought.

At the head of the bed, there was a semblance of a pillow; the bed was covered with what used to be white sheets. A mosquito net was draped over the bed. At a side window, an old air conditioner chugged along trying to turn out some cool air -- it only partially succeeded. A telephone was situated on the bedside stand. There was a wooden chair in the room, part of the back was broken out.

I glanced at my watch. It was past 2300 hours. That meant it was morning in Washington, D.C. I sat on the edge of the bed and picked up the telephone. A G.I. operator came on.

"This is Colonel Moench. Can you ring me through to the Pentagon?"

"I'll try, sir," the voice answered.

The telephone route from Kunsan outward was torturous. The local operator rang Osan Air Base and a female Korean voice answered. Then the Osan operator rang Fuchu Air Station in Japan. Now there was a Japanese operator. The Fuchu operator rang PACAF in Hawaii. Finally, a Pentagon operator came on. The voice from the Pentagon was very faint and somewhat garbled.

"This is Colonel Moench calling from Korea. Give me Colonel George Johnson in Air Force DCS/Materiel." She couldn't hear me so

I repeated the words -- this time shouting. Finally, I spelled out George's name.

There was a wait as the Pentagon operator rang information for the number and then I heard a telephone ringing. A secretary came on and I asked for George. It was difficult to hear and I think we were both shouting -- but we did communicate.

"John Moench, you old S.O.B., is that you?"

"It's me, George."

"And how the hell are you?"

"I'm out in Korea. I just arrived at Kunsan and I need some help."

"Name it," George answered.

"George, this may sound silly as all hell but I want you to send me a couple American flags -- if you can, get me one with the fringe on the edges for use in my office. You may not believe it but this base doesn't have a flag to fly and seems unable to get one. How about going to supply at Andrews and shaking them down for a few flags and sending them to me by way of a courier pouch. And throw in a Pentagon telephone book while you're at it. I think I may be calling for more help before this story ends."

"You walk into a problem?"

"Seems so. For starters, the grass on this base is knee high and I sense that I will find out a lot more tomorrow. I just arrived today and already I seem to have more than I can pray over."

"The grass is knee high? Don't your men know how to use a lawn mower?"

"It appears that we don't have any lawn mowers. I ordered the building of idiot sticks and will figure out the next move tomorrow."

"Well, have fun. I'll get the flags en route to you today. Stay in touch."

I heard a click indicating that George had hung up.

"Well, there goes another chit," I thought as I opened my navigator case and pulled out my toilet articles.

It took me a while to locate the pull chain for the light in the bathroom. I had searched for a wall switch to no avail and then tried fumbling around in the dark bathroom for a possible pull chain -- finally my hand hit it. The light turned out to be a small bulb hanging from the center of the ceiling.

As the light, dim as it was, flooded the bathroom, I found myself disgusted and amazed. Apparently, the fixtures were hand made at the time of the original construction by the Japanese. The tub and hand

**bowl were made out of heavy, cast concrete, the outer surface was hand polished with small decorative tiles placed on the inner, water side. The hand bowl hung crazily -- apparently, it was much too heavy for the supporting wall. The tub was severely cracked -- I was certain that it would not hold water in spite of some gunk that someone had smeared on the cracks. A pipe ran up the wall to a rusted shower head that apparently had been added at some later date. There was only one faucet. Turning to the hand bowl, I saw two faucets and tried them. One worked. Obviously, the plumbing did not include hot water. And then I saw the mirror! Cracked and with most of the silver peeled off the back, only parts of my face were reflected and that which I could see was distorted.**

**"Shit!"**

**The utterance seemed to bring on the urge and I decided to try out the commode. This was the one item that was somewhat modern but it was far from new -- brown stains coated the interior. Mounted on the wall above the commode was a flush water tank. As I took my position on the commode, I prayed that it would work. Alongside the commode, I noted a half roll of toilet paper held by a wire. Glancing around the room, I saw no other toilet paper. "When I see this mama-san of mine, I'll have to tell her to leave an extra roll," I thought.**

**Fortunately, the toilet flushed -- but with a loud sucking sound that startled me.**

**Returning to the bedroom, I opened my B-4 bag and took out my uniforms and hung them in the closet. There were some rusted wire hangers in the closet and, to keep my uniforms from getting stained, I wrapped them with toilet paper.**

**"All I need now, is to get the G.I.s," I thought as the roll of toilet paper all but disappeared.**

**I was pleased to note that the rubbish in the closet had been removed and it had been swept out. I had to guess that something like a vacuum cleaner was not to be had.**

**My uniforms hung up, I placed my other clothes in the available drawers of the dresser. I had to wonder why something so simple as a dresser drawer could not have been repaired. And I could not help but think that, if this was the way the Commander lived, how did the troops live? Soon, I would find out.**

**With my clothes unpacked, I pulled an envelope and note pad from my navigator case, thought a while and then wrote a letter home.**

*Dear Mary:*

*I have arrived safe and sound.*

*Kunsan is a bit of a surprise. I haven't been here a full day and, already, I can see that my hands are going to be full.*

*My Deputy is a Lt. Col. Davidson. I can't say that I'm impressed but I am trying not to jump to quick conclusions. I did meet the departing Commander from Kunsan in Japan. Long story.*

*The quarters here leave a lot to be desired -- they're not something I would like to see you and the children facing. For laughs, I have learned that my billet is called the "Waldorf Astoria."*

*It's been a long day and I'm going to hit the sack.*

*Give Michele and Jeff a hug for me.*

*Love,*

*John*

**The note was short and it bothered me. But there was no need to worry Mary by telling her of the growing array of problems -- she had enough on her hands being alone with our two children -- both of whom were probably giving her fits.**

**I had two sets of pajamas with me but, notwithstanding a noisy air conditioner, it was so hot in the billet that I decided to sleep in my shorts. I pulled the mosquito net aside and crawled in. Then, I reached out and shut off the table lamp. I was exhausted. Almost immediately, the sheets were soaked with sweat.**

**I never did understand why a mosquito always seemed to find a person's ear but there it was. And there was more than one. Cursing, I reached out from under the mosquito net and turned on the bedside lamp. Then, I noticed an aerosol can on the lower shelf of the bedside table. "At least something is right," I concluded as I reached for the can. After shaking it, I pressed the nozzle. Nothing came out. It was empty! In anger, I threw the can at a wall. Then, with a few more unhappy utterances, I began a swatting exercise. After killing four mosquitoes, I decided that the proximate enemies have been destroyed and I turned off the light.**

**Somewhere in the distance, I could hear music being played -- loud music. And not just from one source but from several sources.**

**Apparently, every billet had a stereo and all were running at or near full volume. I had to wonder how long they would continue. I pulled the pillow over my head.**

**Soon, a fitful sleep engulfed me -- but it was short-lived.**

**The sound was hard to describe. At first, I thought it was the struggling of the air conditioner. Then I realized it came from some other source. Perhaps someone was trying to break into my quarters? I remembered that I had bolted both doors but the bolting devices were rather flimsy. Had I unpacked my pistol, I would have reached for it -- but it was still in my navigator case and well away from the bed. Finally, I reached out, felt around for the lamp on the bedside stand and turned it on. The noise stopped.**

**I lay there for a while trying to figure out what the noise had been. Then, as a precaution, I slipped out from under the mosquito net, opened my case and pulled out my pistol. Loading the chambers, I slipped it under the pillow, snapped out the light, and sought again to sleep.**

**It could have been fifteen minutes -- it could have been a half hour. But there it was again! This time, I sat up in bed, my pistol in hand. "What the hell is going on?" I thought as the racket continued. Then I realized that it seemed to be coming from the bedroom stove. I wished I had a flashlight but I had not thought to pack one.**

**Slowly, trying to make no sound, I slid out of bed, pistol in hand, and felt my way toward the stove. The sound continued and, still trying to make no sound, I placed my hand on the stove. I was correct! The noise was coming from the stove!**

**Unsure of what could be making the noise, I hit the side of the stove with the gun barrel. Immediately, there was one hellacious racket. Obviously an animal, or animals, had come down the stove pipe and had been inside the stove.**

**Turning on the bedside light, I opened the stove's door and peered in. There was no animal inside. "Well, I'll be damned," I thought. "Whatever it was seems to be able to climb up and down the inside of a chimney pipe. How in hell can that be?"**

**Puzzled but too tired to pursue the question, I closed the stove door and crawled back into the bed. Over the sound of multiple stereo sets blasting the night with different music, from the airfield I heard a jet aircraft taking off, the after burner roaring.**

**And then I was asleep -- more correctly, half asleep -- perhaps much less than that.**

**Nothing was working correctly -- absolutely nothing. And my mind would not relax. Since receiving the assignment orders to Kunsan Air Base, I had gone through all sort of mental turmoil. And, now that I was there, things only seemed to get worse.**

**Subconsciously, I still heard the loud, booming music coming from the surrounding officer quarters. And then there was the air conditioner -- it rattled and banged with no sense of cool air emerging. Once or twice, the stove again became alive with whatever inhabited it. Periodically, my hand slipped over my pistol as I tried to get my heavy eyes open, peer into the darkness of the room and make sense of all that surrounded me.**

**Then, periodically, I drifted into a dream world -- more like a world of nightmares.**

**First, I dreamed of Mary and our children but I could not touch them. I had left the Virginia apartment in much less order than I had wanted in order to expedite my move to Korea. Now my mind returned to accomplish all the things I had not done.**

**Then I found myself in the aged staff car -- the "blue bomb" -- and it would not start. Eventually, I had the engine out of the vehicle and was trying to repair it but I did not seem to have the correct tools. Suddenly, I realized that all the tires were flat. And then a G.I. appeared on the scene. I tried to talk to him but he just shrugged his shoulders and smiled. I yelled at him but my voice made no sound.**

**More frightening, my half sleeping mind focused on the nuclear weapons on the base -- the Koreans were stealing them! I watched but seemed unable to do anything. I screamed orders to persons who would not listen. Then I found a gun in my hand and tried to load it but the bullets would not fit. I tried to run and grapple with the thieves but my legs would not move.**

**Soon the flags I had ordered from my friend in the Pentagon arrived but they were all messed up -- they did not even look like American flags. I kept turning them every which way but they still did not look like American flags.**

**Now I was swimming in water and I awakened to find the pillow and sheets literally sopping wet with perspiration. The temperature in the room was intolerable.**

**Suddenly, I realized that I had a terrible pain in my middle. I knew what it was -- the grease saturated fried chicken I had eaten at dinner.**

**The end of my first Korean day and the beginning of the second was not what anyone would desire. I wondered if there were those who**

**cared that I and a half thousand other Amricans were at Kunsan Air Base or even that there was such a place on Mother Earth?**

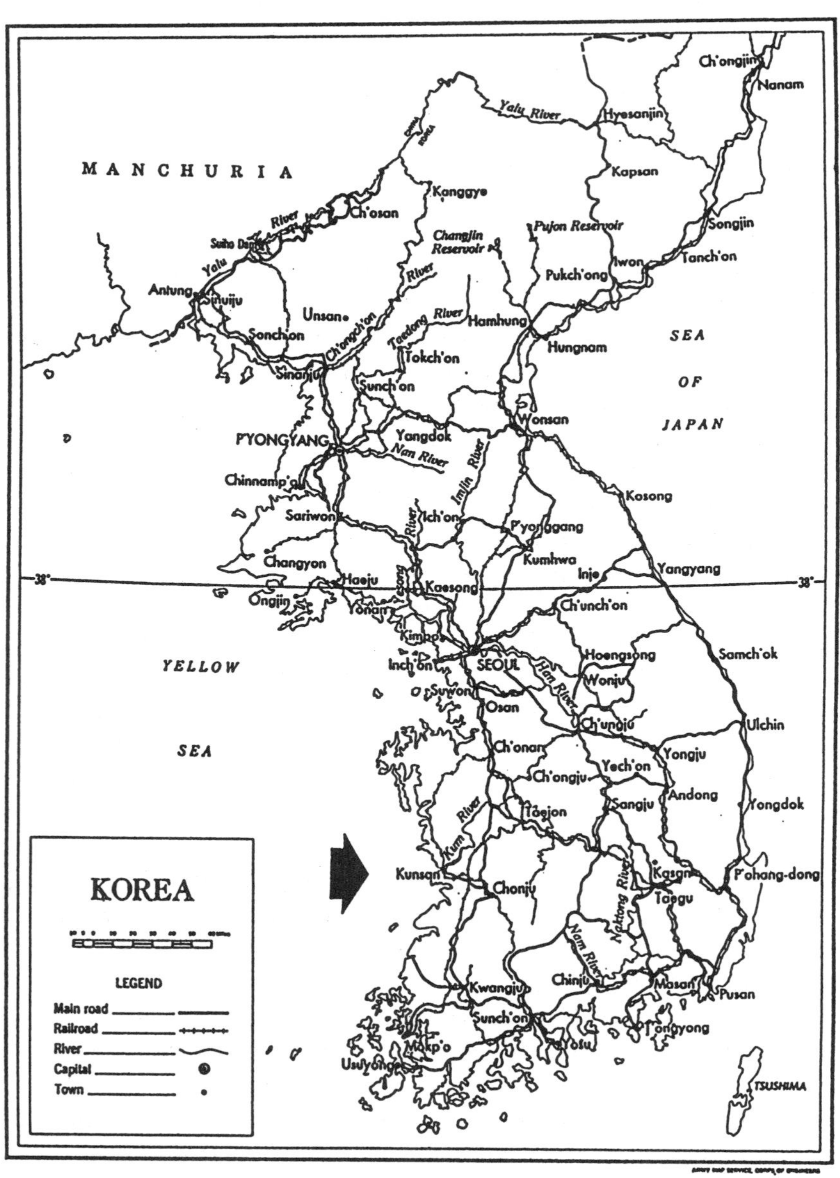


**KUNSAN in the REPUBLIC OF KOREA**

# THE BEGINNING OF DAY TWO
# A TUESDAY

The alarm clock had been set to go off at 0600.

It seemed as if I had just gotten to sleep -- perhaps I had. Light was beginning to creep in through the windows. I eased myself from under the mosquito net. The bed was thoroughly soaked from the perspiration of the night. My body ached. The window air conditioner was still making a terrible noise but no cool air was coming out. I decided to take off the front of the air conditioner -- the filter was totally clogged with dirt and, as a result, the coils were covered with frost. I turned it off.

The cold shower did a great job in waking me up -- the cold shave hurt even with a new blade in the razor.

A clean uniform on, I polished my shoes and prepared to head to the Officers Club for breakfast. Then I remembered Davidson's advice and placed my camera, pistol and ammunition in the wooden box and snapped the padlock shut.

As I was about to leave, I noticed that there was a two-burner electric plate on the floor of the living room. Looking further, I saw a beat up aluminum pot. Apparently, this was the way one heated water for a shave and a clean up. Obviously, it provided no solution to a real bath.

Outside, the morning air was refreshing. The heat of the prior evening and night had dwindled considerably. True to the terminology "The Land of the Morning Calm," there was not a whisper of a breeze. The sky was clear of clouds but there was a heavy, smoke-like haze in the air. Later, I would learn that the smoke came from the many grass and straw-fed fires used for cooking -- and from the stolen pieces of roadway macadam that were used to augment those fires.

With daylight, I could now see that my billet was one of about a dozen similar buildings set in a line. Then, further down slope, there was a second row of such buildings. Still further, there were several others. From the exterior, they looked substantial -- at one or both ends of each unit was a brick chimney -- but I already suspected what the heating systems might be like -- and the interiors.

Settling myself into the staff car, and careful to avoid the protruding spring, I turned on the ignition key. After a few tries, the

*With daylight, I now could see that my billet was one of about a dozen buildings set in a line.*

engine sputtered to life. Full day number one was about to start -- perhaps I would count the day as number two.

As I drove to the Officers Club, I tried to obtain an appreciation of the buildings and grounds that came into view. Around the living quarters, much of the grass had been beaten down -- but, elsewhere, it was "knee high." Here and there, some small clusters of scraggly pine trees could be seen but, in the main, the base was treeless. At some time in the past, a number of the roads had been surfaced with macadam but most were now mostly dirt surfaced. Ruts and potholes abounded.

Heading toward the Officers Club, I noticed that some of the quarters were occupied by Koreans. Children were already playing outside. Here and there, I spotted a Korean uniform. I had to wonder how the base quarters had been allocated -- by what formula a certain number was set aside for the U.S. and for the Korean forces. And the Koreans had their dependents on the base! That raised interesting problems. I wondered if the Korean children went to school -- if so, where? And what responsibility did I have relative to the Koreans

**living on the base? Was there a "status of forces" agreement that set this forth? And did the Korean Commander report to me -- or just how were we to get along? There just had to be some agreement and rules governing this whole thing but I had no idea what they were. I made a mental note to ask Davidson about this.***

**Looking farther out into the base areas, I took note of the remaining buildings. They were as I had seen from the air on my arrival -- mostly rusted tin shacks.**

**But this was not the early fifties -- the Korean War had been, by virtue of the Armistice, relatively quiescent for over a half decade. Why was what I was looking at virtually unchanged, only deteriorated, from that which had existed during the Korean War? Something was wrong -- terribly wrong!**

**During the Korean War, the U.S. forces were hastily thrown into battle with only temporary accommodations and often minimal support -- as they were in the conflict in World War II. For most living and operational use, first tents and then hastily constructed temporary buildings were the order of the day and, sometimes, both were viewed as a luxury. Front line men usually did not even enjoy such accouterments and were often happy just to have a trench or a foxhole.**

**At Kunsan Air Base, among the facilities that survived the ravages of World War II were the Japanese built quarters. Prior to the outbreak of the Korean War, these quarters, somewhat upgraded from the Japanese profile, were occupied mostly by U.S. Army personnel -- to include dependents. During the Korean War, by some sort of miracle, these quarters were not destroyed during the North Korean advance south and their later withdrawal. But they did not go without damage -- possibly the result of a combination of North Korean military action and the work of local South Koreans who were inclined to convert virtually everything movable to their own ends.**

**After recapture of Kunsan Air Base, the skeletons of the surviving Japanese quarters become billets for officers and civilians --**

---

* Well before my arrival at Kunsan Air Base, when the unit was the 6170th Air Base Squadron, an order was issued by the 314th Air Division tasking the 6170th ABS "to draw up a joint use agreement between that organization and the tenant ROKAF organization." (Source: HRA files.) Apparently, this had not (or could not) be done. Frankly, passing to base level the responsibility to sort out an international arrangement was not the way to do things -- it amounted to "passing the buck."

**the latter being a few secretaries brought in by Fifth Air Force, an Information and Education Specialist, Red Cross personnel, nurses, transient USO entertainers, visiting reporters and visiting military, government and other VIP.**

***During the Korean War, front line men were usually happy just to have a trench or a foxhole. Shown here are men of the 25th Division dug in south of Ch'orwon in April 1951. (U.S. Army)***

**In short order, the Kunsan Air Base population increased to some 7,000 personnel -- primarily USAF but also to include U.S. Army, U.S. Navy and U.S. Marine Corps. And with that influx of personnel, the first order of the day was tents -- to be followed with hastily constructed temporary metal buildings. In the meantime, U.S. Army engineers had sought to stabilize (and raise for drainage) much of the new housing areas with excavated fill -- which resulted in a sea of mud.**

**Typical of the Air Force units at Kunsan Air Base, the 13th Bombardment Squadron, living and operating mostly out of tents, sought to keep above the mud by building sidewalks from scrap lumber -- scrap lumber was even turned into fences.**

**Half a decade later, the survivors of these temporary buildings were virtually untouched except by weather, rust and terrible wear and tear. Korea had not been a place where USAF monies were to be spent. And many of the wartime improvements, such as they were, disappeared into the Korean country-side or fell into disrepair as the U.S. base population of 7,000 was drawn down to about 500 and given**

**notice of ultimate withdrawal. Most buildings, even sand-bagged aircraft revetment structures, literally evaporated; tons upon tons of bombs and ammunition were either destroyed in place, transferred to the ROKAF or sent to Japan; the remains were turned over to the fledgling ROKAF as "military assistance" -- the mood was much in parallel to the slogan of the previous KMAG: "Kiss My Ass Goodbye."**

***(Above) Typical of the Air Force units at Kunsan Air Base, the 13th Bombardment Squadron, living mostly out of tents, sought to keep above the mud by building sidewalks of scrap limber. (Below) As the war dragged on, more and more sheet metal buildings were introduced to replace or augment tents. Scrap wood was turned into fences to keep individuals on walkways and roadways.***

***(R. B. Ennis)***

*Half a decade later, the survivors of these temporary buildings were virtually untouched except by weather, rust and terrible wear and tear. (The building at right in above photo matches the building in center photo on previous page. This photo taken before the major Air Force withdrawal from Kunsan Air Base already shows the effects of budget and personnel cut backs.) (R. B. Ennis)*

★★★★★★★★★★★★★★★★

**Rapidly, my mind became so cluttered with ponderous and disturbing thoughts that I was at the Officers Club before I realized it. Davidson was waiting for me when I arrived. A glance told me that he had taken pains to polish his shoes. His uniform was proper and pressed. "Perhaps," I thought, "I had judged him wrongly."**

**Even before Davidson and I sat down, a neatly dressed Korean waitress was standing by with a pot of coffee. Davidson introduced her as "Annie, our Number One waitress." Then he told her that I was the new "Number One Colonel." Annie smiled and asked if the "Number One Colonel" wanted juice. When I asked what kind they had, Davidson answered that all they had was canned tomato juice and canned grapefruit juice. "Take the tomato juice," he suggested, "the grapefruit juice tastes like canned metal."**

**"Tomato juice is fine with me," I responded. "I got sick of canned grapefruit juice in War Two. I never could understand why the citrus industry couldn't turn out a better product. We used to use it as a mixer for gin. In Europe, in War Two, we had nothing for mixers**

**until the war was all but over. Still, in spite of rationing, we had a regular supply of booze -- particularly when we invaded France and captured some of the German stock. In an emergency, our Flight Surgeon would release some of his combat whiskey. For a while, in France, we sold captured cognac at a dollar a bottle -- we used French champagne, initially at twenty-five cents a bottle, as a mixer. We didn't have ice until the war was over."**

**"No problem with booze or mixers here. That's one thing we got plenty of. We may be short of food but we have plenty of booze. And we have an ice plant on base and, as long as it works, we make out O.K."**

**For the moment, additional comment on the subject did not seem necessary. I already had the food item as a "must look at" agenda point. I wondered how really bad it was. Soon I would learn. Apparently, the booze situation needed no "looking at."**

**Breakfast was a single menu -- a take it or leave it selection consisting of reconstituted powdered eggs, fried potatoes with onions and pork sausage patties. The patties tasted rancid. There was white bread toast but the canned butter turned me off -- I had too much of that type of butter in War Two. Also available for those who wanted it were stewed prunes. Annie kept our cups full of coffee. The coffee wasn't bad and I commented to Davidson about it.**

**"One thing we do have at Kunsan is good water and that helps to make good coffee. Fortunately, we have had no breakdowns at the water point and our supply of Filter Aid and Calcium Hypo has been adequate -- I don't think the Koreans know what this stuff is and, as a result, it doesn't get stolen. But wait until you get to Osan. They suck up their water from the river that runs by the base. When you realize what's flushed down stream in that river's water, it's a wonder that everyone isn't sick or dead. They filter and chlorinate the hell out of it but, if you hold it up to the light, it looks like there are hairs floating in it. The Flight Surgeon up there says its some kind of algae that gets through the filters but he assures everyone that the water is safe. Me, I'd prefer to drink Kunsan water."**

***[What Davidson did not tell me was that, in the past, the base frequently had no coffee -- and no sugar or even canned butter. This fact I would establish long after I left Korea and read some of the previously recorded history covering Kunsan Air Base. Citing from related history on file at HRA:***

***"One entire shipment of coffee, . . . seven hundred and twenty pounds, was not received. In the succeeding shipment, coffee in an amount of four hundred and***

*eighty pounds, part of a total of seven hundred and sixty pounds, was not received. Another item not received in full was butter. Food Service was authorized 1,980 pounds of butter of which only 1,280 pounds arrived -- constituting a shortage of 720 pounds. The continued shortages of coffee and sugar . . . caused a certain amount of deprivation in the meals served to personnel at the mess halls. It was indicated that such items were loaded on metal constructed rail cars from the Quartermaster Subsistence Supply Point [but], in spite of lack of evidence indicating pilferage or tampering, these items were not in the rail cars upon arrival."*

*To my endless surprise, losses such as described were of such frequency that they seemed to be accepted as the norm of the Korean environment and were seldom investigated -- even less were these events developed through discovery, arrest and punishment. The standard practice was simply to write off the missing supplies on a Report of Survey.*]

**"Does that include water in the city of Kunsan or only on the base?"**

**"Hell no! Unless one wants to get sick, possibly die, he should not drink Kunsan City water or eat food off base."**

**"Is that true of all Korea?"**

**"Seoul is a possible exception. It all depends on where in Seoul. There are a few places that are pretty good but one has to be careful."**

**"Well, if I get time to go to Seoul perhaps you can tell me about the good spots. But right now I think you and I have enough to do here without thinking about Seoul."**

**Davidson was not a good poker player. The change in expression on his face when the subject turned to Seoul suggested some sort of problem but I was not going to pursue it.**

**"So we have great water, good ice and lots of booze at Kunsan? And from what I observed last night I gather that we also have lots of female entertainment -- josans."**

**Davidson's face flushed but he did not respond.**

**"You get any milk here?" I asked as I noted that the small pitcher on the table held what appeared to be some heavy, yellow canned milk.**

**"Powdered -- tastes like chalk. When we serve cereal, the men try to struggle through it but no one likes it."**

**"Ice cream?" I asked.**

**"We fly it in from Kimpo once a week."**

**"Why, if we have an ice plant, don't we make our own?"**

**"No equipment for it."**

**"Has it been requisitioned?"**

"Actually, I don't know. The on-going system has been to get it from Kimpo -- the Army supply. That's the way it has been working and I don't think anyone has sought to get it changed."

"How about waffles or pancakes -- are they ever served at breakfast?"

"Pancakes sometimes -- but no waffles -- at least not any since I've been here," Davidson replied.

"Doughnuts and sweet rolls?"

"The Red Cross unit serves doughnuts -- we don't serve any."

"How about bread. This toast tastes pretty good but does our bakery make up whole wheat or rye bread?"

"I've never seen any. Frankly, I don't think they get the ingredients for anything but white bread. Maybe they don't even know how to make whole wheat, rye or some other items. The bread and rolls they do make are good. Periodically, they turn out corn bread. And now and then they do turn out cookies, pies and cakes."

"Dry cereal such as bran or corn flakes?"

"We have it but, as I stated, with the powdered milk no one really goes for it. Moreover, the cereal we get often is infested with bugs. If you are inclined to eat dry cereal, I suggest you carefully examine the stuff before you pour milk on it."

The additional discussion during breakfast was wide-ranging. Davidson had a hand-written paper with the names of the officers and some enlisted men, dates of rank and security clearances. Opposite my name he had written: Unknown security clearance. I avoided comment on the assessment. Opposite Davidson's name I read "Secret." "My God," I thought, "how can the base run when the Deputy Commander has only a Secret clearance and persons junior to him have higher clearances?" Suddenly, I was beginning to see new problems -- but I was not certain of the cause. Alongside some names, I read "no clearance." Akers, Benson, Wild and Sergeant Young had Top Secret Clearances. Lieutenant Jones had a Secret Clearance. Sergeant Butler in weather had no security clearance. I noted that Davidson's list did not include any tenant personnel and I reminded him to begin work on that. Obviously, Davidson did not know where I was coming from or where I was going and I let it stay at that.

We then talked about the alert aircraft, personnel, leave policy, supply, the on-base Koreans, VD rates and more. Regarding the on-base Korean population, it seemed that we just co-existed with each element, the American and the Korean, doing its own thing. Davidson was unaware of anything that resembled a "status of forces" agreement

-- to the best of his knowledge, no one had ever asked about it before. And, mostly, that described the relationship between the permanent base element and the deployed tactical alert element -- there was no "host-tenant" agreement. Overall, it appeared that things "just happened" -- which was about how I had begun to believe all things at Kunsan Air Base functioned. I knew that I could not live with this arrangement and I would alter it but it would take time and some careful thought -- perhaps I did not have the time for careful thought? I was discouraged but not beaten.

"Laundry?" I asked.

"Fair. We have a base laundry but it keeps breaking down. Frequently it runs with only one washer and one dryer. When that happens, even with double shifts, we can get back-logged. It's a matter of repair parts for old machines -- and that's not just a matter affecting laundry equipment -- its typewriters, trucks, everything. It's not unusual to wait six or twelve months to get our requisitions filled. Sometimes, the only way we stay alive is to put someone on an aircraft and send him to Japan for parts. This may sound funny, but, at one point we had so many broken typewriters that we were down to pens and pencils to get our work done. As to personal laundry, most of the men use their mama-san. You will see clothes, sheets and other stuff scattered on the ground around the buildings -- that's how the mama-sans dry it."

"And for soap -- what do they use?"

"Now and then we do get some laundry soap in the exchange but mostly it's hand soap or nothing."

The mama-san subject having been raised, I suggested that Davidson have someone tell the mama-san who took care of my quarters to keep a supply of toilet paper in the bathroom.

"That's not the way we do it, sir."

"What do you mean?" Here it was again -- the new kid on the block who didn't understand how things were done in Korea.

"What I mean is that everyone takes care of his own toilet paper. And we don't get enough issue. To supplement the issue, a person can purchase toilet paper in the exchange -- or use up *Stars and Stripes*. When we do get a shipment at the exchange, you will see a rush to purchase a supply. The exchange usually sells out in a day. The problem is that any toilet paper left out is stolen -- either by the men or by the Koreans. Many of the men buy or steal toilet paper for their josans. They don't have Kotex out here and the girls use the toilet paper to make sanitary napkins. Every man heading for a john takes

**his own roll of paper with him and locks up what is not used. I'll see if I can locate a couple rolls for you but I would suggest that you keep it locked up in that box in your bed room. And remember that your mama-san may use more of it than you would suspect."**

*"You will see clothes, sheets and other stuff scattered on the ground around the buildings -- that's how the mama-sans dry it." Obviously, this system did not work very well in rainy weather or in winter. Shown here are some of the Japanese built base billets that were allocated to ROKAF officer families. Note that there is no supplemental heat (the absence of center metal chimneys) as in the case of the modified buildings used as U.S. officer billets.*

**"For Christ's sake!" Momentarily I was dumbfounded. There had to be a better answer. Davidson seemed to enjoy my being confounded by the situation.**

**"Why don't we have the exchange carry Kotex and let the men purchase it if that's part of the problem?" I asked.**

**"We only have two American women on the base, sir. One works as a recreation specialist and the other is a Red Cross lady. The exchange system won't allow us to carry Kotex. They have it up in the Osan and Seoul exchanges because there are more American women based there. But you have to be a woman to purchase it. Rules you know."**

**Oh boy! My plate of problems was running over and I had hardly started. And here I was on a nuclear base with responsibility for over half a thousand men and my focus was on toilet paper and Kotex! This was incredible!**

**I had not told Davidson about the animals in the stove but, to break the current trend of discussion, I decided to raise it. Undoubtedly there would be another suggestion that I was a less-than-knowing "new kid on the block" but I had to face it.**

**"Had a bit of surprise last night."**

**"What happened?" Davidson asked.**

**In response, I related my waking up with the racket and eventually tracing it to the stove. Davidson laughed.**

**"It's the rats, sir."**

**"The rats?"**

**"Yes sir. We don't know how they do it but they can get up on the roof of a hootch and climb up and down the inside of a chimney pipe. It's sort of a game they play. What you do is, before you go to bed, you bang the hell out of the side of the stove. That usually sends them scampering and they generally do not come back for the rest of the night. Some of the guys light a piece of paper in the stove but, with the heat as it is, that isn't the easiest thing to live with."**

**"Why don't you put some mesh over the chimney tops?"**

**"Don't have any mesh."**

**"Has it been requisitioned?"**

**"I'll have to check. I think we requisitioned some a while back. Most likely, it was out of stock or Fifth Air Force supply considered that we didn't have enough budget to cover it. We sort of learn to live with these problems. Screen wire is the same thing. I understand you told Sergeant Young to fix the screens on your office windows. The problem is that we don't have any screen wire and have been unable to get any."**

**I looked at Davidson in disbelief. An Air Force base that didn't have enough toilet paper and couldn't get hardware wire or screen! It was absolutely unbelievable. In disgust, I got up from the breakfast table. As I did so, Annie scurried up with the bill. Reaching for my billfold, I took out a twenty dollar bill.**

**"Can't use that here, sir," Davidson cautioned, "it's illegal. You have to use Korean occupation currency."**

**"You mean that the Officers Club can't exchange currency?"**

**"No sir. It has to be done at the finance office. Black market you know. The Koreans would love to get their hands on green money. It sells for a premium."**

**"The Japanese clubs exchange currency."**

**"This isn't Japan, sir. Things here are controlled by U.S. Forces Korea. Actually, it's illegal for a service person to possess any**

**green money. Here, let me pay. And give me your green money -- I'll get it converted for you."**

**Again I was the new kid on the block seemingly unable to find my way around without a seeing eye guide dog. I was burned up. Apparently, I was being looked upon as needing a lot of sympathy and help. Grudgingly, I fished all the green money out of my billfold and handed it to Davidson.**

**"O.K. Here's my green. But a question: Can civilians carry green in Korea?"**

**"Civil servants -- no. Regular U.S. and other civilians -- yes."**

**I figured that was the situation. I had seen it operate in Europe where the military forces were governed by one set of rules and the non-military population by another. And with two sets of exchange rates in force, one for the military family and another more favorable one for other persons, indirectly the military persons were called on to subsidize the local economy. That a black market money exchange existed had to be expected.**

**"And I guess there is a bit of black market in money?" I asked.**

**Davidson nodded his head.**

**"All right, let's get down to that place we call a headquarters. On the way you can tell me more about the local environment."**

**"That's easy," Davidson answered. "As I said, don't drink the local water and don't eat the local food."**

**"How about Annie and the other Koreans -- do they eat our food or theirs?"**

**"Both ways."**

**"And they don't get sick?"**

**"Their systems are used to the stuff out here. We -- we're tender."**

**I sensed a broader problem but I knew that this was not the time to unravel the situation -- there were just too many things that confronted me. To be effective, I knew I had a lot of "learning" to get done -- and a very short time to get it done.**

**"O.K. Let's get this show on the road."**

**On the way out of the club, I asked Davidson if he knew what had happened to all the buildings that had been on the base when it was occupied during the Korean War and following by the 3rd Bombardment Wing and until that unit's redeployment in 1954. All I got back was a shrug of the shoulders.**

**In the back of my mind, I recalled a copy of *The Invader Review** -- the newsletter of the 3rd Bombardment Wing -- which copy had crossed my desk and which copy had displayed a panorama of Kunsan Air Base following the unit's movement from Kunsan to Japan. Why this recollection popped into my mind, I did not know, but, suddenly, I had a concern for I had counted no such number of buildings as I observed the base on arrival. If I recalled correctly, the displayed panorama showed a collection of buildings on Kunsan Air Base that literally ran from horizon to horizon. With a population of 7,000, this was understandable but now, counting both Koreans and Americans, the population was more like 1,500. What had happened to the buildings that had, not too many years prior, been occupied by the remaining 5,500 persons and the attending support activity? Had these buildings been demolished, had they been sold or had they been stolen? I suspected that I would never know the answer.****

***One small corner of the Kunsan Air Base housing panorama as it existed in 1952. Only a small fraction of these and other housing, logistics and other units remained at the time of this account. As to what happened to the original buildings -- there apparently was no record. (J. Lovejoy)***

---

* Vol. 1, No. 11, September 27, 1954.

** Some insight into this issue may exist in the recorded effort undertaken in 1956 to obtain *officer custody* for "all buildings and facilities at each on-base and off-base site" and to establish "formal real estate accountability." (Source: HRA files.) There is a strong suggestion in all this that, during the phase down of the U.S. Air Force in Korea prior to 1957, much of the existing construction/property was literally abandoned -- in which case such items could have been sold or stolen without record.

# THE SECOND STAFF MEETING

**Departing the Officers Club, Davidson joined me in the staff car. Apparently, he had walked to the club. As we left, there seemed to be a good number of vehicles parked in front and I wondered what the pecking order was -- who did and who did not get a vehicle. But I knew that volatile question would have to wait.**

**"Is the base briefing laid on?" I asked.**

**"Yes sir. I asked every section head to give you a briefing on his responsibilities and the status of things as a part of this morning's staff meeting."**

**This was not the way I expected things to be structured but I decided to go along with what was planned.**

**"And what are you briefing on?"**

**"Nothing, sir. The section heads will cover everything."**

**"Did you do a dry run of the briefing?"**

**"No sir. When we packed it up last night, there was still a lot of work for the section heads to complete and I thought it best to let them do their own thing."**

**I was not pleased with the answer as it smacked of "dodge and weave" but, for the moment, I did not pursue it as a new problem had just come into view.**

**"That six-by-six we just passed. It had only one tire on each wheel. It should have two. It's a dual-tired vehicle. What's the problem?"**

**"We don't have enough tires to go around, sir. We run most of the dual-tired vehicles on one tire. It's all we got. If we put two tires on every six-by, we would have operational only half of the trucks -- the other half would be on blocks. We do get a number of blow-outs using only one tire but we really don't have an option. It's been like this ever since I arrived here. We have tried to get it straightened out but so far no luck."**

**"But why not enough tires? Have they been properly requisitioned? Have you talked to Wing?"**

**"Certainly, but we keep getting not-in-stock or other responses. As to Wing, I don't think the Commander or anyone cares. To the bottom line, we just don't get enough tires. And, as to the ones we do get, they are mostly recaps and the mileage is terrible. The roads here**

**are one hell of a mess -- you will see when you get off base. Between potholes and jagged rocks, off base blow outs can be considerable."***

**Shit! Here was another problem and again I would appreciate what it was all about *when I learned about Korea.***

**"How about Osan? Are they running their six-bys on one tire?"**

**"No sir. Not that I have noticed. I think the Wing Commander must have a special supply source -- or something."**

**Whoa! Osan had tires and Kunsan did not have tires and the Wing Commander apparently did not know or, if he knew, he did not care. My suspicions and anger rose but my thoughts were diverted at what I now saw.**

**"Why aren't these drainage ditches cleaned? They're all silted shut."**

**"Just don't have the manpower, sir."**

**"But you've got enough manpower to play baseball."**

**Although it was still early in the morning there were several men out on a baseball diamond. The grass on the ball field was well worn down and it suggested that it had been having a good amount of use.**

**"Command requirement, sir. Part of the command sports and morale program. We have to field a team to compete in the inter-base competition of Fifth Air Force. The Commanding General at Fifth Air Force is pretty hot on the subject."**

**"So you can't clean out the drainage ditches because you don't have the manpower but you can support a baseball team? And, apparently, Fifth Air Force thinks this is all great?"**

**"That's correct, sir."**

**"Is the team an extra-curricular activity or is it something full time?"**

**"Full time. If the men also had to work, I guess they would be too tired to play ball."**

**I was not what one would call a sports enthusiast and I knew it. Thus, I had to temper my opinion as to what I had just heard. Subordinating my real thoughts, I still had to wonder about baseball having a higher priority than the accomplishment of essential work. Suddenly, I was reminded of some of the ex-Commander's words in**

---

* While maintenance of off-base roads was a ROK responsibility, I would soon learn that, due to the limited work done by the ROK and even though it was illegal, equipment and fuel permitting, the road to Kunsan would be graded by Kunsan Air Base means. (See HRA files.)

Japan: "You'll enjoy the hell out of Korea. Just relax and go with the flow. Some things that go on in Korea may be a bit unusual but one learns to live with it." Perhaps I should *go with the flow* and claim that I didn't have time to be a Commander as I had baseball to play?

By now we were at the headquarters building and I pulled into my parking slot. I had to wonder what the hastily assembled base briefing would be like -- I hoped it would not be a total mish-mash.

★★★★★★★★★★★★★★★

The key staff personnel were already in my office when I arrived. Present were the Operations Officer, Major Akers; the Supply and Transportation Officer, Major Peterson; Major Benson who was the Communications and Electronics man; Captain Wild covering Air Police and security; Captain Polk in charge of Engineering; Captain Pastiak, the JAG; a Chaplain who turned out to be Father Collins; the dentist, Lt. Grossman; and Lieutenant Tommy Jones who had greeted me on first arrival and who turned out to run personnel and a lot of administrative things in the headquarters offices. From the tactical fighter unit there was present a Major John Turnbull.

"Good morning, gentlemen."

There was a series of half-hearted "good mornings" in return.

"O.K. Let's get started. Davidson, what's the line up?"

"Major Akers is first up, sir. He will cover the basics."

Without waiting for Major Akers to begin, I posed a question.

"What's the weather supposed to be today?"

There was a bit of foot shuffling. It was obvious that no one knew.

After a period of strained silence, I spoke.

"O.K. One of the first things a Commander needs to know is the weather. No Commander can operate without knowing the weather situation. If you are going to fly an aircraft or fight a ground war, you better know what the weather is going to be. Davidson, call our weather man, if we have one, and have him front and center with a weather briefing."

"Yes sir." Davidson scurried out the door.

"All right, Major Akers, what is it that you have to show me?"

To say that the briefings that followed were on the pitiful side would be to compliment the exercise. On the surface, it appeared that these officers had never been subjected to professional military briefings. I listened to the entire exercise and then sat quiet for a while.

Major Turnbull's briefing had been short -- he simply noted the number of alert F-100s on the field and stated that all were in commission. The tone of his briefing was in the nature of a challenge.

As I was contemplating my next step, Davidson returned and informed me that the Sergeant in the weather office, a Sergeant Butler, did not answer when he called. "We had no flying scheduled this morning so he must be off doing something else," Davidson advised.

The answer was far from reassuring. Weather support was needed for more than the support of the local C-47 and L-20 -- it was needed for general operations -- for the whole base.

I knew that the ball was in my court. Inwardly, I was raging. Emotionally, I wanted to kick or fire almost everyone. But I knew that was not a solution to anything as there would be no replacement. I had what I had and I was going to have to live with it -- or most of it. Seeking to control myself, I realized that everything had to be taken one step at a time. And right now the problem was the briefing to which I had just been exposed.

"Gentlemen, as an overall assessment, while you have done some good work in a short time, your briefings just don't fly. If we have senior visitors coming to this base, one of the first things we are going to lay on is a briefing. If the briefing is done properly, it will tell those visiting persons that we know what we are doing -- if you can lay on a good briefing it will tell me that you know what you are supposed to do and are doing. If any briefing element is a flop, it will tell me and any visitor that you and all of us are incompetent."

Already having concluded that Davidson would not know how to develop a good base briefing, I decided to pressure him and the others by turning to the most junior officer present.

"Lieutenant Jones, would you take over the task of organizing a base briefing -- something that begins with who we are -- command lines and all that, our base organization, the enemy situation as it affects us locally, our peace and wartime roles, our resources, our problems. In that regard, since arriving yesterday, I have heard a lot about budget problems but no one briefed on it -- it needs to be covered. And no one discussed construction -- that is a key element in any briefing. In relation to intelligence, prepare something on the background of the local situation -- cover a little history of the base during the Korean War, lay out the road and rail situation, be prepared to cover our withdrawal plan in case of an enemy advance -- if we have such a plan. With respect to the ROKAF and ROK Army presence on and around Kunsan, develop a special briefing section --

something that can be added depending on the audience. Finally, in relation to our wartime role, prepare some charts that depict our activity in case of a Korean War and in case of General War. But be damned careful that nothing sensitive is close to that Korean girl who is supposed to be my secretary. And, Davidson, I want you to figure out how we can conduct a Top Secret briefing in this office without the whole damn local community listening in on us. Major Turnbull, I know that you are a tenant but you are a most important tenant -- in fact, you are mostly why we are here. Do find some way to integrate a meaningful overview of your operations into this briefing with, of course, a Top Secret cover -- it is very key to the whole.

"As to the make up of the briefing, find something on the order of 20 X 30 paper and do some drawing -- grease pencil is O.K. But try to make it look good. And try to have it all ready for a dry run in not more than two days from now. All you other chaps help Lieutenant Jones. For the record, I have given Lieutenant Jones a Top Secret clearance." From the look on Jones' face, I was certain that he was surprised. The actual, formalized granting of the clearance, I would handle separately.

I could detect a lot of consternation in the faces in front of me but I hoped things would sort themselves out. From the reaction I got from Lieutenant Jones, I suspected he was going to enjoy his new assignment. According to the data Davidson had furnished me, Jones had only recently been commissioned and this was probably only his second or third duty station. "What a way to start," I thought.

Davidson hung back as the others departed.

"Sir, Lieutenant Jones has never been put in for a Top Secret clearance. Out here, we have to go through Wing to get clearance approval from Division and I think they have to get it from Fifth Air Force. And, unless a background check is on file, we have to ask for one. Granting Lieutenant Jones access to Top Secret information is going to give Wing fits when they find out. It is just not done that way out here. You can't . . ."

"Davidson, don't tell me what I can and can't do. I just did what I did as a matter of command expediency. And I would add that I am granting you a Top Secret clearance -- and I may do more. When it comes to fighting a war, we can't have procedure get in the way. Certainly there are risks in something such as this and that is why there is a Commander -- to make decisions and take risks."

Davidson shook his head and left the room. Somehow, I had the feeling that I might be reported to Wing and the informant might well be Davidson. But I was going to get to Wing and Division before Davidson or anyone could get there to light a fire under my butt.

As soon as Davidson had disappeared, I called for Lieutenant Jones to return.

"Tommy, I want you to complete a message for me. It will need serial numbers mostly -- and fill in any other blanks. The message should be addressed to the Commander of the 314th Air Division with information to the Wing I'll sign it. Here, let me draft the body of the message."

SUBJECT: SECURITY CLEARANCES

IN ORDER TO CONDUCT THE ESSENTIAL BUSINESS OF THIS ORGANIZATION, I HAVE THIS DATE ISSUED INTERIM SECURITY CLEARANCES AS FOLLOWS. KINDLY EXPEDITE THE GRANTING OF FINAL SECURITY CLEARANCES.

CLEARED FOR TOP SECRET INFORMATION:
LT. COLONEL WALTER DAVIDSON
MAJOR STEVE PETERSON
CAPTAIN JESSE POLK
CAPTAIN JOSEPH PASTIAK
SECOND LIEUTENANT THOMAS JONES
SERGEANT ------------- BUTLER

JOHN MOENCH
COLONEL

Handing the draft message to Jones I asked him to put it on the wire four hours after I took off for Osan on the morrow.

Jones looked at the message. "Sir, how about yourself? We have nothing on the record."

"Tommy, I've got all the security clearances I need -- it comes with being Commander. If the system can't catch up with me, I am not going to worry about it. Just fire off that message and let's see what happens."

"Yes sir."

Lieutenant Jones seemed pleased at how things were progressing. For my part, intuitively, I already had a sensation that he was a fine officer worthy of trust and development.

# THE "WILD" RIDE

With the organization and construction of a base briefing turned over to Lieutenant Jones, I turned to Captain Wild.

"All right, Wild, let's you and me take a ride."

"Your car or my jeep?"

"Your jeep is fine."

On the way out of the headquarters building, I remembered the mosquito problem of the previous night and told Sergeant Young to get me a few aerosol bombs. From the expression on his face, I detected that I had not given him a simple task but I did not intend to explore the situation -- soon I would know if Sergeant Young was capable or not.

Driving away from the headquarters, I asked Wild how many men he had in his Air Police unit.

"Something under two hundred, sir."

"That gives you how many on a shift?"

"About forty-five. When things are tight, I double-shift the men -- have them pull sixteen hours."

"How often do you have to do that?"

"More times than I would like but I don't have much in the way of alternatives -- sometimes men have to double-shift for days at a time."

"And how do you spread the men?"

"It varies. Right now we are running with the senior Sergeant on duty as acting head of operations -- he happens to be my Deputy as I don't have an officer assigned. Normally, he and I rotate between the day and night -- we both work about twelve hours a day -- I have him working today as I wanted to be available for whatever you had in mind; two men are handling the watch and communications; six are standing by as an emergency reaction team; two are on the front gate; six are doing aircraft security; eight are on roving foot and vehicle patrol -- they have two vehicles to use; two are working the city of Kunsan in one vehicle; one is covering the water point; one is covering the fuel and storage area; six are held as relief of those on posts -- we try to give everyone a crapper and cold or hot drink break every two hours; the remainder are covering the perimeter."

"That leaves you with less then ten on the perimeter -- am I counting correctly?"

"You're correct, sir."

"And how many miles of perimeter do you have to cover?"

"About ten."

"And that means that one man has to cover a mile or more of the perimeter?"

"That's correct. But that assumes I have everyone present for duty and healthy. Sometimes, I have one man covering as much as two miles of perimeter."

"And you have how many covering the nuclear storage?"

"Eight between the nuclear and conventional weapons storage."

"Meaning you have only from four to six men on the nuclears?"

"That's correct, sir."

I sagged in the seat as I contemplated what I had just learned. Four to six men guarding a bunch of nuclear weapons in one of the most forward and vulnerable positions that one could find. It seemed preposterous -- totally unbelievable! But I was reminded of the ex-Commander's comment that nuclear weapons were not my worry -- this was a Fifth Air Force matter.

"How many dogs you got out?"

"None at present. We don't use dogs in daylight -- only at night. We have a dozen German Shepherds. I run a heavier guard at night and use every dog that's healthy on night operations."

The answer made sense but it didn't help my mood.

"Where's your radio?" I asked.

"We don't have radios, sir."

"You don't have radios? Well, how in the hell do you communicate?" I was shocked.

"We have a fixed telephone line to the front gate and to some of the permanent guard positions such as the entrance to the nuclears and the tactical alert area. But, beyond that, nothing. If someone gets in trouble, they shoot. And then we send the reaction team to find out who shot. It isn't very sophisticated but it's all we got."

Jesus Christ! In the interior of the United States a nuclear storage area would be covered with double chain link fence, lights, roving dogs and sensors, interior and exterior guards and more. And here we were almost in no-man's land, virtually surrounded by enemies, and with almost nothing.

"The fences around the nuclear and conventional bomb storage sites -- what are they?"

"I'll show you, sir. Mostly nothing. The Koreans steal the fences as fast as we put them up. They use the wire for nails. Here and there we have a standing fence but it is very spotty. We have some concertina spread around in critical positions but, from time to time, it also gets stolen."

"And lights at night?"

"We have some pole lights here and there -- they do a reasonable job."

"Sensors?"

"None, sir."

"Mine fields?" I was searching.

"None, sir. It would be too dangerous for the local population. Actually, we don't own any mines."

"What kind of weapons do you have?"

"Depending on the assignment, the men carry pistols, carbines or shotguns. Around the nuclear weapons we limit the men to shotguns -- no carbines. That's directed by policy."

"So, if you are hit by a group armed with rifles what do you do?"

"We have some rifles held in the Air Police Command Center that the emergency reaction team can draw but that's all. The standard item on the base is a carbine. We do have some Thompsons."

"How about thirty or fifty caliber machine guns?"

"One fifty. We have two weapons carriers with a fifty caliber mount but only one gun. We keep it and the boxed ammo in the Air Police Command Center."

"Grenades or mortars?"

"Some frags and tear gas grenades but no rifle launchers -- and no mortars."

The news of personnel and armament limitations had so occupied my mind that I had not paid attention to where we were or what was passing by and it infuriated me.

"What's that building?" I asked pointing to a ramshackle one story tin structure.

"It's the Enlisted Club, sir."

"Fine. Let's stop. I want to see what it's like."

Captain Wild pulled the jeep to the side of the road and put on the emergency brake.

"Sir, I wouldn't go in there if I were you."

"And why not?"

**"Sir, that's a pretty rowdy place -- and they don't appreciate officers coming in. You go in there and you are likely to get punched in the face if not knifed. I wouldn't go in there without support -- never have."**

**I looked at Wild in disbelief. The head of the Air Police and the person responsible for base security and he was unwilling to go into the Enlisted Club without support? What would be my next surprise?**

**"What's that forty-five doing on your hip?"**

**"I can't use it against Americans -- it wouldn't be right."**

**"Forget the question. I'm going into that club and you can come or stay put -- I don't care."**

**It was still early in the day and I doubted that there would be drunks in the club at that hour. So long as no one was inebriated, I was not concerned. But, one thing for certain, there was going to be no building on the base that I would not enter. Wild shrugged and fidgeted but continued to sit in the jeep. I looked at him in disgust. The thought struck me that I was being tested -- was I a person with guts or not?**

**The Enlisted Club was hardly more than a tin shack. But that was a description that covered most of the buildings on the base. The door swung open easily.**

**Inside, I stopped for a minute to allow my eyes to become adjusted to the dark. A few men lounged about. Some of those present were drinking at the bar. One of them saw me and sort of sloshed his way up to me, sticking his face in front of mine. He was wearing two stripes.**

**"No officers allowed in here, buddy."**

**I grabbed his shirt front and pushed him up against the wall -- his drink crashed to the floor -- some of it spilling on my uniform. I should not have acted in this manner -- it was foolish and it could have led to grave consequences all the way around -- but the G.I. had triggered a growing time bomb within me.**

**"'I'm not *your buddy*! I'm your Commanding Officer and when you address me you use the word *sir*. Do you understand?"**

**I was aware of a movement of the other men in my direction. For what purpose, I did not know. Perhaps Wild's assessment was about to come true. The hairs prickled on the back of my neck as I tensed myself for the unknown.**

**"Cool it, man." The voice came from a huge black in civilian clothes. "This is the our Colonel. Sorry, sir. He just had a bit much in**

**the way of early morning beer. He had a hard night on the perimeter. We'll take care of him."**

**Things happened so fast that I can't recall what really took place but, in seconds, the man I was holding was surrounded and whisked off to the side of the room. The black who had addressed me spoke again.**

**"Sorry about that, sir. The men out here get up tight now and then. A good drunk keeps them cool. It won't happen again. I apologize for him."**

**"And what's your name?"**

**"It's Sergeant Anderson -- Amos Anderson but don't kid me about *Amos and Andy*. My parents stuck me with this name and I have to live with it. 'Been here for almost ten months now. Got two to go and I'm back to the big PX land. 'Come from Virginia. It'll be good to get back there."**

**"My wife and children are back in Virginia right now," I answered. "Arlington." I could see that the ice was broken. I stuck out my hand and it was grasped solidly.**

**"That's where my family is," Sergeant Anderson responded. He was a powerful fellow -- not one with whom I would want to tangle.**

**"Small world."**

**"Yes sir. Small world."**

**"Take care of your friend," I added as I stepped back outside.**

**"We will," Anderson replied as he saluted and winked.**

**Wild was still in the jeep. He noted the spilled drink on my uniform but said nothing about it. He knew I was pissed. But I felt good. If this was a test, I thought I had passed.**

**"Colonel, next time you do that, let me have some of my men here. There's just no need for you to take chances."**

**I didn't answer but, briefly, I thought about the terrible impression I would make if I found it necessary to move anywhere around the base with an escort of Air Police. It would be an unheard of attitude of confrontation -- and it would not work.**

**Wild put the jeep in gear and drove off.**

**"Any particular priority, sir? Any stuff you have a need to see real quick?"**

**"Not at this point. Just drive and talk. Tell me what we go by. But first tell me about the policy on civilian clothes. One of the chaps I met in the enlisted club was wearing civvies. I presume that they are authorized."**

"Yes sir. They are authorized for off-duty wear on base -- they are not authorized for off-base wear in Korea."

The answer seemed reasonable. We were not at war but, still, there was only an armistice between the North and the South in Korea.

For the next half hour, we drove around the base with Wild pointing out the enlisted barracks; the enlisted mess hall; storage buildings; the motor pool; the water point; the Post Exchange; the ice plant; an earth-mounded, dug-in command post which he assured me was a stupid construction project directed by someone at Fifth Air Force -- he alleged that it was worthless due to the level of the water table at the base; the existing nuclear storage "huts" and the concrete nuclear storage igloos under construction.

At the nuclear storage site, I did observe that the "buddy system" was in effect -- the guards monitoring that area and each other. At least something seemed right.

But, when we were inside the nuclear storage area, I was struck by the proximity of the adjacent Korean village -- literally on the other side of a questionable barbed wire fence. I stored the knowledge but did not comment. I could not understand how Fifth Air Force could be happy with this situation -- certainly I was not.

Alongside the village, on the other side of the presumed security fence, I observed a drainage ditch. On the bank of that ditch, Korean women and children were washing clothes, beating them with sticks over stones. And, adjacent to the washing routine, there were others cleansing vegetables. From somewhere upstream, a sickly green, slime-covered flow of water dumped into the whole -- it had to be raw sewage.

Eventually, we arrived at the Engineering yard -- this was Captain Polk's area of responsibility. Over the gateway to the yard there was a sign.

| WE HAVE DONE SO MUCH FOR SO LONG<br>WITH SO LITTLE<br>WE ARE QUALIFIED TO DO ANYTHING<br>WITH NOTHING |
| --- |

Pointing to the gateway sign, I commented about the "up beat" nature of the motto and then asked Wild, "Did you ever hear of the 3rd Bombardment Wing -- that was a B-26 Invader night intruder outfit that operated out of Kunsan during the Korean War?"

"No sir."

"Well, during that war, that Wing was based here at Kunsan. Actually, the last bomb to be dropped during the Korean War was by a 3rd Wing B-26 Invader that flew out of Kunsan -- a Lieutenant Donald Mansfield was the pilot. From a report I read, Mansfield and his Navigator, Lieutenant William Ralston, released at 2133 hours on July 27, 1953. Twenty-seven minutes later, the Cease Fire went into effect. This is a pretty significant element of Kunsan history.

"Anyhow, I was in Europe at the time but I recall some comment that reached me that the 3rd had supply problems not unlike that which we seem to face and I think that the motto of their supporting 3rd Supply Squadron was *Because of Us, They Shall not Want.*

"Do you realize that most of that which we enjoy here today, even though it is primitive, is a result of the hard work of the 3rd Wing and other outfits that pioneered this base. And they may well have had a hell of a lot harder time here than we are having. Did you ever think of that?"

"No sir."

Suddenly, Wild became very quiet -- I could sense that a serious introspection had taken over. I had tossed into his mental framework some new considerations. And I hoped I had made a point. We were not the only ones to suffer -- and we were not engaged in frontal combat.

*Above and right, the motto and insignia of the referenced 3rd Supply Squadron at Kunsan Air Base during the Korean War. (R. B. Ennis)*

**And then we came to the war reserve materiel yard and I asked Wild to stop. I was reminded of the war plans I had briefly scanned at PACAF. Could it be that key elements of the war reserve materiel stored at Kunsan Air Base were actually for aircraft no longer in the combat inventory of the USAF? This was a frightening thing to contemplate but I was beginning to consort with the unbelievable and the horrible.**

[***That rather unbelievable things could happen in the military system was not new to me. At the time, I recall reflecting on the careful plans I had put together (circa 1946) to withdraw from storage and recondition over 1,000 T-6 Texan aircraft for transfer to South American and other countries to support an aviation training program.***

***Many parts in an aircraft were then categorized as "local manufacture." With over 1,000 aircraft to be put through the San Antonio Air Material Area production line, I thought it made sense to calculate what the "local manufacture" workload would be and mass produce the items instead of manufacturing them individually on call.***

***As a result, a pilot group of aircraft was sent through the rehab line and record was kept of the "local manufacture" needs. Then, these items were extrapolated to the total need and placed in production.***

***But, when it came to the 1,000 aircraft on the production line, the "local manufacture" parts were not there and the production line came to a standstill.***

***As it turned out, the parts, having been made, were transported to the supporting supply section for subsequent reissue on call. But, once there, some regulations-oriented person(s) dutifully categorized them as "non-stock" in that they were officially labeled as "local manufacture," and they were then all sent to the scrap yard. Fortunately, the San Antonio Air Materiel Area was able to buy back these items from the junk dealer before they were destroyed.***

***Stupidity, lack of understanding, whatever one may term it, had, as so often, destroyed the advantage of those who sought to understand, think and plan ahead. I continually admonished my staff and others to forever be watchful for that person(s) who would, most likely in all innocence, screw up the best laid of plans.***

***"The best laid plans of mice and men . . . ." During my military career and following, so many things were upset by the emergence of the totally unexpected that I cannot recount the total. And none of it had a foundation in substantive thinking -- only spontaneous and often very irrational and inexperienced thinking.***]

# THE WAR RESERVE MATERIEL YARD

There was one thing I could appreciate -- comparatively speaking, the war reserve materiel yard had a good fence around it -- a high fence with rows of inter-laced barbed wire with reinforcing metal spacer bars between the posts. The fence was about ten feet high and, at the top, was an anti-climb-over set of three barbed wires strung on forty-five degree angle brackets. There was a formidable entrance gate which was padlocked. Wild had a key. I noted two pole lights -- one at each side of the yard.

Inside the war materiel yard there were crated aircraft parts, mostly tail and wing sections, and some other boxes and crates. But, by and large, the yard had stacks of crated drop tanks -- an essential for most fighter operations.

Walking down the rows of stacked materiel, it was easy to see that most of the items had been in place for some time. Not only was there a growth of grass sticking out from under the boxes and crates but all of the boxes and crates were extremely weathered. In some cases, the nails on the crates had rusted through and boards had become detached.

Mentally, I did a calculation of the number of drop tanks in the stacks -- several hundred -- which could mean enough support for over a hundred sorties -- hardly enough to fight a war of any consequence but still enough to get started. And drop tanks, just like bombs, had to be in place. Typically, one wanted at least enough war reserve materiel in the forward areas -- fuel, bombs, drop tanks, ammunition, rockets, etc. -- to cover 30 days of operations for the units that would deploy into and operate from the base area.

And then I looked at the nomenclature on the drop tank crates. It was as I suspected when I reviewed the out-dated war plans at PACAF -- they were for fighter aircraft no longer in the active Air Force inventory! And, if I could determine this, so could the North Koreans, the Chinese Communists and the Soviets!

"Who cuts the grass in this yard?" I asked.

"The Koreans -- the same persons who come in and harvest the grass on the main field. I always put a guard on them to make sure that all they do is cut grass."

**The answer did not allay a growing suspicion that our enemies could have knowledge of everything that went on at Kunsan Air Base. It would only take one grass cutter to report on the full of what was in the yard -- and on most of the base. Soon, I would learn that the situation ran even deeper than that -- but that would be a number of days later. At the moment, I was confused -- and worried.**

**Certainly, the logistics system in the Air Force knew that the drop tanks I was looking at were useless -- except for some possible employment by the ROKAF. With that being the case, why were they here? But I knew that gross mistakes could be made in the Air Force logistics system and simply go undetected. Was that at which I was looking simply one great big mistake perpetuated from year to year by a system too big and too overworked to examine details?**

**[*At the time, I was reminded of the drop and bomb bay tank situation that developed at the outset of the Korean War when I was serving in the office of the Director of Programs in Air Force Headquarters. Major General Frederick H. Smith, my boss, returned from a budget meeting and threw a package on my desk with the words that "something is wrong with this." It was a budget request prepared by the Air Materiel Command at Wright-Patterson Air Force Base and it covered drop and bomb bay fuel tanks. I took the easy way out and ordered to the Pentagon the civilian who had authored the budget paper. The next day, when that person arrived in my office, I began to review with him the details in the budget request. This review went routinely until I realized that one line covered drop tanks for fighter aircraft no longer in the Air Force inventory. From there on the situation grew worse. Apparently, working with a much out-dated aircraft program, this person had ordered tanks not only for aircraft not in the projected inventory but aircraft that would never see action in Korea in even the most bizarre of circumstances. Included were drop or bomb bay tanks for, among other aircraft, the entire Air Force inventory of B-25s and some other aircraft that had been relegated to training and administrative uses. The most costly error was an already on-going emergency procurement of bomb bay tanks for all the B-29 aircraft in the Air Force inventory to include those in storage. In this latter case, production was already proceeding on a twenty-four hour basis. That afternoon, without consulting with General Smith who was away at the time, I ordered a halt to that production.*]**

Then a startling thought struck me. Could it be that this was all one great big, low cost cover and deception operation? If so, what was the grand scheme of things -- the plan?

I had been involved in such operations from time to time, all "close hold" matters, but none were of the scope that here seemed possible. Was it that Kunsan Air Base was an element in the equivalent of General Patton's fake army in England in World War II? Or was it that Kunsan was set up simply as a "draw fire" trigger intended to cause a strike that would alert the Strategic Air Command and other forces? If either of these possibilities was valid, the odds were that I would not be told. And that caused me to think of the security clearance problem that had already bugged me. Was this whole thing being orchestrated and manipulated by "Mickey Mouse" individuals with special "need-to-know" clearances to be held by only a handful of persons?" Were the nuclear weapons that I had yet to inspect real weapons or false weapons? And would I ever know?

My mind spun but I knew that I could talk to no one in my command about my sudden concern. Perhaps I would not even learn anything when I reported in at the 314th Air Division at Osan? Could it be that the run around I had gotten in the Pentagon, at PACAF and at Fifth Air Force was the result of knowledge that could not be passed to me? Could it be that the 314th Air Division did not know what was going on? Maybe I did not want to know the truth? But would the powers-to-be not be astute enough to know that I would recognize and question the situation? Could it be that there were persons well up the line who knew of a problem but were unable to attack it head-on and they had selected me for the job on the assumption that I would attack it from below? On reflection, I dismissed that thought -- the Chief of Staff was too strong an individual to play such a game. But it might be that he was not informed?

Trouble, trouble, boil and bubble. Suddenly, I saw myself proceeding on two courses -- one real and one false. In such a situation, how did I stack up priorities? I would have to think about this development -- think very hard -- and right now was not the time.

I could sense that my long, introspective quiet was bothering Wild. Wild, I was certain, would not recognize what I had discovered as he was not a pilot. But had not some of the pilots on the base recognized this? Major Peterson, the Supply and Transportation Officer, was rated but his time had been in transport aircraft, not fighters, and his background in war plans and logistics was next to nothing. He could easily miss the point I had discovered. And, most

**likely, none of the other pilots who might recognize the situation were involved in or concerned about war materiel storage. Had the strange mix of marginally qualified officers I had inherited been carefully selected because they did not know the job and would not suspect a real purpose of Kunsan? But then there were the enlisted men -- surely one or more of them might notice what I had seen -- still the short tour in Korea might not generate interest as I could already detect that the prime objective of most was to get along and go along -- get the tour over with and go home. And, in the meantime, enjoy life to the fullest.**

**Turning my thoughts to Wild and looking at my watch, I suggested that we head to Operations. It was already past lunch time. "I might as well skip lunch and get that check ride in the Gooney Bird out of the way," I thought. "And I hope that Major Akers is ready when I get there."**

**With my thoughts returning to security, en route to Operations, I asked Wild if he ever ran patrols outside the base perimeter -- the answer was that, except for security on the pipeline and the storage tanks in Kunsan City along with G.I. scrutiny in the city itself, he did not. "Regulations really limit the Air Police to on-base activity," was his response. "And if I had an off-base patrol encounter something serious, so long as we were not fired upon I don't know what my rules of engagement would be." And what about intelligence on the surrounding area? The answer was that, other than what he got from the local ROK police, he had none. What this all added up to was that the population on Kunsan Air Base sat behind a theoretical line in the sand with no outreach intelligence and, until the line was crossed by an unfriendly force, at which time it probably would be too late to act, the hands of everyone were tied. I knew where the problem originated -- in Washington, D.C. with the Joint Chiefs of Staff and the Congress!**

**Except for thanking Wild for the morning's tour, we had no further conversation. I just could not make small talk and anything beyond that would probably get out of hand.**

**Wild pulled up in front of the Operations building where Major Akers was standing -- patiently waiting for my arrival.**

**[*"Yours is not to reason why; yours is but to do or die." I knew the words. And I also knew that, in the course of history, many a military man, or formation of men, was sent on a mission the purpose of which would never be explained to them. That they might perish without knowing why was immaterial. This was the nature of the military commitment, the chain of command, obedience and more.*]**

# INTRODUCTION TO THE KUNSAN GOONEY

Major Akers saluted and informed me that the Gooney Bird was ready to go.

"Not so fast," was my answer. "First, let's go through a weather check."

"It's all done. Weather is O.K."

"You don't understand, I want to go through the weather routine. So let's start it over."

The weather "officer" was a Sergeant -- Sergeant Paul Butler. His name had already surfaced. He had the regular weather maps and hourly sequences posted. He informed me that, if he had a weather question he could not answer, he would call the weather office at Osan. He stated that Lt. Colonel Davidson had contacted him relative to staff briefings and he assured me that he would have a weather briefing for me every morning at 0800 hours. Regarding the alert aircraft, he said that they got their target weather on a tactical line from their home base. The ROKAF seemed to have their own weather network and, except when their communications were down, he was not called on to provide them with data. Sergeant Butler had a repeater line to the tower to keep them informed of the local weather and to support their hourly broadcast from the Kunsan Radio Range. The Sergeant seemed to know his business and appeared well qualified and motivated. For a change I was impressed with what the personnel system had sent to Kunsan Air Base.

"Sergeant, how long have you been out here?" I asked,

"Just over six months."

"And where did you come from?"

"Langley. Tactical Air Command."

"Like it here?"

"Frankly, no sir. But everyone has to pull the bad ones along with the good ones."

"Married?"

"Yes sir -- and with three children."

"Ready to go back home?"

"The sooner, the better."

"Do much sight-seeing in Korea?"

"No sir. And I don't go for the josan treatment either. I think the guys that play that game are playing Russian roulette."

The answer pleased me. Apparently not every person was josan addicted.

Scanning the Sergeant's weather map, I noticed a low pressure area that looked like the beginning of a typhoon in the Central Pacific. Sergeant Butler confirmed my observation.

"If it continues to form," Butler stated, "it will be the first one of the year. We're just entering the annual typhoon season. It runs for about three months. I'll be watching it."

"O.K. Sergeant. Keep an eye on the thing." Then turning, "Akers, let's go to the aircraft. Did you file a local clearance?"

"We don't bother with that here," Akers answered. "We only file when we go cross-country. That's the system that seems to have been in place for a long time -- it was going on when I arrived."

I looked at Akers in disbelief. Again I saw that I was being treated as the new kid on the block. The answer translated into: This is how we do it here, stupid!

"Suppose we have an accident? Where is the record?"

"Sergeant Butler knows we are flying."

"Sorry. No good. From now on all flights off this base, even if it's just around the traffic pattern, will file a clearance. And, to be sure that all the pilots understand, write up a base regulation on the subject. As Operations Officer, you can sign it but let me look at it before you do. Frankly, I'm surprised that the base has not been written up on the subject during an IG inspection."

"Yes sir."

I knew that Akers preferred the informality he had inherited but he took my direction in stride. "He probably already has me pegged as a headquarters S.O.B. or an Inspector General type," I thought, "and, maybe, he's right. But clearances are supposed to be filed."

Dutifully, Akers asked for my serial number and proceeded to fill out a clearance form. When it was complete, I scanned it. Then he signed it as pilot and we proceeded to the aircraft. A Sergeant was standing by the aircraft.

"He's our Engineer," Akers volunteered.

"Ground Engineer or Flight Engineer?"

"Both."

"On flight orders?"

**"Yes."**

**"What's his name?"**

**"Sergeant Alexander Phillips -- he likes to be called *Alex*."**

**As we approached the aircraft, I stuck out my hand.**

**"Sergeant Phillips, good to meet you. I'm John Moench."**

**The Sergeant had started to salute but stopped and, quickly wiping some grease off his hands and with an apology for the grime, shook hands with me.**

**"Welcome to Kunsan, Colonel."**

**"How's the aircraft, Alex?"**

**"About the same, Colonel. We still have one engine running in the red -- it's been that way for several weeks. I think it's the thermocouple. It powers up O.K."**

**"Can't you replace the thermocouple?"**

**"Can but don't have one. I've had one on requisition but nothing has arrived."**

**"An engine running in the red is a Red Cross -- is it not?"**

**"Yes sir, but the pilot can sign it off."**

**"Anything else wrong with the aircraft?"**

**"The radio compasses are still acting up. Major Akers knows about it. I'm not a radio man so I can't fix it -- just don't know how. I can replace a set but not fix one."**

**"We have two radio compasses on this Gooney Bird," Akers cut in. "We can't get them to point in the same direction. I have tested them in clear weather and it appears that both of them are off the same amount but in opposite directions. What I do is average them out. It bothers me but, so far, I have made some pretty good instrument approaches using that system."**

**I thought a while. Actually, the aircraft should have been grounded. I didn't like the idea of flying with one engine in the red. But, if we lost an engine, we still had a second one and a Gooney Bird, particularly one that was empty, had no trouble flying on a single engine. As to the radio compass problem, at least for today it wasn't an issue as the weather was beautiful.**

**"All right, let's do a walk around. If everything else looks O.K., let's take it off but watch the oil temperature and pressure when we do. If they hold, let's continue with the check out. And, by the way, what's the check out routine?"**

**"Informal, sir. We only have a handful of pilots on the base. I have looked at Wing regulations but haven't found one on the subject. I do make sure that a person has a questionnaire on the aircraft in his**

Form 5 -- if not, I get him to fill one out. You need to fill one out for the L-20 as you have none in your file -- I checked. I'll bring one around to your office -- along with a copy of the L-20 Pilot's Instruction Manual.

"Regarding the actual flight check, if a person has prior time in the aircraft, we limit the check ride to one of familiarization and a few touch and go landings. And, should you wonder, we have had no aircraft accidents in recent years -- I checked the records in file on this -- and I trust we will not have any. We have enough problems here without adding to them by having an aircraft accident."

For a change, I liked what I heard. But, on reflection, I wondered about the clearance procedure for the ROKAF and the rotating alert fighters. Before we fired up the engines on the Gooney, I had to ask Akers the question that was burning in my mind.

"Does the ROKAF file a clearance with us when they fly?"

"No sir. They do their own clearances."

"Air defense operational launches of the ROKAF?"

"I think they come direct out of the Osan Command Center."

"How about the F-100s?"

"Same thing, sir. They do their own clearances."

"What about transient aircraft?"

"They file with us."

So I had three independent aircraft operations on the base. What would be my next discovery? Fortunately, there was only one control tower. But that raised another question.

"Do the ROKAF pilots speak English?"

"Enough to get by -- but it takes time for a new person to key into the pronunciation and syntax."

There it was again -- the separation of the newcomers from the old hands. I smarted at the suggestion that, as a newcomer, I might not understand the ROKAF use of English.

"Do we conduct English language instruction for the ROKAF?"

"No sir. That's a responsibility of the Advisory Group -- that and flight and other instruction. The only problem is that they don't have anyone assigned to Kunsan to do the job."

"What about in-flight emergencies -- counsel and advice to pilots in trouble -- how do we communicate?"

"We call someone from the ROKAF or the alert area to come to the tower. We don't have stand-by operations people in the tower -- there is just not that many bodies available out here."

"O.K. Let's start engines and taxi out."

# THE CHECK RIDE/ORIENTATION FLIGHT

The Engineer was correct. As we advanced throttle to takeoff power, the cylinder head temperature on the one engine moved into the red danger area. But oil temperature and pressure held. And there was no indication of loss of power on takeoff. And so we rolled down the runway and were airborne over Kunsan Air Base.

Major Akers was riding check pilot in the right seat and, with the wheels in the well, I elected to do a wide circle of the airfield. I wanted a good look at what I had to work with -- a better look than what I had obtained from the in-coming Gooney Bird from Japan or what I had, so far, obtained from the ground.

After several swings around the airfield, I headed for the port city of Kunsan.

Dropping to about 500 feet, I flew over the road that went from the base to the city. A few sections of road were hard surfaced but most of it was dirt. The traffic on the road consisted mostly of animal drawn carts, A-frames and just people walking. There were some straw roofed huts along the road with the land on which they were placed built above the level of the rice paddies that dominated the area. Approaching Kunsan City, I pulled the aircraft up to about 1,000 feet.

From the air, Kunsan City, for all its some 80,000 population, looked very small. Most of the buildings were one story shacks. In the center of the city, there were a few ramshackle buildings to the two-story level. One building seemed to rise to three stories. There were scattered vehicles in the streets -- mostly old buses and a few trucks. The bulk of the traffic was simply people walking. Assessing the size of the city and considering the population, I concluded that they must sleep a dozen or more to a room.

There was a tanker in the port and I pointed it out to Akers. He replied on interphone.

"The tanker has fuel on it for the Koreans and for us. See those storage tanks in the port area."

I looked and signaled a "thumbs up."

"They pump into those tanks and, to get it to base, we pump it through a tactical pipe line. You may have noticed the pipeline sections along the road to Kunsan City."

I nodded to indicate that I had seen the disconnected pipes and Akers continued.

"I'm not directly involved in the pumping but I understand that, every time we pump, we have a major problem with the Koreans. Apparently, they know when we are ready to pump and they come from miles around to steal fuel. What they often do is disconnect the pipe and that is not only one hell of a mess and loss of fuel but it is a fire hazard. When the base gets ready to pump, we call for helicopter coverage out of Osan to augment our security on the pipeline. But, no matter how much security we put on the line, the Koreans are going to do taps and disconnects. I have been told that we lose as much as twenty percent of our in-coming fuel each time we pump."

Damn! Wasn't there something that wasn't a problem?

"See that low mountain to the side of the city?" It was Akers on the interphone.

"The one with the road running into it on one side and out the other side?"

"Yes. That's the one. Know what it is?"

"No."

"Well, I understand that, in the Korean War, when the air base was evacuated as the North Koreans came south, the last bug out element of security from the base was ambushed and slaughtered in that tunnel. Allegedly, people from the village next to the entrance did the job. It's called *The North Korean Village*."

I was getting a scattering of Korean history to which I had not previously been exposed but I was not certain that I liked what I was hearing.

"You got any other historical tidbits that you want to tell me?" I asked.

"Well," Akers replied, "see that large plant across the Kum Gang inlet to the north -- the one with the stacks belching smoke?"

"Yeah. I got it."

"Well, that's a smelter operated by the United Nations under one of those UN economic assistance programs. It's for copper. But from copper you also extract gold. There is a UN civilian in charge but I would bet my pants that a lot of the gold coming out goes into his pocket."

"What makes you think so?"

"He has exchange privileges at our base and I see him once in a while. It just strikes me that he complains too much about how the

**Koreans are stealing all the gold. I think it's a cover up for what he is doing. But I can't prove anything."**

**This was not my problem but it disturbed me. It seemed that all Korea was involved in thievery -- from toilet paper on up.***

**"What's the city I see to the east?" I asked.**

**"That's Iri. The main road from Kunsan City runs toward Iri and on towards Chonju where it joins a north-south main road. Going north, you run into Kongju and, from there, you head toward Osan -- going south the main road takes you to Kwanju. From Iri east, the roads are all but worthless."**

**"Have you traveled these roads?"**

**"No sir. But I've observed them from the air."**

**We flew over Iri. It was a smaller version of Kunsan City. For the present, I had seen enough.**

**"Let's head back to the base. On the way, I want to run a simulated single engine -- I'll throttle back the one running in the red. Then I'll run an instrument approach and shoot a few touch and go landings. Is there anything else you want me to do to write me off as checked out?"**

**"Nothing," Akers answered. "If you are satisfied, so am I."**

**The Engineer and Akers were correct again. The radio compasses pointed in different directions as I approached the Kunsan radio range -- about thirty degrees separated the needles. I lined up in the middle of the needles and, as Akers had forecast, I came straight in. Then we did three touch and go landings. The air was relatively quiet and the landings were smooth. After the third landing, we taxied to the parking ramp in front of Operations.**

**"You're all set Colonel. I'll put a check out sheet in your Form 5 and write up the flight. If you go to Osan tomorrow, do you want me to be co-pilot?"**

**"Right. If I decide to go, I'll let you know the takeoff time. How do you read tomorrow's weather?"**

**"I think it's O.K. We could have some early morning fog or haze here. If we go, we may have to make an instrument let down at Osan but that's no sweat. They do have a GCA at Osan that is pretty good. They usually pick you up at about fifteen or twenty miles out. It's faster to make a GCA let down than a range let down."**

---

* In verification research for this story, Josephine F. Lovejoy, who was stationed at and provided this author with various K-8 photography of the Korean War time frame, told of the chapel organ being stolen "piece by piece" and being found assembled and in use in a local Korean church. "Thou shalt not steal," did not appear to be a prevalent concept in Korea.

"Good, see you later."

Someone had brought my staff car to the flight line and I crawled into it, fired up the engine, and headed for the headquarters.

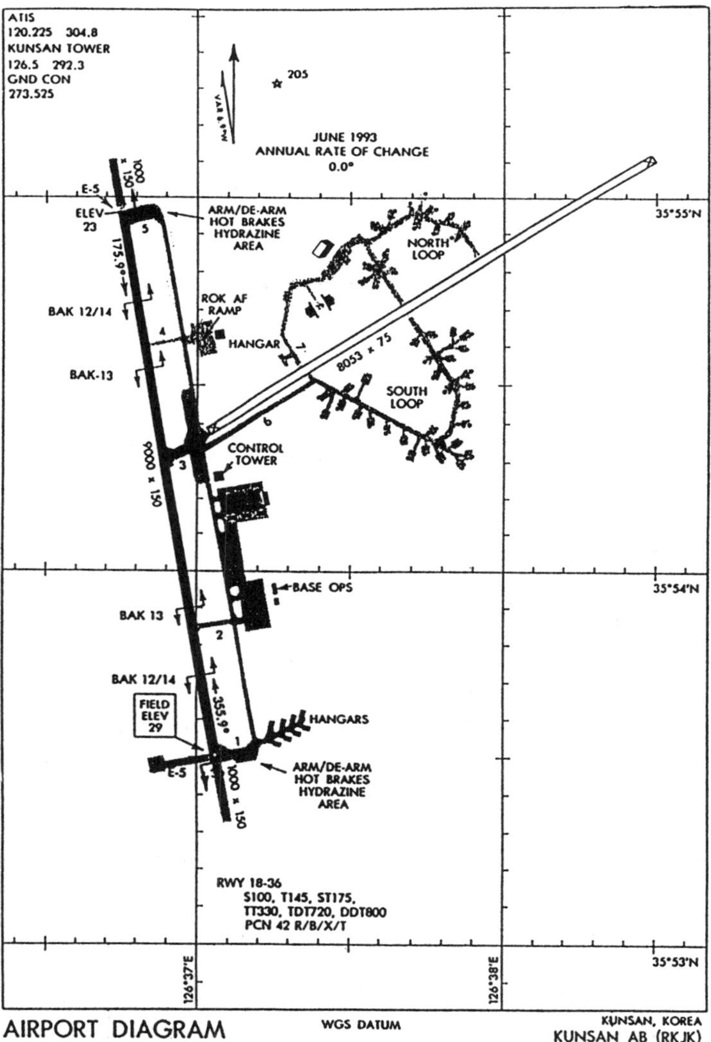


*Above is a post 1990 published diagram of Kunsan Air Base, then known in Air Force and ROKAF circles as K-8. Base Operations has been moved from the position marked by a building symbol -- ▭ -- on this chart to a position proximate the north-south runway. Hangars have now been constructed at the south end of the field and the parking area parallel to the north-south taxiway has been expanded. Other improvements have been made. The 8,000 foot NE/SW runway and dispersal area to the east of the north-south runway remain in place but unused.*

*[I was beginning to assemble in my mind a range of background data covering the base and adjacent area but I smarted that no such data had emerged during my stopovers at PACAF or Fifth Air Force. To me, a knowledge of history was vital to any current action. One has only to reflect on the significance General Patton placed on history in the operation in North Africa in World War II to realize how important such understanding is to military leadership.*

*That others may have known even less than I currently did was hardly a comfort. That even data on the proximate post-Korean War period -- the deployments, the construction, the problems on and off the base and more -- was somewhere over the horizon of most was discouraging.*

*Three plus decades later, when preparing this account, by accident I would learn of evidence of North Korean atrocities at Kunsan and of the Korean War construction of the then main NE/SW runway, roads and facilities following the expulsion of the North Koreans. To drain away water, the construction personnel of the 808th Engineer Aviation Battalion built French drains across the planned runway area which consisted largely of virtual quicksand of the paddy areas -- a base so fluid that a weight at one site would cause the surface to rise at some other location. During this work, laborers could easily sink waist deep in the paddy ooze. To overcome this situation, in addition to drainage and removal of the unstable materials, a massive quantity of fill was required. Fortunately, there were above sea-level hill resources nearby to include conglomerate and sand. But access to these sources of fill required the movement of large numbers of Korean graves.*

*While it was true that the Kunsan Air Base site was that of an early Japanese airfield, that airfield was unimproved and very limited. Thus, to accommodate the current combat aircraft, a hard surface, extended runway was necessary. How it was determined that the first runway would be constructed on a NE/SW axis has been lost in history. Eventually, that runway was extended and then replaced by the existing north-south runway. In the meantime, the number of water crashes that took place off the beach of Kunsan Air Base from the NE/SW axis runway was sufficient to resurrect the "One a Day in Tampa Bay" worries of the B-26 Marauder at MacDill Field, Florida as now applying to the B-26 (A-26) Invader at Kunsan Air Base.*

*The following six photos furnished by Colonel George H. Chase, U.S. Army (Ret) depict some of this 1951 base construction environment and activity.*

*A North Korean "execution pit" found on one of the hills at Kunsan Air Base.*

*Lieutenant George H. Chase stands next to one of the Korean bodies unearthed for relocation. The hill in the background is at the south seaward end of Kunsan Air Base.*

***One of the borrow pits from which earth was obtained to build the Kunsan Air Base runway and other foundations.***

***Korean civilians, unfamiliar with equipment much beyond that of the shovel and A-frame, gather to watch the giant American earth-movers. Here they stand and squat behind an American NCO on the route from a borrow pit.***

*A B-26 Invader comes in for landing on the new Kunsan Air Base runway. Offshore islands that would be used by North Korean infiltration teams are in the distance.*

*A B-26 Invader prepares for takeoff. Tents and C-47s are in the background.*

*Heavy use of Kunsan Air Base during the Korean War coupled with the deterioration resulting from the devastating Korean winters and the fragile sub-base soon necessitated that the NE/SW runway be resurfaced. In spite of this significant runway overlay, the NE/SW runway eventually was abandoned for all but emergency use. Years later, with the advent of Soviet satellites, the activity at the increasingly important Kunsan Air Base would be carefully monitored -- see vertical photo on next page.*] **(Photos below are from HRA files.)**

***Vertical photo of Kunsan Air Base, Republic of Korea, circa 1985.***

# THE JOSAN POLICY MEETING

When I arrived at the headquarters, I found that Peterson had assembled Davidson, Wild and Pastiak. Lieutenant Jones told me that there were some papers on my desk that needed signing but I decided, first, to get the josan thing over with.

"Come in, gentlemen."

"Have a good flight?" Davidson asked. I saw a glimmer of a smile on his face. I suspected he wanted a reaction to the Gooney Bird's engine running in the red and the radio compass problem but I was not going to oblige.

"It was O.K."

Seated at the conference table, I opened the discussion.

"Tell me about the josan situation on this base."

For a minute, the officers just looked at each other. It seemed that no one wanted to reply. Then Davidson spoke.

"Sir, if you want us to fix you up with a josan, that can be done."

I must have turned a dozen shades of ever-deeper red.

"I'm not asking to get fixed up! I want to know what the hell is going on. What's this about truck loads of josans being brought into this base every night?"

There was some strained quiet. Finally, Davidson answered.

"Colonel, it's been a long standing policy. This is an isolated base. The situation in Kunsan City is horrible -- sanitation, everything. A year in near isolation is not good for the morale of the men. We do get a few of the men off on R&R to Seoul with some getting to Japan -- but most of the men spend their full tour right here on the base. For morale purposes, we bring in professional entertainers but they are strictly off limits. We have an on-base Quonset set aside for overnight housing of these entertainers. A guard is kept on that building to preclude any American entering. For other company, it was found desirable to bring girls from the city to the base rather than trying to run a bus service to the city. The Korean bus system is the pits -- dirty, unreliable, crowded, the windows are not even safety glass. Each on-base club manager knows what the activity will be in his club for the evening and he just orders up the number of josans he thinks would fit in. Then we dispatch some six-by-sixes to the city. There is a collection

**point in the city and we load up the girls on a first come, first served basis. It has been working fine -- no problem. Once in a while we do have a fight over a josan but that is infrequent."**

**"Is this system known by and approved by higher command?" I asked.**

**"Frankly, I don't think they know about it," Davidson answered.**

**"And how long has this been going on?"**

**"Long before any of us got here."**

**"So a truck load, or more than one truck load, of josans arrives at the gate. How are they processed in?"**

**"We check their papers but, sometimes, we just count 'em, sir."**

**"And then you count them going out?"**

**"Yes sir. Sometimes the count is off but most of the time it balances out."**

**"And, once inside the base, they are taken directly to the clubs?"**

**"Yes sir."**

**"And once in the club, can they go outside?"**

**"Yes."**

**"And, once outside, can the men take a josan to the barracks?"**

**"We discourage that but I'm sure it does happen."**

**"And, perhaps a josan can step outside on her own and circulate through the barracks and no one would mind?"**

**"Possibly."**

**"And, quite possibly, the josans come with the idea of making a bit of cash -- income? Could I be correct?"**

**"Possibly. Yes sir." I could see that Davidson did not like the cross examination.**

**I leaned back and searched the faces at the table Here I was -- in plain language, I was commanding a whorehouse. There was no way around it. In a manner of speaking, this was an established perk for being assigned to Kunsan Air Base -- the much touted "Riviera of Korea." Could it be that this was one of the reasons the base had gotten its name and reputation?**

**But this was not only a military installation, it was a nuclear base -- or, at least, it was advertised as such. How could I allow this to go on?**

**"And these josans -- they carry identification papers?"**

**"Yes sir." The answer came from Wild. "All Koreans are supposed to carry identification papers of some sort. For our regular**

Korean employees, we issue a G.I. identification card. For casual workers, such as the grass cutters from the villages, we issue a pin-on tag they are required to wear. As to the josans, they usually carry identification issued by the Korean officials. And, when possible, we check this identification as they come in. Sometimes, with a crowded truck, it's a bit difficult -- but we try."

"What kind of Korean identification do the josans carry?"

"Either call girl or prostitute."

Bang! There is was! Confirmed! I was running a whorehouse!

"Sir, some explanation." It was Wild again. "Here in Korea almost any girl who relates to an American is viewed as a prostitute. Your secretary is categorized as a prostitute. Basically, other than the grass cutters, the Korean women who enter the base are categorized in three ways: *call girls*, *prostitutes* and *all others*. This categorization determines the physical checks they are required to get. This is all run by the Koreans. A call girl has to have a physical once a month; a prostitute gets a check twice a month; and all others are supposed to get a check every two months. This is really a VD certification -- it's done by the Korean doctors."

"It's really a square-filling exercise," Joe Pastiak added. "Typically, the Koreans don't get a physical -- they just pay off the doctor. Unfortunately, the real reason behind a lot of this, in addition to the immediate financial shakedown, is the matter of the long term Korean shakedown. The officials reason that a Korean girl associating with an American may end up with the American wanting to marry the Korean. What they do is build a record that would make it difficult, if known, to obtain entry for the girl into the U.S. So, if an American wants to marry a Korean girl, he has to buy the record from the police. The price of all this varies but it can run as high as two thousand dollars -- sometimes more."

Damn, it gets deeper! Obviously, my staff knew of the system and allowed it to go on -- they may even have supported the concept. Certainly, none of them was suggesting it be changed.

"Suppose we stopped bringing the josans on the base?" I asked.

"We'd have one hell of a morale problem -- probably a mutiny. Things are bad enough out here. If we denied the men this bit of diversion, I think there would be a blow up." Pastiak was very serious.

Somehow, I couldn't stomach the system -- but I could see that an abrupt change could trigger unwanted results. And I was not about to set up a bus schedule to the city as an alternative. Perhaps there was

**a middle ground? I could see that I was going to get no ideas from my staff -- so what would it be?**

**The room was quiet as a tomb. I was trying to think through the "impossible." My staff just sat there waiting for my decision. Mentally, I tried several solutions and threw them away. Damn! This was not something I wanted to have to deal with -- but here I was and there was no escaping the situation. I could let things go as they were, which would mean that I approved the system, or I could make a change.**

**For a minute, I contemplated the Osan Wing Commander learning of the on-going josan system and frying my butt. Then, laughing to myself, I contemplated throwing the whole subject to my Chaplains but I knew that they couldn't handle such a question.**

**Finally, I decided on a change.**

**"O.K. This may be the most unpopular decision I make but I don't intend to be the commander of a whorehouse and that is how I would describe this situation. Second, I don't want josans running all over this base in the daytime let alone at night. This is a military installation to include nuclears. I'm already worried about the nuclears even without the josan problem. So, as of tomorrow, make that the day after tomorrow, I want a new procedure in operation. I will allow a man to bring a josan on the base but he must sign her in and sign her out at the gate -- in person. When on the base, the man can only have the josan at a club, at the recreation center, at any general event such as baseball or church -- and travel must be by the most direct route practical. If a josan is found wandering around the base on her own or in company of someone violating these rules, or in company of someone other than the one who signed for her, I want the sponsoring person to be disciplined."**

**"On the basis of what charge?" Pastiak asked.**

**"*For a failure to protect government property*! I will consider the signed in josan as government property until signed out at the gate."**

**"It will be hard to make it stick," Pastiak answered.**

**"Unless you have a better idea, it has to stick. But, something else, I don't want any of this in writing -- not a word. Brief our own and tenant heads on the policy and let's monitor the result."**

**I could see that my staff was not pleased at the decision. And I wasn't happy with it myself. In my view, it still left me running some sort of a whorehouse.**

**I looked at my watch. To my surprise, it was already dinner time. I asked Davidson to join me.**

# THE INSPECTION REPORT

**Davidson and I had a drink at the bar. There we were joined by some of the other officers. It was obvious that they were interested in what this new Commander was going to do about what and I imagined that all sort of rumors were flying around. A few of the officers asked some question, there were some mild gripes, most of the men just stood by and listened.**

**Jones had, at Davidson's request, exchanged my money for Korean currency and he joined us at the bar -- handing me a large wad of strange bills. I looked through the mess and finally figured out what the various items were worth in American dollars -- then paid for the drinks.**

**At dinner, I was joined by Davidson, Akers and Jones. I noticed, that following a drink, Davidson's hands, which had been slightly trembling when we arrived at the club, had stopped shaking -- was it alcoholism I was looking at?**

**Again, it was a choice between fried chicken or fried steak and everyone urged me to order the chicken -- which I did. Actually, I hated chicken and, worst of all, fried chicken. I had grown up on a chicken farm and, by high school, had eaten so much chicken that it almost nauseated me. But I thought even less of chewing through tough steak regardless of how much steak sauce I put on it.**

**I tried to carry on some light conversation with those at the table but it was difficult -- I just had too much on my mind.**

**I asked Akers about having the L-20 ready for a check ride for me in the morning but he advised that Osan had ordered us to fly a Korean body to Seoul for intelligence examination. The statement caused my neck hairs to stand on end.**

**"What body?" I asked.**

**"One of our perimeter guards found it on the sea wall," Davidson answered. "It was sort of half on and half off. We tried to get the local Korean officials to take it but they refused -- they said that the head was on our side of the line so it was our problem. It seemed like a drowning. He had clothes on but there was nothing in the pockets and there was no wound mark on the body. We put him in a reefer and notified Osan. He's probably frozen stiff by now."**

"You mean you put him in a food reefer?" I was somewhat taken back.

"Yes. We don't have any other way to store bodies. We do this all the time when we have a fatality to deal with. We did slip him in a body bag."

Well, how about that! I guessed that the answer was the best of solutions available. I had a hard time imagining my soon-to-be-eaten chicken coming from next to the body of a dead Korean but I guessed that I may have led too sophisticated a life in the past. I brushed it aside and the subject was dropped.

Jones stated that, based on a call he had received, it was known at Osan that I was at Kunsan. He stated that the people at Osan were pretty unhappy that I had not first reported up there. I decided that I might as well fly up to Osan in the morning and do a formal check in with the 314th Air Division -- but, in relation to that decision, I made a tactical error in assessment as I was to learn that the concern about check in had come from the Wing Commander -- not the Division Commander. On the plus side, I had already learned enough about Kunsan Air Base that I could talk sensibly to anyone at Osan -- I was not to be pushed around.

Akers agreed to have the Gooney Bird ready for flight at 0800 hours. I told Davidson that there would be no morning staff meeting and to pass the word around. As to the L-20 check out, I told Akers that we would delay it for a day or two.

Reflecting on the Korean body now stored in the reefer, I asked if this was or was not a frequent occurrence. In answer, I was assured that it was infrequent but "now and then" it did happen. And what was the outcome of such an occurrence? No one knew. And then I asked a question that threw everyone off.

"Did anyone check his nose or his ass hole?"

Eyes at the table darted from one to another. No one wanted to ask the obvious question. Finally Davidson answered.

"I guess no one did but what would it be that would interest us?

I knew I had hit upon an upsmanship situation and I decided to use it to advantage. Certainly, by tomorrow, there would be talk about this one.

"I gather you people haven't been exposed to enemy agents. Often, one of the identification marks of an agent can be found in tattoos inside the nostril or on the inside of an ass hole -- a number. I think it would be significant for us to know if the body that washed up on the sea wall was that of a North Korean agent -- don't you?"

There was fidgeting at the table. I knew that I had scored but there was no point in pressing the issue -- the point had been made and I let it drop.

"Have we gotten General Joyce's bio and photo yet?" I asked. The shaking of heads told me "no." I noted that the question seemed, immediately, to cause Davidson's hands to again begin shaking. Since I had told him to obtain a bio and photo for both General Joyce and Colonel Musgrave, apparently my comment placed special pressure on him.

And then Annie brought our chicken dinners. The chicken was greasy but tolerable. Annie produced some jelly for the bread. We had a round of cold beer served with the dinner. I kept watching Davidson's hands -- following the beer, they again became steady as a rock.

"Had your first bout with G.I.'s?" Akers asked.

The question seemed to embarrass the others.

"Not yet," I answered. "How long do I have to wait?"

"Doc says that about forty-eight hours is all that is normally needed. Has he given you some pills yet."

"Doc is not here," Davidson reminded Akers.

"Sorry," Akers added. "I've got a good supply and will bring some by your office -- it's lomotil -- works pretty good -- we refer to it as *Instant Cement.*"

The conversation drifted into things back in the U.S., family, politics and more. In the meantime, my mind had a focus on the trip to Osan. What would be the topics of discussion? Already I was worried about the impact of the findings in the war reserve materiel yard. What else was there to worry about? Finally, I turned to Davidson.

"I know it's late but would you get me the last inspection report on the base and our response -- and bring it up to my hootch. I'll take some cold beers up with me to satisfy any thirst we might generate. If you want someone to come up with you, O.K. -- but don't make it a crowd. I just want to review and discuss the reports -- to learn what the inspectors have said about this base and how we responded. And if there are things not done that should have been done, I want to know before I get a tit in the wringer at Osan." Then, as an after-thought, "Do you have a vehicle?"

"No sir."

"Well, take mine. I could use a walk." That Davidson did not have a vehicle assigned to him concerned me. As the Deputy Commander, he needed one if he was going to do his job. But why had not the ex-Commander assigned him one? I was puzzled. Was it that, in spite of conversation to the contrary, Davidson had been viewed as a non-thing by the ex-Commander?

"I'll drive you up to your quarters," Wild suggested.

"No, I'll walk. It will help me think."

When I got to the Waldorf Astoria, it was about 2300 hours. Davidson was waiting for me. He had Major Peterson and Captain Polk with him. Their presence suggested that the problems raised by the inspector had been mostly in the support area.

While Davidson, Peterson and Polk sat quietly sipping on a beer, I read the inspection report -- actually several reports as Davidson had included the current and some earlier inspection reports. To my surprise, they were rather shallow. None of the items that concerned me were in the reports. Why? Mostly, the inspector's reports concerned administrative items -- which the base seemed, per the reports, to be handling. Apparently, Jones was doing a good job -- as had been his predecessor. The inspector's reports did gripe about the condition of the buildings -- Polk's and his predecessor's replies were centered heavily on the lack of personnel and supplies. The inspector's reports also raised some hell about the staff car suggesting that it should be turned in for salvage but there was no offer of a replacement. The issue of single tires on the dual-tired trucks did come up in one report but it was set aside by a comment dealing with the lack of supply -- there was no further action. Apparently, the inspector had reviewed the defense plans for the base and gave them a passing score. I had not had a chance to look at these plans and the inspector's reports tended to give me a good feeling but I had to wonder if the inspector knew what he was looking at. As I finished the inspection reports, it was not what they said but what they did not say that worried me. No real discussion of base defense, no discussion of general security, no discussion of nuclears, no discussion of the alert aircraft, no discussion of fences and other essentials, no discussion of radios and personal armament, no discussion of food, no discussion of medical -- the list of non-discussed items was enormous.

"How come these inspection reports don't cover the alert aircraft, don't hit on the manpower situation, say nothing about fuel storage and pumping problems -- just about miss a whole lot of things?"

"My guess," Davidson answered, "is that the inspectors just want to get in and out of here -- to fill a square. No one likes to come to Kunsan so the inspectors just do the minimum look-see, go home and collect their pay checks. An inspection report is an inspection report. I don't think anyone grades inspection reports -- the object is just to have one. Plus, you will find that the personnel assigned to the Osan inspection system are not all that swift. Most likely, the next inspector to come this way will be a feather merchant in the Osan IG office and he won't be able to wipe his butt. That, in my view, is a blessing."

I had to wonder if Davidson might not be correct. I was worried about the situation at Kunsan but who was to say that the situation at Osan was much different -- I had not been there and did not know. Perhaps General Joyce was going through some of the same trauma that I was going through? The thought had not occurred to me. As to the inspector being a civilian rather than a military person, I was surprised. But I was not going to pursue the point.

"What about an inspection by a nuclear team?" I asked. "When was the last time we had the Atomic Energy personnel here -- or a similar Air Force team?"

"Not while I've been here," Davidson answered. "If we had a nuclear inspection, I wasn't involved."

"And I didn't find anything like that in my files," Peterson added. "However, the nukes belong to Fifth Air Force -- not us."

Something was wrong. Again my mind turned to the question: Was it that the "nuclear weapons" were not really nuclear weapons -- only dummies -- only "Silver Bullets?" I would have liked to raise the question with my staff but I knew I dared not for, if this operation was a tremendous cover and deception plan, or something like it, its success depended on the base and all concerned "playing it for real." And, by God, until I learned that things were not "for real," I had to assume that they were -- and I was going to play it to the hilt.

"What guidance on nuclear matters have we gotten from the Wing Commander at Osan?" I asked.

"None," Davidson replied.

The answer bothered me but with sleep beginning to overcome me, I had to call it quits. I thanked Davidson, Peterson and Polk for staying with me on the inspection reports. As an after-thought, I reversed my instruction on the morning staff meeting and told Davidson to take it and do what he could to polish the base presentation. I could see that he did not look forward to the task.

In minutes, we had said "good night" and I was alone.

With Davidson, Peterson and Polk gone, I tried to assess the evening. These were some of my key officers, Davidson especially, but they seemed limited in their grasp of needs, problems and opportunities. At no time during the evening did these officers come forth with serious analyses or recommendations. Something was wrong -- terribly wrong. Was it me? Or was it them? Was it everyone? And what about that Wing Commander at Osan? More and more, he was beginning to come across as no more than an annoying title.

I attempted a letter to Mary but it was so short I tore it up. What could I tell her of the day that would be on the plus side -- virtually nothing. I recognized that letter writing was going to become a chore. The solution: I had to get a tape recorder -- there was no other way. Perhaps, in a day or two, I could get to the exchange and purchase one.

Mentally, I then sought to list the topics to discuss in Osan but my thoughts trailed off. I fell asleep in a chair with my clothes on. I did not even turn off the light.

I dreamed a lot. Most of it centered on being in a battle of some sort and finding that the shells did not fit the gun I held. I kept dreaming it over and over. Finally, I managed to force a shell into the gun but, when I fired it at the enemy, the bullet just dropped out of the end of the barrel.

And then my dreams shifted to the josan problem. Was all of Korea one great big whorehouse? Could it be that, at Osan, truck loads of josans were nightly imported to the various clubs? By my cutting down on the josan activity at Kunsan Air Base, was I violating some unwritten policy of General Joyce -- or the Osan Wing Commander?

Suddenly, I was no longer dreaming -- I was awake!

Had my dreams awakened me or had there been a noise? With one eye, I searched the room. I was disturbed to find that I had left the light burning.

The temperature was terrible and my clothes were soaked through. Finally, I got up, opened one of the left-over cans of beer and drank. The beer was warm but, at least, it was liquid.

The can of beer emptied, I tossed it into a waste basket; turned off the light; slipped off my shoes, socks, shirt and trousers; placed my pistol under the pillow; and slid under the mosquito tent. I was dead tired. Soon, I found that I shared the tent with a mosquito -- it had found my ear. I slapped and killed it.

When I drifted off to sleep, I did not know.

# DAY THREE -- A WEDNESDAY

The alarm clock shattered my sleep.

For a moment, I did not know where I was. Then reality reached me but I was still half asleep -- exhausted.

I reached out from under the mosquito net for the still sounding alarm clock and stabbed at it to turn it off. On the third try, I succeeded. I was beat. Whatever sleep I had gotten, it was not rest.

Slipping out of the bed, I took off my sweat-soaked underwear and, gritting my teeth, took a cold shower. It brought me back to life. Somehow, I had to find a way to get hot water into my hootch -- the idea of being limited to hot water by way of a hot plate was not a long term solution.

As I dried myself, I decided on several things and picked up the bedside telephone. I asked for Lt. Colonel Davidson. On about the fifth ring, he answered. My mind had been trying to get thoughts lined up for the check-in at Division and I felt that, before I flew up there, I had to fill in more squares.

"Davidson, this is Moench."

I heard a drowsy "yes sir." Apparently, he had been sleeping when the phone rang.

"Davidson, a modification of today's schedule."

The "yes sir" was a little more clear.

"Instead of leaving for Osan at 0800 hours, make that a departure for 1200 hours. It's about an hour up there so that should put me in Osan just after lunch. Hopefully, the boss and the staff up there will have had a good lunch and they might be on the drowsy side. Advise Major Akers of the time switch. If we have any passengers for Osan, have them at Operations by 1130 hours.

"At 0800 hours, I want to meet Major Turnbull of the tactical fighter unit. Ask him to be in my office at that time. Tell him that I would like him to give me an expanded briefing on his operations and walk me through his area.

"I'll be down for breakfast in about thirty minutes. During breakfast, you can fill me in on anything that happened last night -- bring Captain Wild if you want. Also, I want you to think about what I will face at Osan and brief me on anything, absolutely everything, that you think will come up. Finally, I would like to know the layout of the Osan base -- if you have a map of Osan, bring it with you.

"As to the 0800 hours morning briefing, slip it to another office and give the overview job to the next senior person -- as I recall, that is Major Akers."

The "yes sir" I heard was not a statement of enthusiasm. I knew I was beginning to drive Davidson up the wall -- but he was my Deputy Commander.

Returning to the bathroom, I undertook my morning shave -- this time with water heated on the electric plate. I had not yet met my mama-san but she seemed to be doing O.K. All my dirty clothes had been washed and ironed and my shoes had been polished. Apparently, she was trying to show me what she had done as the washed and ironed clothes were carefully laid out on the wooden box in the bedroom -- not placed in the drawers or hung up. To my surprise, I saw that there was a small vase with some flowers on the stand next to my bed -- I had missed it the night before.

Dressed, I put a change of clothes and a shaving kit in my B-4 bag. I was going to place my pistol in the bag but decided against the idea and locked it in the wooden box. Locking the door to the Waldorf Astoria, I slipped into the driver's seat of the blue bomb. This time, on the first try, the engine caught. It must be the weather, I thought.

En route to the club, I passed the now familiar Korean housing area. Again the young children were out playing in the dirt. I paused for a minute to watch them -- thinking about my own children back in Virginia. And then I realized how little they had to play with -- only makeshift items. Some of the children were playing with an old tire -- rolling it back and forth in some kind of game of tag. Others were just digging in the dirt. Suddenly, I decided that I had to do something special for these Korean kids.

I was already seated and having a cup of coffee when Davidson arrived.

Breakfast was a mirror image of the day before. I could see where a year of the same thing would wear on a person -- already it seemed to be wearing on me and I was only in my third day. There was one thing different this morning -- there was a jar of orange marmalade on the table. Annie was there with her broad smile and continuous coffee refill. As she poured coffee, she proudly announced that a shipment of marmalade had come in and that she had a jar for each table. Somehow, even though this was only day number three, Annie was already coming across as an American.

"Where does Annie live?" I asked Davidson.

"She comes from one of the local villages."

"Her English is pretty good."

"I think she's been working in the club since the Korean War. For them, it's learn English or no work."

"What does she get paid as a waitress?"'

"I have no idea but it's not much. The Korean manager takes care of it."

"Don't we have a role in this -- like setting hours, wages, audit and other things?"

"I really don't know. I never did try to get into the issues of club management. It sort of runs itself. And I believe that *if it ain't broke don't fix it.*"

"Well, as of now, get into it and tell me how it works. I suspect that, without some control by us, the situation is ripe for kickbacks, theft, black market and more. Do it as discreetly as possible as I don't want a backlash."

I could see that Davidson did not like this new assignment but I did not care. I was certain that, in the days ahead, there would be many assignments that he and others would not like.

"Have you started the briefings on the josan policy?"

"Yes."

"And . . . ."

"No one likes it."

"But are they accepting it?"

"It's hard to tell but I think there will be some cooperation. Changing long-standing policy isn't an easy sell job. Frankly, sir, many of the men think that your being so new here you don't understand the problem."

The hair on the back of my neck bristled.

"And what is it that I do not understand?"

"Well, a lot of the men think that your policy is going to drive up the VD rate."

"And why is that?"

"I don't want to go into detail, Colonel. But the fact of the matter is that sex in not a clean issue and, by having access to the barracks, the men can obtain some semblance of sanitation. They think that you are driving them out of the barracks -- possibly into Korean hootches -- and they postulate all kinds of bad things happening as a result."

I leaned back in my chair and looked at the ceiling. It was an old story. I had heard it many times before. But I was not going to buy it.

"We'll see," I answered. "Now tell me about last night -- did anything happen that I should know?"

"We picked up a couple slicky boys on the perimeter. They were sneaking out some radio stuff that had been stolen from a barracks. Captain Wild will turn them over to the local authorities today. Right now we have them in our jail."

"And what will the local authorities do with them?"

"Probably nothing. The slicky boys will pay off the local police and we might find them back on the base in a night or two. Our Air Police have captured these guys before and I think they may have roughed them up a bit."

"How much?"

"I didn't see them -- only heard some comment. My guess is that the slicky boys will have some sore muscles for a while. I suspect that our Air Police did do some clubbing of the slicks before they packed them into our jail."

Davidson sat quietly for a short time. Apparently, he wanted this information to sink in. He might have been seeking my approval or disapproval. I did not respond. I knew the problem, especially the frustration of the security personnel, but, for the moment, I had other things on my mind.

Davidson continued.

"Major Akers tells me that you know about the tanker in port. We expect to reconnect the pipeline in the next few days and then pump. I have alerted Osan for some helicopter support to cover the operation. We may begin to reconnect the pipeline today in which case I would expect to see the Koreans moving to the pipeline area by tonight -- or by early morning. As soon as we begin to reconnect the pipeline, they know that a pumping is about to start and they literally come from miles around to camp next to the line with their cans and buckets. I'd like to shoot them but we can't."

"What can we do?"

"Next to nothing. It's a sorry situation. All too many Koreans live by stealing. They will steal anything and everything. It's a losing proposition. Actually, I think this reflects long-standing Korean mores about which we can do nothing. After a while, you'll understand."

There it was again! The new kid on the block did not understand. I boiled but said nothing.

# A BRIEFING ON OSAN

"Tell me what you know about Osan. What will I encounter up there? What are the personalities of those with whom I must work? What has been going on at Osan? What is the skinny?"

Without his saying, I knew that Davidson was uncomfortable with the questions. Suddenly, I began to suspect that he had never really interfaced with the Osan environment. But then I could be wrong. Perhaps he had interfaced with Osan and failed to get anything done? Perhaps he had been to Osan and screwed up?

"As to the people you will encounter at Osan, it's hard to tell," Davidson began. "We are in the middle of the silly season with a good number of senior officers rotating. The new Division Commander, General Joyce, came over from Japan -- I don't really know anything about him. As you directed, I have been trying to get his bio and photo but, so far, it has not arrived.

"There is this new Wing Commander at Osan, a Colonel Musgrave. I haven't met him but I've heard all sort of stories about him -- none of them are good news. I think that all of the senior Division staff -- all the Colonels -- have rotated and I don't know the names of those replacing them. As I said, this is the silly season."

"I have to assume that our Army friends on the DMZ go through the same thing. Have you given much thought to the fact that this would be a good time for the North Koreans or Chinese Commies to pull something? With key personnel in transition, it seems that, militarily, this is a most vulnerable time."

"I guess everyone worries about such things but one can't do anything about it. We're in Korea and things just happen or they don't."

I hadn't wanted to get into defense planning but here I was. Apparently Davidson was unable or unwilling to shed much light on Osan so I thought I might as well get at the Kunsan Air Base defense plan -- it might come up at Osan -- who could tell?

"What's our base defense plan look like -- I mean, in general terms, how do we function in the case of an attack? Do we have a perimeter defense plan; how do we augment security in the alert and nuclear areas; how does the ROKAF fit into the plan; can the ROKAF trigger a base alert; just what happens when the siren goes off? Do we have a withdrawal plan? In what situations can the F-100s do a precautionary launch -- and who can order it? How do we operate in case of the loss of communications? And when was the last time the base defense plan was fully exercised?"

"Sir, I can't recall when the plan was exercised in full -- the Air police do some limited security exercises but not the whole base. Actually, I don't know if we really have an overall base defense plan that means much of anything. I'll have to talk to Major Akers -- that's an operational item and he must be doing something about it. Perhaps Captain Wild knows something? Regarding any precautionary launch by the F-100s -- I guess that's part of Major Turnbull's responsibility -- we just don't get into the alert aircraft situation."

In my wildest dreams, I had not expected that answer. Here we were out in almost no-man's land, the Chinese Communists were directly across the Yellow Sea and the North Koreans were less than thirty minutes jet flying time to the north and, apparently, my Deputy sat dumb and happy -- perhaps the whole base sat equally unprepared for a military emergency? Perhaps this was mostly the case in all of South Korea?

"I just heard what you said but I find it hard to believe. You mean that, as Deputy Commander, you don't know if we have a defense plan for this base? And, if we have one, you're telling me that, in your recollection, it was never fully exercised? It sounds as if we are anything but a military organization out here. Suppose I was killed -- how would you operate -- what would you do?"

"Colonel, I have just got to tell you how it is. We're manned at less than two-thirds strength; we don't have all that much in the way of talent; our logistics are terrible; sometimes the biggest problem we face is just getting food -- it all adds up to the fact that we don't do a lot of things you would expect to be done -- like cutting grass."

"Well, let's see if we can't change a few things. When I get back from Osan I want you and Akers to brief me on the base defense plan -- whatever it is -- and, if we don't have one or one that makes sense, your job is to get us one. Then, figure that an enemy attack may hit us within a week or so. It may be a test run or it may be the real thing but, either way, we better be ready. Your job, as well as my job, is to do a job while also being prepared to defend our unit in the case of attack. If we don't have a plan with everyone knowing his job in that plan, in an emergency we will be no more than a rabble and we will be slaughtered."

"Yes sir." Davidson was far from pleased and there went his hands again -- trembling.

"Now, let's get back to Osan. Certainly, you can tell me more than you have so far."

Davidson thought for a while and was about to answer when I interjected a troubling thought.

"Who can trigger the sirens on this base?"

Davidson paled at the question.

"I don't know, sir. I think they are controlled by the Air Police."

*Don't know -- think* -- it was driving me up the wall.

"In after hours, do we keep a duty officer in the headquarters?"

"No sir. We are manned too thin for that."

"Well, as of tomorrow, I want a duty officer and a duty enlisted man, preferably three stripes or more, in headquarters every night. You write up their responsibilities and give the duty officer a button to activate an alert. As a part of the duty officer write up, spell out the rules governing a base alert. If this is not in the base defense plan, put it in there. When you are finished, brief me on the duty officer's responsibilities, the rules regarding the triggering of the sirens, the electronic hook-up of the sirens and where they are located."

Davidson's face had further whitened. I could see that I was pushing him by continually asking him to do things and posing questions to him he could not answer but I could not stop -- I had things to do.

"O.K. Let's get back to the Osan thing. What else can you tell me?"

To my surprise, Davidson's mood suddenly changed and his answer was remarkably forthright and informative.

"Well, I guess the first thing you will see is that Osan just does not look like Kunsan. That's the Air Force headquarters in Korea and it seems to get all the priority. I understand your focus on grass and you will be pleased or unhappy to know that at Osan they do a reasonable grass-cutting job and, based on the last time I was there, they seem to have a good number of lawn mowers. And the buildings are better than here. I think all the roads on the base are paved. Finally, you will see a good number of American girls up there. Most of the American girls are secretaries -- some, but not all, are really "stateside rejects." They have a pretty good Officers Club and the VIP quarters on Hill One-Eighty are superb. If you spend the night, they will put you up in those VIP quarters -- it has its own mess and the food is outstanding -- not like here. I suggest you visit the Officers Club -- it's a pretty good set-up and the meals are usually good. But, if you go by the Officers Club, all I can say is be ready. The *silly season*, when it comes to the secretaries, is called the *mating season*. Every secretary tries to stake out a claim on someone for the next year and, as a Colonel, you are a prime object to be claimed."

"You got to be kidding," I blurted. But I sensed not only was he not kidding but, somehow, he had been there and either had been claimed or rejected. "Continue," I added.

"In the way of physical facilities, the headquarters building is a bunch of inter-connected Nissen huts. They have several hangars on the flight line. As to aircraft, in addition to alert fighters, they have some T-33s and Gooney Birds -- the General's Gooney is really plush. And they have several helicopters as well as L-20s.

*The 314th Air Division headquarters building complex of Nissen huts as viewed from Hill One-Eighty. Aircraft hangars are in the background beyond which is the runway, the river and some mountains.*

"I do suggest you visit the Osan Command Center. It will give you an idea of how primitive things are out here. Believe me when I say that it's not high tech. It's a joint command center with both Koreans and Americans in it. Mostly, it's oriented to air defense.

"We may have a man or two for you to fly up to Osan for treatment in their hospital -- we usually do. I'll talk to the medical Sergeant about it in the morning.

"While you're up there, if you get a chance to talk to Materiel, I think there are some things you might put pressure on. Probably the biggest item, outside of food which is Army controlled, is the old matter of tires. You have seen how we operate. If we have many more blow outs, we will be dead in the water. You will note, when you are at Osan, that all their vehicles run on two tires."

Davidson had opened up. This was, without doubt, the most expansive coverage of issues he had provided to me since I arrived. Apparently, he had been sitting on his thoughts for some time. I wondered what took him so long to come clean. I could see that he was searching to see how I took this information. It did disturb me that the priorities might be going to Osan but I would have to witness some of this for myself.

"With all these things bothering you, what have you done to correct the situation?"

"Colonel, I don't think you really understand. I have only been the Deputy here. For about two weeks, from the time the last Commander left and you arrived, I have been serving as the Acting Commander. In that time, I could not get anything done -- I was a lame duck who just had to go along with the past and wonder about the future. In the past -- well, we just sort of existed -- we just tried to make the most out of a bad deal. I don't think anyone really cared about what happened out here. I think we could all have starved to death and no one up the chain of command would have noticed or cared."

"As you see it, were the Kunsan problems beyond the capability of the Wing Commander to do something constructive?"

"Frankly, Colonel, I don't think Kunsan is really on the Wing Commander's agenda."

"Past or present?"

"Both."

"Well, let's change that. As my Deputy, you can get anything done in my name that needs to be done. Just don't make any fool mistakes. Let's get some of the right things done -- and fast. And, if we have to kick some butt, let's kick it."

I could see that Davidson's hands were now shaking rather hard and I again wondered what the problem was. His comments on Osan were a rather brilliant portrayal compared to the past. Had I misjudged my Deputy? I thought it best to change the subject.

"What can you tell me about the U.S. Air Force Advisory Group -- the MAAG? We have a ROKAF squadron here, but Akers tells me that there are no MAAG personnel stationed here at Kunsan. The subject may come up when I visit Osan. Any thoughts?"

"Not really. I have never gotten into ROKAF operations or the MAAG -- it's the 6146th Air Force Advisory Group -- some call it AFAG. The AFAG headquarters is located at Yongdongpo in the western part of Seoul and south of the Han Gang. Its offices are in the ROKAF headquarters building. The support functions and living quarters for unaccompanied personnel are situated on a Han Gang island and they are sorry -- it's the location of the Seoul Auxiliary Airfield and, when the river rises, it floods. Accompanied people and their families live in quarters on the Eighth Army's Yongson Military Reservation in downtown Seoul. I've been there and the housing is pretty good -- nothing like what we have here at Kunsan -- and better than what is at Osan."

I made a mental note to visit with the AFAG commander. Undoubtedly we shared in some common problems. But that matter could wait.

"Have you laid on the meeting with Major Turnbull?"

"It's done."

"Good. Let's go."

I gulped down the last of my coffee and left some Korean currency on the table.

"Too much," Davidson cautioned. "You're tipping. It is an insult to tip a Korean. We don't tip."

The new boy on the block again -- I could see it in Davidson's eyes. I picked up my money, looked carefully at the bill Annie had laid on the table, and then sorted out some notes that matched.

"Let's move." I was angry at the world. And I had suddenly become extremely apprehensive about the forth-coming visit to Osan. Somehow, I felt I was walking into a buzz saw and that the exposure by Davidson might have been set forth as some sort of bait to lead me into something untoward when I reported to the 314th Air Division and to Wing -- probably to teach me a lesson. I was particularly disturbed that, in the short time I had been at Kunsan, the focus of all too many problems appeared to center on the Wing Commander. Instinctively, I could envisage that he and I were going to clash. Hopefully, I would be wrong but the evidence was mounting that I would be correct. With all the problems on my plate, the last thing I needed was a difficult relationship with the Wing Commander at Osan -- with Colonel Musgrave. I knew that I had to play my cards carefully.

# KUNSAN'S PRIMARY TENANT

Major Turnbull was waiting for me when I arrived at my office.

"Come in Major."

The Major appeared uncomfortable -- nervous. He had been to one of our base staff meetings and seemed arm's length at that time but still relaxed. What had changed? Had he been instructed by his home base not to cooperate with me? I was puzzled.

"Care for a cup of coffee?" I asked. I had found that Miss Lee did know how to make a reasonable cup of coffee.

"Thank you, no sir."

I could sense a lot of ice in the air. But I was totally unsure as to the cause.

"'Been here long?" I asked.

"Two weeks. I rotate back to Japan in another two weeks."

"And the air and ground crews -- what is their rotation -- the same for everyone?"

"No sir. The air crews are generally rotated every two weeks. Except for bringing an aircraft in or taking one home, they don't get any flight time here. And, without time in the cockpit, they can get pretty rusty. The ground support crews normally spend a month -- the same as I am doing."

"I understand."

For a while we sat in silence. I had asked for an expanded briefing on Turnbull's activity but, studying him, I decided to pursue another line of thought.

"How can I help to make your life better?" I asked.

It was obvious that Turnbull had not expected that type of question. And, suddenly, I realized that he might have thought I called him relative to some sort of problem, probably one caused by him or by someone in his unit -- perhaps he knew of something having happened and expected that I would know. I observed that his mood changed quickly and whatever was bothering him rapidly became a non-thing.

"This rotation stuff is a drag," Turnbull replied. "We get here and we go through target study, we check out the aircraft, once a day we run up the engines, we study tech manuals, and, then, we do it all over again. The men try to stay occupied by playing cards, reading, listening to music and the like, but it is boring as all hell. I know that

**you can't change that but, if there is one thing that you can do, it is to improve the food we get. Our officers get food from the Officers Club and our enlisted men depend on your G.I. mess. Frankly, the food stinks."**

**"Your mess set-ups in Japan are one hell of a lot better, aren't they?"**

**"They sure are. And none of us can figure out why the base here can't do as good. We are only a few hundred miles apart."**

**"Well, I have only been here for a few days but, already, I appreciate what you are telling me. As to a fix, I can't yet tell you what it might be or when -- only that I recognize the problem and intend to do something about it. Now is there something else I can help on?"**

**Turnbull thought for a while and then answered:**

**"Colonel, does it bother you that we sit here strapped to the ground with almost nothing around us in the way of local defense -- nothing other than a few old guns manned by the ROK Army? Right in our area, all you have around us is a handful of Air Police and nothing beyond that. Somehow, the situation strikes me as very peculiar. We have more protection in Japan. Sometimes, I think we have been put out here as some sort of bait. Do you think that is possible?"**

**I could see that this was not a sudden thought -- it was something that came from deep inside the Major -- probably it was a matter of discussion among the men of his unit. Certainly, it was not thoughts that would lead to good morale.**

**"I trust that is not the case. But let me address just the issue of air defense, again admitting that I have only been here a few days. Let me say that, on the surface, I do find things a bit on the open side. I would, as example, like to see some better guns or even missiles around this base but, from a command position, one cannot reflect concern downward -- you can't and I can't. We both have a job to do. And, when it comes to air defense, consider that we not only have a ROKAF squadron here but there are other units to the north and east." Purposefully, I did not want to comment about the adequacy or inadequacy of the Kunsan Air Police situation -- or beyond.**

**Turnbull's appreciation troubled me for it coincided with some of my own thinking -- but it was not something to which I could openly agree -- or even hint of agreement. Further, I had to recall how, as a Major, I looked to Colonels to have the answers. Turnbull harbored a worry and seemed to need an answer so I thought it best to give him an**

answer -- possibly something that would be repeated to his men and to others. Hopefully, something positive to offset the mood I detected.

"Did you ever think that your unit would not be in Japan if you were not standing alert here -- possibly your unit would not exist at all without your being here in Korea?"

"What are you talking about, Colonel?"

I knew I had Turnbull's attention.

"Well, let's begin with what your aircraft are targeted to hit."

"I'm not allowed to answer that question, sir."

"I know that so let's just make some assumptions. The first assumption is that the U.S. is not going to rush off to drop nukes on a country that has no nukes. And that rules out North Korea and, possibly, China. So we have only the Soviet Union left.

"Now, with the national defense budget what it is, unless a force has a nuclear role it really sucks hind tit when it comes to money. And the only way the Air Force tactical fighters can play in the nuclear game is to be based forward -- in Europe and here in Asia. If we had nuclear rights in Japan, you could launch from there but we don't have those rights. So your only alternative is to stand nuclear alert here in Korea. If you did not stand nuclear alert in Korea, your unit would probably not be in Japan and, probably, it would not even be in the Air Force program. In other words, the aircraft and crews you have here in Korea preserve in the Air Force program a full fighter unit -- your unit in Japan -- your job and that of your buddies."

"I never thought about that," Turnbull answered. "But what about the Navy and the carriers -- are they impacted by the same policies?"

"Hell yes. The carriers are assigned nuclear tasks along with everyone else. It's play the nuclear game or lose budget money.

"Now," I continued, "as to any military unit serving as a trigger, let me begin by saying that the two U.S. Army Divisions we have north of us on the DMZ serve as a trigger -- the North Koreans hit those units and they know that they are attacking not South Korea -- they are attacking the United States. And we have the same thing in Europe with the forces deployed there. This is part of the U.S. commitment. Are these forces a *trigger*? Possibly -- but a necessary trigger. And a *trigger* is not *bait*.

"Then there is something else. If the Soviets attack the U.S. with missiles, and they would be foolish to do it without missiles, the time of flight is about thirty minutes. With our radars in Alaska and northern Canada, we would pick up the missiles shortly after launch.

Although SAC could launch it's missiles and quickly roll the strategic bombers, unless they took out your capability here, you would be up their tail pipe before SAC got its first weapons to target -- that excludes, of course, the airborne alert aircraft flying on the periphery of the Soviet Union. So now the Soviets have a problem. Will they seek to hit you, and others like you in the Far East and Europe, right away and trigger the U.S. attack or will they let you sit in the hope that their attack can be launched without detection? What your unit stationed here does is complicate the Soviet attack plan. Suppose, in reverse, the Soviets had nuclear aircraft on alert in Cuba, or Mexico, or Canada -- think about what a pain in the ass that would be for us.

"Stated differently, your unit and others like it give the Soviets a great big pain in the ass."

I could see that Turnbull was absorbing the whole thing and I decided to take it one step further.

"Now to the matter of air defense. You probably have less air defense coverage in Japan than you do here -- yet, your Japan base is not much further from enemy forces than you are here in Korea. Worse, in Japan you are not sitting on a ten minute alert. And you have no nuclear weapons in Japan. Thus, in the event of the big one, the chances of your forces here doing damage to the enemy is greater than the chances of those at your home base in Japan."

"How come no one else talks to us along these lines?" Turnbull asked.

"I guess it ties to the fact that strategy is not often passed downward. Certainly, the specifics of the invasion plan of Eisenhower were held close. The big thing in the military establishment is to trust the upper echelon to do its job and for the upper echelon to trust that the lower echelons will do their job. When I put a man on the perimeter and tell him he has a certain job to do, I don't expect to lay out for him the entire base defense plan. We are on the perimeter of the United States and, just like the guard I send out, we have to work our sector of the problem and trust that others work their sectors of the problem."

Turnbull settled into a relaxed, reflective mood. I knew that I only half believed some of what I said but that had to remain a private thought. Overall, it seemed that it was time to take another direction and I asked Turnbull if he would walk me through his area. He agreed.

There were eight F-100s in the alert area -- six of them had nuclear weapons fitted below -- at least the external configuration was that of a nuclear weapon -- but they could have been "Silver Bullets."

All six aircraft were on the described ten minute alert. One F-100 had the engine unbuttoned and was being worked on by several mechanics.

"We can be off the ground in under ten minutes," Turnbull assured me.

"And how do you get your orders -- how do you communicate?" I asked.

"We have a dedicated tactical line to our base in Japan and one that comes from Fifth Air Force at Fuchu. We get our operational launch from CINCPAC in Hawaii by way of Fuchu."

"Not through PACAF?"

"No. PACAF is not in the operational stream of things."

"What can you do if communications to Fuchu or your home base fail?"

"Mostly, we sit and wait for them to come back on. If the base still has communications to the outside world by way of your lines, we might get a relayed message by way of the Osan Command Center."

"Do you check the circuits periodically to see if you can talk to the Osan Command Center?

"It's not on my operating SOP, sir."

"Have you ever visited the Osan Command Center?"

"No sir."

And those answers told me that I had something more to do.

"How about a precautionary launch?"

"I don't have that authority, sir. That would be something I would be ordered to do and it would have to be authenticated. It takes two recognized authorities to execute a precautionary launch."

Which meant that, if an attack rolled into the base and communications were out, the F-100s would be sitting ducks tied to concrete. Why would I, as the senior officer on the scene, not have certain authority to order a precautionary launch? Someone in the operations system was not thinking. On the other hand, I surely would not want Davidson making such a decision in my absence. What a hell of a situation!

"The stored nuclears -- those not on your birds -- who are they for?"

"Beats me," Turnbull answered. "No one has clued me in on that one. I guess someone at Fifth Air Force knows but I don't."

"And, as of this moment, that makes two of us," I added. "I guess that is one of those things we are not supposed to know."

Turnbull introduced me to some of his pilots and ground crew personnel. Then, noting the time, I decided I would have to leave.

"One last thing," Turnbull added as we were about to depart company, "have you had a chance to study your fire and rescue support capability?"

"No, not yet."

"Well, I think you should. In particular, take a look at your flight line fire truck."

"Why?"

"You'll see."

Turnbull was smiling as I left. Obviously, there was some sort of joke in his comment. I decided that the next stop would be the flight line fire truck.

I had to wonder why my eyes had not caught it! The flight line fire truck was backed up on a mounded dirt ramp. Chocks in front of the wheels held it in position. I went into the shack in which the fire team was located. Someone called attention.

"At ease," I ordered. Then, looking around the room, I asked, "Who's in charge here?"

"I am." The voice came from the rear of the room. The owner of the voice walked forward. "I'm Sergeant Willis, Stan Willis. Is there something I can do for you?"

"Certainly. Can you tell me what's going on with the fire truck outside blocked up on that ramp?"

The Sergeant smiled. Even before I heard the words, I could hear it coming.

"Things are a bit rough out here, Colonel. If we didn't have the truck up on the ramp, we couldn't get it going. We don't have a starter for it. We get it going by pulling the chocks and letting it roll down the ramp. When the speed is up, we let out the clutch and pray that it kicks over."

"Do you have foam in the truck?"

"Yes sir. But we don't have a back-up supply."

"Does the ROKAF have a fire truck?"

"They have a water pumper -- that's all. And it isn't a big one."

Suddenly, I had still another problem on my hands. I thanked the Sergeant and headed for operations. It was getting close to departure time for Osan. I had to wonder why the inspection reports did not list the fire truck situation as a problem. Was it possible that the inspector saw it but reported nothing? Or was it that he didn't wander far enough from the headquarters to see it? Either answer was disturbing.

# ON TO OSAN

Major Akers and Sergeant Phillips were waiting for me in the Operations building. Akers had the clearance filled out. There was a room at the side of the building that served as a passenger lounge and about a dozen men, some with baggage, were seated. I could see that an ambulance was parked outside by the aircraft.

"We have one stretcher case," Akers reported. "The others are regular passengers -- mostly reassignments."

"What's wrong with the stretcher case?"

"Broken bones. Accident last night. They have him strapped in good. He needs some setting and cast work that, with our Flight Surgeon gone, we can't do here. He's pretty well loaded with morphine and should sleep most of the way up. Grossman said that all he could do was a temporary splint job. One of the medical Sergeants will fly up with us."

"O.K. Lets load up and get rolling."

The flight from Kunsan to Osan was uneventful. The one engine kept reading in the red but, otherwise, it ran perfectly. The radio compasses continued to point in different directions but, eventually, one got used to it. GCA picked us up well out of Osan and it brought us around for a controlled landing. On the way in, I observed the river running by Osan from which the base's drinking water was drawn -- it was a sickly yellow. On landing, a Follow-Me jeep picked us up at the end of the runway and guided us to a parking spot in front of the control tower and the Osan Operations building. An ambulance immediately pulled up to the aircraft to receive the stretcher case.

"Do you plan to spend the night?" Akers asked.

I cursed myself for not having discussed this with him.

"Did you bring a change?"

"Yes sir. I always do when I fly around Korea. One never knows about the weather, the aircraft or what else can go wrong."

"O.K. I recommend you hang loose until about four or five this afternoon. If things go fast, we may want to get out of here. Otherwise, we may have to bunk here for the night and leave tomorrow morning. One way or the other, I'll leave a message for you at the Operations desk. If we are going to stay overnight, I'll be back to the aircraft for my B-4 bag. Leave it unlocked or have Sergeant Phillips somewhere around."

Akers had called in my code status and I saw that a staff car was pulling up to the aircraft. It was a new model -- not anything like the clunker I had at Kunsan. I pulled off my headset and combed my hair, straightened my uniform and was about to head for the exit door when I had a thought.

Looking at Akers and Phillips, I asked: "Do you want to continue to fly an aircraft in the red line and with the compasses screwed up?"

"No sir." The answer came as one.

"Well then, let's see if we can't solve the problem. You both go to the transient aircraft shop and tell them that you just arrived from Kunsan; tell them you have a new C.O. and that he's an S.O.B.; tell them you were ordered to get this Gooney Bird fixed or you and everyone in transient maintenance were going to have a new and uncomfortable assignment. Throw my name around and use some strong language. Tell them that your C.O. is already on his way to see the Commanding General to discuss major problems and he doesn't want the Gooney Bird to be still another problem to bring up with the General but he damn well will if the aircraft is not fixed by tonight. And let me assure both of you that, if you don't succeed in this mission, I may let each of you know what an uncomfortable assignment means."

I could see that Akers and Phillips were unsure of whether I was crawling over them or the transient aircraft shop or what. They both saluted and uttered a "yes sir." I saluted back and proceeded down the ladder.

The G.I. driver was holding open the door of the staff car. He saluted as I neared. Seated inside, I told the driver to take me to the 314th Air Division headquarters.

Yes, without doubt, Osan was quite different from what I had found at Kunsan. As Davidson had reported, the grass at Osan was cut; drainage ditches were clean; buildings appeared to be in fair condition; the roads were good; well lettered signs told a person where facilities were located -- and all trucks had two tires! Mentally, I gave Davidson a "Brownie Point." But, as I reflected on the Osan/Kunsan comparisons, I found myself giving the Wing Commander a demerit.

There was no guard at the entrance to the Air Division headquarters so I just walked in. The Commander's office was easy to locate -- it was right off the entrance -- there was a large "Commanding General" sign over the door. I stepped in and announced myself to an

American secretary who I presumed worked for the Commander. I was to learn that her name was Barbara.

"I'm Colonel John Moench. I just flew in from Kunsan Air Base. I'm the new Commander at Kunsan. I would like to see General Joyce. Is he in?"

"Did the General know you were coming? I don't see you on his schedule."

"No, he did not. And he may not even know that I'm in Korea. But I am here. Kindly so advise General Joyce."

The secretary was flustered. Obviously, I had broken a routine. With an "Excuse me," she got up and went into the General's office. In a few minutes, she returned.

"General Joyce asks if you would give him a few minutes. He has some visitors to take care of right now. As soon as possible, he will see you."

It turned out that the "few minutes" would be some twenty minutes. I saw two somewhat disturbed Colonels hurry into the General's office. As they passed, they gave me disapproving glances. Later I would learn that they were the Personnel Officer and the Wing Commander. Obviously, the General wanted some information in front of him before he saw me. I was pleased with myself. Apparently, I had succeeded in arriving unannounced in spite of word reaching Kunsan that, with displeasure, it was known that I was in Korea. Undoubtedly, the word originated in a lower staff level and not from General Joyce. Perhaps, as had been reported to me, it originated with the Wing Commander?

"The General will see you now," the Secretary announced.

I went in, saluted the General, and reported in good military fashion. General Joyce was a tall, well-built individual with thinning, speckled gray hair and a pleasant face. Immediately, I liked him. He stuck out his hand. The handshake was firm and his eyes reflected confidence. He invited me to join him at a sofa and have a cup of coffee. The secretary was already bringing in two filled cups.

"How come you didn't stop here on your way to Kunsan?" he asked.

"My orders stated that I was to report to Kunsan and take command -- and that's what I did. You may know that your predecessor asked me to report early -- sort of an emergency situation. He implied a serious problem at Kunsan and I gave up leave in order to get there as fast as I could -- had to get my orders recut and pull a lot of strings to do it."

General Joyce did not have to tell me -- I could see that he was unaware of the communication of his predecessor. I could also see that he was impressed with what I told him.

"Well, the main thing is that you are here. And, having already been at Kunsan, what can you tell me? I have, on occasion, flown in and out of your base but, since taking this job, I haven't been down there for a deep look-see -- I'm still trying to get settled here at Osan. I'll try to get down your way in a week or two."

Here was my chance and I knew I had to make the most of it. General Joyce was new so he would not be on the defensive regarding the past. What I had hoped for was an open mind and I sensed that I had encountered one. But I knew that I was not going to make friends with some subordinates to the General -- persons who probably had not briefed him on Kunsan, persons who probably didn't even know the problems at the base, and persons who may never even have been there.

"General, I'll be as frank as I can. I have only been at Kunsan a couple days -- actually, I arrived about this time three days ago. In overview, I have never seen such a mess. I find it difficult to believe that our military establishment can place men out in the front line and then not support them logistically, with personnel, with much of anything. I intend to get the place shaped up but I can tell you that I may make a lot of persons unhappy in the process. I hope that, of the persons I make unhappy, you are not one."

The General was obviously taken back. In that he did not have knowledge of what I was talking about, he could not really comment. And, certainly, he wanted his command to run properly. The General had heavy eyebrows and a firm mouth and chin line. All of these and other facial elements tightened as I spoke. His reply was serious and well-formed.

"John, I don't pretend to know what your problems are at Kunsan but you can be assured that, within reason, I will do everything to support you. I want to hold a weekly staff meeting here at Division and I would like you to attend. I'll let you know the schedule as soon as I can figure it out. And, at that staff meeting, don't be bashful about reporting on your needs. The staff persons here may think they have done a good job and, in the circumstances, they may have done a good job. But, if you have major problems at Kunsan facing you and they can help, they should join with you in solving those problems."

That's all I wanted. I felt the Commanding General was on my side. Now I had to deal with the Wing Commander to whom I was directly subordinate -- on paper, at least. But, before I could get to the Wing Commander, General Joyce was to give me some bad news.

"John, I have looked at your personnel file. I find it very interesting. This job at Division is not a bowl full of cherries and I have a lot of things that need to be done but damn few people who know what they are doing. Noting all the plans and programs experience you have, I must tell you that, as soon as I can locate another Colonel to fill your slot at Kunsan, I want you to come to Osan to serve as my Director of Plans and Programs. Among the officers I have assigned and in-coming, I have no one qualified for that job and, with all the politics, resource and other issues I face, I need someone who knows the score."

This news came as a shock. I didn't relish coming back to a staff job. While I could see that the job at Kunsan was going to be an enormous headache, it was still not a staff job -- and I was tired of staff work. But I knew that General Joyce had made up his mind and he was the boss. Inwardly, I sensed that, if I had reported into Osan on the way to Kunsan, I would have never reached the Kunsan destination. And I had to shudder if, in the meantime pending the arrival of a new Colonel to serve as the Kunsan Air Base Commander, what Lt. Colonel Davidson would have done -- or not done -- as Acting Commander. The thought was frightening. For his part, General Joyce had every right to assume that Davidson was capable -- my guess was that the ex-Commander of Kunsan probably gave Davidson a good Efficiency Rating and who at Osan would discern the short-comings of which I was fast coming to learn?

"General, one request."

"Yes."

"Can we keep that decision between the two of us until it actually happens? I fear that, if it gets out, I'm going to be considered a lame duck at Kunsan and it will fracture any progress to get the mess down there cleaned up -- and it does need one hell of a lot of cleaning up -- and I don't exaggerate."

General Joyce looked at me for a minute and then answered.

"It's a deal."

With some additional words of encouragement to get the job done and to call on him if I needed help, I left the General's office and proceeded to the office of the Wing Commander. On the way out, I made a point of talking to Barbara, his secretary.

I learned Barbara had been in Korea for several years. I complimented her on her dedication and she seemed pleased. I could tell that other officers apparently considered her no better than an office fixture -- for me, she was the General's secretary and a door to knowledge. Before I left, she gave me a copy of the General's bio, his photo and a copy of Colonel Musgrave's bio and photo. This would be one task Davidson did not have to fulfill.

The staff car that had brought me to the Division headquarters was waiting for me. As I got into it, I noted the three tall flag poles in front of the headquarters and the three symbols -- the United States to the left, the United Nations in the center and the Republic of Korea to the right. Looking beyond the headquarters building, I could see a significant hill.

"It must be One-Eighty," I thought.

Much like Kunsan, there were few trees on the base -- even on One-Eighty.

*Three flags flew in front of the headquarters of the 314th Air Division. In the background is Hill One-Eighty.*

# THE WING COMMANDER AND THE DIVISION STAFF

With my next stop to be the Wing Commander, I quickly scanned the Musgrave bio Barbara had given me. Frankly, I was not impressed. Musgrave was, indeed, "an old Colonel." His assignments, I noted, had been entirely at base level and primarily in administrative work.

I didn't need a seeing eye dog to tell me that Colonel Musgrave and I were made of different cloth and I could readily determine that, in all probability, he and I would not view problems in a similar perspective.

Colonel Musgrave did not ask me to sit down -- did not offer me a cup of coffee. Obviously, he was extremely unhappy with me and I guessed it stemmed from my having made my first entry direct with General Joyce. Perhaps he was angry about other things?

According to the organization chart, I was subordinate to the Wing Commander -- as I recall, it was the 6314th Wing. And I perceived that Colonel Musgrave saw himself faced with a junior Colonel who apparently did not live by his rules and one who felt he could deal directly with the General. Finally, I knew that he had no idea what I had discussed with the General -- he could only wonder -- perhaps he concluded that there was some special relationship between General Joyce and me and he was off balance.

I was hardly in his office a minute when Colonel Musgrave emphasized that I was subordinate to him and that I should have reported to him when I arrived -- not to General Joyce. I countered that I was responding to a direct, personal communication from the Commanding General of the 314th Air Division -- not a message from the Wing Commander. Colonel Musgrave, not knowing about the message to which I had reference, was thrown off guard. He could have confronted General Joyce on the matter, but he didn't come across to me as having the guts.

From that point on, the discussion became increasingly more difficult. I suspected that the Colonel had been farmed out to the Korea Wing Commander job for lack of some other place to assign him. He was a skinny guy with glasses and a wrinkled, prune-like face. He did wear pilot wings but I had no idea as to his aeronautical background -- it was not evident in his bio. Instinctively, I did not like him -- and it was obvious that the feeling was mutual.

The ensuing discussion was a decided pain. I took the Wing Commander from one problem subject to another. Step by step, I demanded things for Kunsan but, always, he sought to side-step the issue -- refer to his staff, refer to Fifth Air Force, suggest a need to study the matter. Finally, I did what I did not want to do -- I dropped the names of a few senior officers. I hated myself for it but it seemed to work. Apparently, as the Wing Commander's bio suggested, he had few friends in high places and I could see that he was uncomfortable dealing with anyone who did. Slowly, he became a little more agreeable and cooperative. But I knew that I had created an enemy and that he would trap me at the first opportunity. I resigned myself to watch my rear and live with the situation.

On departing the Wing Commander's office, I asked him about his staff meeting schedule and whether he wanted me or Davidson to fly up to attend those events. He replied that my attending General Joyce's staff meetings was enough. The implication was that he did not want a direct relationship with me. I left wondering what sort of relationship he had with his other subordinates.

My next stop was the Colonel in charge of materiel -- the Division Director of Materiel -- his name was Walter Kincaid. He was new to Korea -- had only been on the job for a little over a week. Kincaid had come from the Air Material Command and seemed to understand logistics but, to begin the conversation, he admitted that what he was encountering in Korea was beyond his wildest dreams.

With the Director of Materiel, I reviewed several problems -- the first was the matter of the truck tires. He professed ignorance of the tire supply situation but, before the meeting was over, I had talked him into our jointly visiting the Osan warehouses. In one of those warehouses we found a good supply of the needed tires. Eventually, he agreed to give me a load to take back on my Gooney Bird. And he assured me that he would look into my other logistic needs. As we parted, I told him about the fire truck with no starter and the safety problem it posed -- I suggested that neither of us needed to face this issue on the next inspection report. I sensed that I was going to get a starter or a new fire truck in short order -- and that some heads might roll.* At the tail of the conversation, I mentioned the tight supply

---

* During this time frame of history, approximately one-third of the Air Force fire fighting and crash rescue equipment in Korea was out-of-service awaiting parts. (Source: HRA files.)

situation regarding foam but did not ask him to do anything. I figured he would look into that situation on his own.

Finally, I decided to push my luck a bit further.

"You have some new staff cars here," I observed.

"We just got a shipment in," was his answer.

"And what is the distribution going to be?"

"Frankly, I don't know. I have to assume that my staff handles that."

"Well, is your staff going to handle General Joyce's torn pants when he visits Kunsan. The single staff car I have down there is so old that two years ago the IG demanded it be salvaged. I really hate to tell you what it looks like -- a jeep bumper, threadbare tires, one windshield wiper, a rope is used to hold the trunk down, springs stick out of the seats -- do I need to go on? General Joyce told me that he would be down to Kunsan in a week or two and I would hate to put him and you, if you come, in that vehicle."

The face of the Director of Materiel turned red.

"You know you're an S.O.B.," he said.

"I am but I'm also a good S.O.B. How about one of those staff cars? And I promise to junk the one I have and make the IG happy."

"I'll have one driven down to you tomorrow. Will that make you happy?"

"It's a hell of a good start."

There was a moment of silence -- then we both laughed. I knew that I could work with this man and I thought I might make one more request.

"While I'm at it, do you have any lawn mowers you could send down to me -- I've got a base with knee high grass."

"Not on your life. General Joyce is hell bent to get this base looking good and we've got every lawn mower we own in use. Besides, just this morning I did look at your Table of Allowances and the associated inventory and I saw that you've got a tractor and draw mower down there -- why don't you use it?"

I was caught off guard. No one had told me about this equipment when I asked about the grass and I had not noticed it in my travels around the base. Something was not right.

I did a dodge and weave answer in which I told the Director of Material something about a tractor not being able to work around the quarters area, and let it drop. Mentally, this was going to be a first order of business when I got back to Osan. Something did not track and I was going to find out why -- and quickly.

From Materiel, I went to visit the Director of Operations. The Colonel holding that slot was Jack Hubbard -- one of my Air War College friends. Like myself, he had been encouraged by the prior Division Commander to report early and he had only just arrived. Between us, we passed some mutual criticism of the system that not only got us to Korea but got us to Korea early. We talked a bit about the screwed up command arrangements in Korea, the North Korean threat, the South Korean forces, relations with the U.S. Army, the terrible state of facilities, the lack of supplies, and more. We were on the same wave length.

Then I recited to him the Wing Commander's restrictions on the Kunsan C-47 -- the restriction that seemed aimed to keep my bird from flying to Japan. When I reminded him that I had about one-third of the Air Force population in Korea on my base and followed that up with the conclusion that one-third of the people ought to get one-third of the food brought in from Japan, he agreed and assured me that he and not the Wing Commander was running operations. I could sense that he already had a run-in with the Wing Commander. The result was that I would get a message authorizing me one-third of the load of any Division C-47 making a supply run to Japan. And, if that was not enough to bail me out at Kunsan, at my discretion, but with notice to him, I would be authorized to fly my own aircraft to Japan. For starters, I could make an immediate flight to Japan to get supplies in hand.

Without a face off with the Wing Commander, I had turned his restrictive policies around. I knew that Colonel Musgrave would be furious when he learned what had happened but I had won something for my men that was vital -- food augmentation from Japan.

At the close of the meeting with Jack, I asked if I could get a tour of the Osan Command Center. He apologized that he had to get some work done for General Joyce but he called in a Lt. Colonel to escort me to the Center.

The Osan Command Center was in a large, two-storied Quonset -- an Air Force Air Policeman manned the front door. On a scale of one-to-ten and with the Fifth Air Force briefing room rated at *ten*, the Osan Command Center hardly rated a *one*.

The Osan tracking system was manual with Korean enlisted persons doing back writing on two large Plexiglas status boards using fluorescent grease pencils. The men marking the status boards wore headsets that apparently connected them to the operational radars. The room was dimly lighted to assist in the viewing of these status

**boards. At the front of the room, there was a row of chairs -- obviously for guests. Behind the front row of seats were two rows of desks for USAF and ROKAF duty personnel manning telephones connected to the operational units. To the rear was a raised dais containing more desks and duty personnel.**

**The Lt. Colonel explained the radar situation and noted the aircraft currently being tracked. The radar coverage extended into North Korea and some North Korean aircraft were depicted on the boards.**

**One track well up in the north part of the Yellow Sea caught my attention - its was moving in a race track configuration. And, if I read the status board correctly, it was a friendly aircraft and moving at slow speed.**

**"What's that fellow doing up in the Yellow Sea?" I asked.**

**"Intelligence, sir. I'm sorry but I can't say more than that."**

***[Later, when assigned to the 314th Air Division as the Director of Plans and Policy, I would spend many hours flying that racetrack pattern -- often flying eight hours after working a full day in the office. The aircraft was a C-47. I was not supposed to know what took place in the rear cabin but a person would have to be a fool not to understand. The rear cabin was fitted with a bank of electronic equipment with language trained operators monitoring North Korean and other communication channels. Tapes were made of all intercepts. If a priority intercept was made, the chief operator had the ability to communicate same to the Osan Command Center. Other than that, the tapes were simply bagged and sent for study by an intelligence center in Fuchu or to the Agency in Washington. The remarkable thing was that the North Koreans and Chinese Communists allowed this to go on without so much as a harassing interception. Flying approximately equidistant from North Korea, Port Arthur and the Shantung Peninsula, the only protection the unarmed C-47 had was the fact that, if navigation went correctly, it was flying over international waters. But navigation did not always go correctly.***

***Several years later, a U.S. Navy EC-121M flying over the Sea of Japan would be shot down by North Korean fighter aircraft with a loss of 31 Americans. Following that experience, a plan for fighter escort of such missions would be devised -- but only in the Korean area and in relation to North Vietnam. Intelligence gathering (snooper) flights on the periphery of Communist China, the Soviet Union and other target areas continued without escort. Overflights by high-flying aircraft obviously***

***continued without escort. That there eventually would be more shoot downs was inevitable. All this was placed in the category of calculated risk by those who ordered the operations.*]**

**On one status board the enemy forces and their readiness were displayed. On another, the status of friendly forces was shown -- the DMZ units, Kimpo, Osan, Kunsan, Suwon, Taegu, and more. About a half dozen radars covered Korea -- one was the unit at Kunsan.**

**Examining the status boards, I noted that one radar operated well into the Yellow Sea. I asked about it and was informed that it was operating from an island called P-Y-Do (the more correct name was Paengnyong-Do) directly off the coast of North Korea -- so close that the North Koreans illuminated the island with searchlights.**

**"You ought to take a flight up there some day," the Lt. Colonel suggested. "It's an experience. You go up when the tide is out and you land on the beach. The sand is well packed -- much like Daytona in Florida. But, you have to land rather close, but not too close, to the water as, when the sand dries out on the up-side of the beach, it is soft as hell and will ground loop you or worse. And you better get your butt off before the tide comes in."**

**[*Subsequently, I would make several passenger and supply flights to P-Y-Do. On one such flight, with the tide in-coming and the time to takeoff becoming very short, a ROKAF C-46, in my opinion much over-loaded with passengers and cargo, started to roll down the beach with the down-side landing gear getting into soft, water-logged sand. In spite of full rudder control, the drag on that gear began to turn the aircraft seaward but the pilot continued the takeoff. Eventually, the aircraft had swiveled a full ninety degrees and was heading out to sea with the gear in the waves and the prop tips hitting the water. I thought the aircraft was a goner but the pilot dropped full flaps and literally pulled the gear out of the water. Never have I witnessed anything of equal comparison.*]**

**From the status boards, I noted that a number of U.S. Army Nike missiles were deployed along the west coast of Korea. I wondered if they were armed with nuclear or conventional warheads but decided not to pursue the point.**

**"What about the Matadors and the nukes?" I asked.**

**Placing a finger to his lips, the Lt. Colonel answered.**

"That's NOFORN. We track those things on the upper dais by an Air Force officer." The Lt. Colonel pointed to the rear. I nodded understanding but I was uncertain that I actually understood.

I could see that some of the radar tracks were keyed to boats or ships in the Yellow Sea.

"What are you tracking out there?" I asked as I pointed to the plots.

"We have some Soviet and Chicom ship movements under surveillance. Unfortunately, we can't do much to counter the North Korean boats they use for infiltration as they look like fishing boats and don't give us a radar return unless they are close in -- normally, we can't even tell them apart in photography. They are equipped with high speed Soviet diesels and, from international waters, they can make a really fast run in and out of the South Korean coast. Once in a while, the South Koreans nail them. The larger ships are often used for intelligence surveillance, communications and resupply."

"Are there any coastal radars?"

"None. Everything depends on coastal watchers and the local population. With the ROK's island-dotted, irregular coastline stretching twenty-eight times the length of the DMZ, it's an incredible frontier to protect. And with more than a little unhappiness in some areas respecting the Rhee regime, infiltration is not something easy to counter. The good news is that infiltration is not assigned to us as a problem -- that's left up to the ROK."

"So what happens around my base at Kunsan is not supposed to be my problem even though it may end up as my problem?"

"You got it, Colonel. It may not make sense but that's the way the ball bounces out here."

[*In one later incident, a North Korean fast boat was discovered and the ROKAF launched against it. What followed was a "hot pursuit" into international waters and, eventually, at night. When the fast boat reached the mother ship, a Chinese Communist ship, it tried to shelter itself by hiding behind the hull while the ROKAF sought to sink it without hitting the mother ship. The chase and attack went on for hours with the ROKAF sending flare equipped C-46s to light the scene and fighters to shoot up the enemy craft. In Korea, such an event was "just another day" and, in the U.S., such events were not worth a line of print.*]

"Do any of the smaller fast boats actually land around Kunsan?"

"Yes."

And so I had confirmed another worry -- North Korean infiltration from the sea supported by mother ships, most likely Chinese Communist, in the Yellow Sea -- possibly just outside Korean national waters -- and I was not supposed to be concerned or involved. This was all incredible. I had to wonder how many boats it would take to support enough persons to overwhelm my defenses at the Kunsan Air Base?

"The Korean fishing boats -- do the South and North Koreans fish the same waters?"

"Undoubtedly."

"Which means that intelligence or other materiel, even agents, could be transferred at sea and we would be none the wiser?"

"We have to depend on the ROK to police such things."

"Do they?"

"Frankly, I don't know."

I then told the duty officer about the Korean body found on the sea wall at Kunsan -- he was not aware of it but showed no interest.

"Do you have a communications intercept working to cover the sea activity?" I asked.

"Without revealing what goes on in the way of COMINT and ELINT, yes we do. But, we don't run it. That stuff is run directly out of Fifth Air Force -- the ROK does some intercepts -- possibly the U.S. and ROK CIA are involved -- I think the Navy may have some capability. We get fed such information as others think we need and that isn't much. To get details on that, you need some special security clearances and a need-to-know certification."

I did not pursue the point. I was all-too-familiar with the array of security clearances and need-to-know certifications that had emerged in the military system and I hated it. In the Pentagon, for some, a mark of success often was not what a person did but how many security clearances he had. Frequently, one could observe Pentagon persons with a stack of fifteen or twenty passes hanging from a neck chain -- and that usually meant the same or a greater number of special security clearances held. This was not, however, the time for me to concern myself with the security system.

"I understand," I said -- then added, "How do we communicate and on what subjects?"

"Mostly by land line and not very good," was the answer. "In case we see something you should know, we ring your ops officer, your Air Police Command Center or yourself. We also ring the ops officer at your alert area. If the information is sensitive, we send it by message. We are limited, however, in that you don't have an intelligence line so we can only go to Top Secret -- no Code Word stuff."

Again, I could see security clearances popping up as an issue but I let it pass.

"What happens when one of your radar sites goes down for maintenance? I don't see back-up coverage."

"We pray," was the answer.

I thanked him for the briefing. Outside, I found the staff car had followed me to the Osan Command Center. I got in and asked the driver to take me to Flight Line Operations. It was late and I decided to spend the night. Perhaps there was more I could learn. Above all, I knew that I wanted to meet "Mike."

When I got to the Gooney Bird, I found Sergeant Phillips. He unlocked the aircraft and I retrieved my B-4 bag. He stated that he thought the aircraft might be fixed by morning. I told him to get word to Major Akers to spend the night and plan a takeoff at 1000 hours. There were still some things I wanted to do and one was to visit the Controller -- old "money bags." I had to understand something about budget -- the subject had already come up too often to please me. And then, if time was available, I wanted to talk to the Director of Personnel.

Settled in the staff car, I asked the driver to take me to the VIP quarters. It turned out to be on Hill One-Eighty -- just as Davidson had briefed me. Mentally, I gave Davidson another "Brownie Point."

As we climbed the road to Hill One-Eighty, I could readily understand why so many military persons, friend and enemy, had died to insure its control -- it overlooked the terrain for miles upon miles in every direction -- it was a near perfect observation point. Rounding the last turn in the road to the VIP quarters, a proximate, rather steep down slope came into view and I could see that it was protected by rows of concertina. Later, I would learn that this concertina, much like the fences at Kunsan, was stolen regularly by the Koreans. At the base of the hill were some Korean structures. Stretching from one, I observed a very long, horizontal antenna wire. I had to wonder why this was tolerated for the reasons related to its use had to be obvious. However, this not only was not my ball game but I had more than enough on my own plate to handle. Accordingly, I decided not to mention to anyone my observation or the obvious conclusion. Surely, anyone at Osan could observe that which I had observed and reach the conclusion I had

**reached. But, then, I knew that there could be considerations of which I had no knowledge. And, once again, my mind turned to the matter of clearances -- the possibility that I did not have the clearances "to know." I wondered who did?**

***[The problems that can result from the practice of imposing overly-tight security restrictions was illustrated in the case of the USS Peublo where, due to security restrictions, neither CINCUNC, COMUSKOREA, Fifth Air Force nor the ROK had knowledge of the operation until the ship was taken on January 23, 1968. The result was that no contingency planning had taken place. Yet, in the ensuing emergency, all eyes turned to those commands for assistance -- assistance which, for many reasons, could not be given. Support from Japan was out of the question with a resultant focus on Korea where hasty recommendations went so far as embracing a nuclear ultimatum. Lack of knowledge and pre-planning relative to the USS Pueblo had left the USAF fighter aircraft in Korea keyed to nuclear operations -- there was no conventional weapons response immediately available although conventional weapons were in place. As to the ROKAF aircraft, they were limited by range, North Korea overflight problems and more.]***

**Then, in what was an emerging pattern of worry about a situation that bordered on combat and certainly a situation in which men's lives were on the line with bullets flying about, I wondered about combat pay. Why was combat pay not authorized for the men who stood on the DMZ and those who manned the guns, aircraft and more in the rear areas? Certainly before, now and later, men would die on this frontier of America of the Free World. Was this not something akin to combat and deserving of appropriate recognition?**

***[On reflection, I was politically naive when it came to the issue of combat recognition. For me, combat recognition would not only reflect the true situation but it would heighten the awareness of the men to the problem at hand -- and reward them for the conditions and risks encountered. But that was not how the situation was viewed from the Washington, D.C. arena. There, to recognize the facts of the situation would be to heighten the priorities that would be accorded not only the Military Assistance Program for the ROK but the U.S. facilities, forces and more committed to the ROK. At the time, the conflict in Southeast Asia was already emerging with a profound forecast as to resources involved and, no matter how many bullets flew in the ROK or how many***

*persons were impacted, the idea of recognizing the situation in the ROK as "combat" or allocating to it adequate funds was politically unthinkable.*

*Some years later, CINCUNC/COMUSKOREA, then General Bonesteel, faced up to the same issues and, rather than describing the situation myself, I quote from an overview by Major Daniel P. Bolger, Scenes from an Unfinished War: Low-Intensity Conflict in Korea, 1966-169, Leavenworth Papers, Number 19:*

> *Until 1968, Korea fell into an odd category with regard to combat pay and awards. In Korea, as in the Dominican Republic intervention of 1965-66, provisions already existed to give combat pay -- but only to Americans dead (one month paid posthumously, of course) and wounded (three months' pay or paid while hospitalized, whichever was shorter). . . . By the U.S. Army's reckoning, soldiers on patrol in the DMZ received the same official consideration as those in garrison at Fort Benning, Georgia.*
>
> *Bonesteel changed that. . . . the general had been pressuring the Department of Army and Department of Defense for designation of the area north of the Imjin River and south of the DMZ's center as a "hostile fire zone." Soldiers and airmen serving in or flying in this zone would receive hostile fire pay and other combat incentives.*

*Eventually, the Joint Chiefs of Staff would reluctantly acknowledge that the forces involved in Korea were "in every sense" involved in combat. But what that meant was politically restricted in application for it implied unacceptable political and funding consequences.*]

**Adding my observations of Osan to my views of Kunsan and comparing both to my brief exposure to the facilities in Japan, I knew that something was terribly unbalanced.**

**Before the Korean War came crashing down with the resultant tornado sweeping the U.S. into it as a major participant, the JCS had stated that, from the standpoint of military security, the United States had little strategic interest in maintaining troops and bases in Korea. In U.S. thinking, Japan was a key in the Far East and there the Eighth Army had bedded down with four divisions -- the U.S. Air Force with several combat units. Life in Japan was relaxed, cheap and enjoyable. And then the North Korean forces attacked.**

**In the Korean War, the American ground forces first clashed with the North Korean forces on the road between Osan and Suwon -- a**

few miles from where I stood. There, some 400 men of Task Force Smith moved in from Japan as a holding unit would be defeated. More U.S. forces would be poured into the battle and, in the end, over 33,000 Americans would die and over 103,000 would be casualties. It was a huge investment but now, at least on the Air Force side of the equation, the environment had turned into a poorly supported and under-funded near shambles -- I had only to reflect on an enlisted men's day room to become angry and discouraged.

The Korean War over, the Eighth Army settled down in Korea for a seemingly permanent stay. For its part, the USAF had placed at Osan the 314th Air Division, which prior to the Korean War had been based in Nagoya, Japan. Japan was still the land of good living while, in the vernacular of the military, the U.S. military forces in Korea, at least the Air Force, "sucked hind tit." Yet, if there was a war in the future, it would most likely involve Korea and not Japan.

Something was seriously wrong in the allocations of attention, funds, units, equipment and more. To what extent I could change things, I did not know. But I knew that I had to try.

*Entrance to a USAF enlisted men's day room. Note sand bags and boards on the roof to hold corrugated sheet metal panels in place. Something was seriously wrong in the allocations of funds and more.*

# THE OSAN VIP QUARTERS AND "MIKE"

The Osan VIP quarters on Hill One-Eighty consisted of several inter-connected sheet metal buildings, one story, interiors walled in Korean mahogany plywood. In the central unit, there was a large community and recreation area. This central area had reasonable furnishings, a small library of paperbacks and a Japanese stereo system with a large stock of stereo tapes. Off to the side was a well-stocked bar and a neatly-dressed Korean bartender. He asked if I wished a drink.

I ordered a Scotch and soda.

As the bartender was serving my drink, a young Korean girl appeared and took my bag. "You room this way," she stated as she disappeared down the hallway. With a drink in hand, I followed her to my room. To my surprise, it was equipped with a double bed. There was a rug on the floor. A relatively quiet air conditioner wafted cool air across the room. There was a private bath with a modern tub and shower. The accommodations were not great but still remarkably better than anything that existed at Kunsan! As I marveled at what I saw, the Korean girl had opened my B-4 bag and was hanging up my clothes. "You got things wash?" she asked.

I had been in the same uniform for the entire day and it was rumpled. The decision to change to a fresh uniform was easy and I advised the Korean girl that I would soon give her something to wash. She replied in broken English with a distinctively Korean character.

"You changy changy uniform. When you changy, I wash. Now you give shoes. I do polish."

She knew what she was saying and I understood. I started to slip off my shoes but, quickly, she kneeled down and took over. And then she was gone.

Somehow, while I was still in Korea, I found myself in another world -- one well away from the rigors and austerity of Kunsan. But I knew the sensation was not something that would last.

A quick, very hot shower and a fresh uniform made a new person out of me. The Korean girl had my shoes, now well polished, next to my bed. She had come in while I was showering.

Outside, the staff car and driver who brought me to the VIP quarters was standing by. I asked that he take me to the Officers Club.

**After arriving at the Officers Club, I told him to return to pick me up in about three hours. He saluted and departed.**

**The Osan Officers Club was located about one hundred meters from the Division headquarters building. It was a solid structure -- not like the ramshackle "Bottom of the Mark" but no where near the elegant Tachikawa club. Inside, a loud party atmosphere dominated the bar room. I could see that the occupants included some twenty to thirty American girls. Some were what Davidson had termed "stateside rejects;" others were quite attractive. I wondered if Mike was one of them.**

**Saddling up to the bar, I ordered my usual Scotch and soda. Then I surveyed the people around the bar. Soon, one of the American girls approached me and asked if I was new on the base. "No, I'm just visiting from Kunsan," I answered. She screwed up her face and left. I think I heard her say: Shit, I thought you were a cute Colonel and I wanted one.**

**An officer at the bar noticed my dilemma and commented.**

**"You're new here, aren't you?"**

**Confirming that I was, he continued and repeated what Davidson had told me.**

**"What you see is the product of the silly season. A majority of the officers transfers out at this time of the year and a new batch arrives. The girls are civil servants and most of them have been here for some time. For them you might call this the mating season. The girls are trying to figure out who they will tie up with for the next year. From their perspective, this is serious business. If they screw up, they will have an unhappy life for the next twelve months."**

**"Is one of them out there called Mike?" I asked.**

**"That's Mike over there," he answered as he pointed to a sort of round-faced girl in a dark dress. "You know her?"**

**"No, I just want to meet her."**

**"Hey, come on," he replied as he literally pulled me in the direction of Mike. "Hey, Mike, I got a Colonel here who wants to meet you."**

**Thereupon, one of the most important and supportive associations of my stay in Korea was about to begin.**

**It was hard not to like Mike. She had a quiet, pleasant personality but, if the situation demanded, she could slip into the strongest of four-letter language. It was obvious that she was well known by everyone.**

"Mike, I'm new here. I got assigned as base commander at Kunsan. On the way out here, I was advised that, if I wanted to learn about Korea, you were the one to see. Until recently, I didn't know that you were a girl -- I thought you were a guy."

Mike laughed deeply. "Who's the cracker ass who turned you onto me?" she asked.

"As I recall, it was someone in Hawaii."

"Don't know who's in Hawaii right now who knows me," she answered, "but it doesn't matter. What do you want to know? I can tell you the name of every S.O.B. who slept with every bitch out here for the last decade or more. I could write a book. I already thought up a title -- it would be *I Knew Your Husband.*"

This was hardly the introduction I expected but Mike soon simmered down.

Mike did know a lot about Korea. She had been in Korea before the initiation of the Korean War. She had worked primarily as a secretary in Operations but had held a lot of jobs right up to senior levels. The military command had evacuated her to Japan when the North Koreans came south -- she got out just before the North Koreans overran Osan and she lost everything other than a mink coat and a decorative plate. As soon as the tide turned, she was given a military uniform and brought back into Korea. And she had been there ever since.*

Mike's knowledge of Korea was immense. She seemed to know every senior Korean; every USAF officer of consequence who had served in Korea was a first name to her; she was a pilot and, on the quiet, flew Korean aircraft; also on the quiet, she piloted USAF aircraft; she apparently was financially well off; she had many unfortunate love affairs the details of which she would gladly recount to anyone; the Koreans respected her and admired her -- I quickly learned that she was known as "Mike-san." And, when it came to social dirt, she knew absolutely everything.

Eventually, we got around to discussing the myriad of logistic and other problems I was facing at Kunsan Air Base.

---

* Civilian secretaries and other civilian support personnel were introduced into Korea as soon as the tide of battle changed. When Kunsan Air Base was reoccupied by the 3rd Bombardment Wing of the Fifth Air Force, the Wing Commander's secretary, Mary Hetherington, was brought forward from Japan. She would soon be followed by others. When the combat units were withdrawn from Kunsan Air Base, most of the civilian employees left and, with funds restricted, a Korean National was employed as secretary for the Base Commander.

As to the import of food from Japan, Mike alleged that the supply flights out of Osan had, in prior years, been a primary source for good living by senior officers and other select persons. "I don't know about this new General," she said. "I think he's a straight-laced guy and the good life is over."

When it came to Colonel Musgrave, the Wing Commander, Mike needed no prodding. She suggested that he was out to make a last stab at getting promoted to General -- in a tortured way, that was part of the reason why he had restricted the Kunsan Gooney Bird from flying out of Korea. "He's a shithead if I ever saw one," she said. "He's bitter about a lot of things. First, he's pretty old for a Colonel and I think he believes he should be a General. Second, he probably recognizes that, short of a miracle, his assignment to Korea could be a dead end road -- and he would like to create that miracle. Third, he hates the younger officers who he views as a threat and you included are going to get run over at every opportunity. I already heard about your meeting with him -- watch out -- cover your ass. Right now, he's spending his time reading and writing regulations more than doing anything really constructive. He's a nit-picking bastard who believes that anything can be solved with a new regulation. He is not a hands-on person -- very unsociable -- does not mix -- bitter -- most of his time is spent cooped up in his office. Except for eating, you will hardly ever see him at the Officers Club. I expect that he's going to give us girls a hard time but that, in six months, he'll be messing around with a Korean josan. I've seen it all happen before."

On more general subjects, Mike alleged that the focus of most of the key Americans in Korea was themselves. Reflecting the turmoil in Korea, apparently, in one prior 18 month period, one unit in Korea went through nine commanders. She alleged that any person who could, after assignment to Korea, pulled every possible string to get out. She laughed when I told her about my being asked to hurry to Korea only to run into the ex-Commander of Kunsan at Tachikawa en route home on an advanced basis.

As an overview, Mike asserted that in Korea relevance had a baseline -- something "better than nothing" was good. To the bottom line, she told me that neither Kunsan, nor Taegu, nor Kangnung, nor Kimpo, nor any other outlying spot had held squat of significance in the past Air Force command in Korea or at Fifth Air Force. "No one will even spend a night at your base -- most will find it difficult to even stop by for an hour or so. But there is something in Korea that attracts Fifth Air Force personnel and that is Cheju-Do. Fifth Air Force didn't have money for barracks and other essentials but they did have money to build hunting lodges at Cheju-Do. And, while virtually no one from Fifth Air Force comes to Osan, Kunsan and other operational sites, hundreds fly to Cheju-Do for hunting. "This may be hard to take but you're at the end of the sucker line and you better get used to it," was her advice.

The problem, Mike asserted, was that the focus of Air Force attention in the Pacific had been everywhere other than Korea. At the end of World War II, the grand scheme of the Air Force was to concentrate on a ring of bases beginning with Japan on the north and then running through Okinawa, Taiwan, Guam and The Philippines. The central focus of all this was Communist China. Money flowed to these selected base areas and living conditions in all of them were excellent -- especially for the occupation forces in Japan. And, with minor exception, the tour in all these areas was two to three years with dependents. Korea was the exception and the hell hole. In Korea, living conditions were primitive even in the capital city of Seoul. In 1949, the U.S. forces that had been assigned occupation duty withdrew. Most of those few elements that continued to be assigned to Korea for Military Assistance or other duty were on a one year in-and-out assignment although a few did have their dependents and served extended tours -- some of the latter had lived in the refurbished Japanese buildings in Kunsan.

Then, in 1950, the North Koreans moved south and all hell broke loose. Mike had been with the residual Air Force contingent in Korea when the North Koreans attacked and immediately the order of the day was evacuation. Everything was going to hell.

At that time, Kunsan was simply a small, left over Japanese airfield with a grass runway and, right after Osan, which was the scene of the first fighting between U.S. and North Korean forces in July 1950, it fell to the North Koreans. When Kunsan was recaptured, Army Engineers quickly moved in to give it a hard surface runway and other facilities. But everything that took place was catch-as-catch-can and established with the idea that, once the North Koreans were "kicked in the ass" and the war was over, the U.S. Air Force units would once again fall back to their "good bases and quarters" in the well established and preferred ring of Japan, Okinawa, etc. -- the air problem in South Korea would be left to "improved" local forces.

After a see-saw battle, the ground lines finally stabilized at the approximate 38th parallel and the "demilitarized zone" was created with the ROK forces, reinforced by U.S. Army divisions, holding north of the South Korean capital city of Seoul. The U.S. Air Force, however, was not about to get tied into a UNC or U.S. joint command structure in Korea and, relying on claims of mobility, it withdrew to the planned ring bases in the Pacific. Unlike the U.S. Army, the U.S. Air Force had no love for Korea or Korean duty.

The result was that, except for brief in-and-out tactical deployments to Korea and some "Mickey Mouse stuff," Korea was virtually abandoned by the Air Force. Those Air Force persons who were assigned to Korea were sent literally to the Air Force "Siberia" and virtually abandoned. The basic plan, she said, was to effect a full Air Force withdrawal from Korea.

"What kind of Mickey Mouse stuff went on?" I asked.

"If I answered that question, I'd lose my friggin job," Mike answered.

Obviously, in years past, Mike must have held special security clearances covering operations she was still not permitted to divulge. I smelled the CIA, non-Korean foreign nationals, overflight of enemy territory, listening and other surveillance operations -- possibly even the training of Special Operations Teams for intelligence, sabotage or other work. As isolated as Kunsan Air Base was and considering its strategic location, it seemed especially well situated for such activity. But I knew that I could not pursue those possibilities of the past. Further, Mike was continuing with her Korean history rundown.

"In 1957, as a result of intelligence confirming a continued build up of North Korean forces, at Panmunjom they were told that the U.S. would no longer stand still doing nothing to enhance the defense of South Korea.

"But believe me when I say that doing anything positive in South Korea, such as permanently deploying tactical air units or spending real money, was not to Air Force liking. As a result, the Air Force limited itself to temporary deployments to Korean Air Bases, primarily Osan and Kunsan, and accepted the left over Korean War facilities, as shoddy and primitive as they were, as a norm. For the fighter pilots who deployed here from Japan and Okinawa, it was a blast -- a temporary home away from home that turned into some real parties. Bombs were dropped at the ranges, guns were fired, exercises went on and then came the booze and the girls.

"In the meantime, facilities and support equipment went to hell. Not infrequently an exercise might be called and it would end before the communications system could get a message through to notify your base that an exercise was on-going.

"But then there developed a need to forward deploy tactical nuclear capable fighters. In the established bases in Okinawa and The Philippines the tactical nuclear operations did not pose a problem. In Taiwan, special arrangements were made which, I think, for a time allowed the Chinese Nationalists to be the delivery agent -- the idea of yellow-on-yellow rather than white-on-yellow. However, in Japan there was a problem as nuclear weapons had been excluded from that country. That meant the whole northern tier of the enemy areas was left uncovered. The answer was to deploy nuclear capable fighters in Korea -- but not on a permanent basis -- only as a projection of forces in Japan or, in some cases, in Okinawa. Still, no one in the Air Force hierarchy wanted to spend money in Korea and everything proceeded on a shoestring. The result was that the jocks and support personnel came to Korea mostly to sit on their asses in makeshift alert status and in lousy conditions -- no parties -- mostly just sitting.

"And that's where we are today." Mike concluded. "We've been operating on a shoestring for years and we're still operating on a shoestring. Fifth Air Force is our *Daddy Rabbit* but there is no desire on the part of most of those at Fifth even to come to Korea to see how the *bunnies* live and die. The Commanding General of Fifth Air Force did spend one night at the house of the 314th Air Division Commander. He woke up with lice or mites falling out of the overhead thatch ceiling with the result that a new roof was ordered. But that is an exception to how the world turns out here."

"So it's a case of *See no Evil; Hear no Evil; Speak no Evil.* If Fifth Air Force does not come to Korea and see the problems, then those problems don't exist and they don't have to do anything?"

"You got it," Mike stated. Then, after catching her breath, she added, "Some Fifth Air Force people do show up now and then but they usually RON in Seoul. The wives in Japan really have it in for Korea -- they've heard about *Moose Calls* and more and they suspect that anyone going to Korea only has one objective in mind and that is freely available sex. You're mostly unmolested at Kunsan in that you have no VOQ, no worthwhile exchange, no entertainment, lousy food and who in hell would want to go to Kunsan City? We're much better off here at Osan but the real fun game is in Seoul -- shopping, entertainment, girls, the works. For reasons you can suspect, the Fifth Air Force has supported a good VIP set up in Seoul, it's called the Seoul House -- spelled *S-e-o-u-l*, not *S-o-u-l* -- and the night life up there can get exciting. There is an especially good night spot sponsored by the

**Eighth Army. It's located up-river from Seoul -- it's called Walker Hill. You need to find time to visit it."**

**[*I did visit Walker Hill but it would be some ten years later at which time it had been taken over by the Koreans and was being run as a high class casino -- and more.*]**

**"As to your Deputy," she offered, "be careful. I think he's got an apartment in Seoul and it may be equipped with a josan -- you probably already know that he drinks too much. He has come up here now and then but he seems just to pass through. I don't know how he was used by the Colonel you replaced -- maybe he wasn't."**

***An aerial view of Walker Hill some years later and after the U.S. Army had turned the facility over to South Korea for development as a high class casino resort.***

**"And how do you know all this stuff about Davidson?" I asked. "Trust me," is all she said.**

**"Since you know so much, tell me why I had only a crooked tree trunk for a flag pole when I arrived at Kunsan."**

**Mike laughed.**

**"There used to be one hell of a flag pole in front of the K-8 headquarters building. Who knows what happened to it? Most likely it was stolen. In Korea, if it's not nailed down it will be stolen. And sometimes the nailed down items are stolen -- along with the nails."**

**Eventually, we proceeded to the dining room for dinner. The conversation lasted for a long time -- it was almost midnight when we finished. As we talked, I heard repeated renditions of a Korean song echoing from the bar. The words and music would haunt me forever. Apparently, anyone who was a veteran of Korea knew this song and at least some of the words. The chorus ran:**

***A-ri-rang. A-ri-rang. A-ra-ri-yo!***
***A-ri-rang. Go-gae-ro nu-mu gan-do.***

**And it seemed that there were three verses that ran:**

***No-reul bu-ri-go neum im eun,***
***Sim ni do mot ga-su balbyung nan-da***

***No-da ga-so, nol-da ga-so,***
***I-ba-mi sae do rok nol da ga-so.***

***A-ri-rang go-gae neun noon moore-go-gae;***
***June deun nim bogo sipu su na yugi wan-ne.****

---

* From the September 27, 1954 edition of "The Invader Review" of the 3rd Bombardment Wing (L) -- the included English transliteration from text slightly different from that shown reads:

Arirang. Arirang. Arariyo.
O'er the Arirang hill going thou art,
If thou leave here deserting me,
Will have a footsore within a mile.

According to an accompanying historical statement, the Arirang song emerged during distant times -- one version is said to have come from the period of the time when Tae-won-goon, the father of the last king of the Lee Dynasty, was rebuilding the Kyung-buck palace. Allegedly, there are many local versions of this song. The song keys to firmness of purpose with a desire for victory against the enemy through trials and tribulations.

Interspersed with the *A-ri-rang* song, I heard many a voice singing grandly of "Pusan U," "Just Give Me Operations," "Air Force 801," and "No Fighter Pilots Down in Hell." Some of the musically-inclined officers periodically joined with the Korean band to play various instruments or to sing. There seemed to be no operational or other worries at Osan -- actually, it seemed like a tremendous fighter-pilot party town. In contrast, I wondered why I had heard no singing at Kunsan? In Osan, everyone in the Officers Club seemed to be having a good time, smiling, happy-go-lucky, singing -- the thought of work, problems and proximate enemies seemed far away. In contrast, in Kunsan, I had already observed that smiles were hard to find and conversation dwelt mostly on work and the problems of the day.

*The Kunsan Air Base (K-8) headquarters complex as seen in 1952. Note the formidable flagpole to the right. Some years later, it had disappeared and only an old, crooked tree trunk served as the flagpole. (J. Lovejoy)*

The night drawing to a close, I excused myself. I had forgotten about the staff car but the driver was outside waiting. He took me up to the VIP quarters on Hill One-Eighty where I tried to get my thoughts together -- "*A-ri-rang*" still rang through my mind.

Mike probably had talked too much. On the other hand, I may have talked too much to Mike. I had to wonder if I could believe all I had heard. I was already aware of a lot of what Mike had to say but she certainly filled in a lot of "holes."

Restless, I stepped into the night air to do some walking -- to relax my mind. From the vantage point of Hill One-Eighty, I could see the Osan Air Base spread out below me -- a large, reasonably-lighted facility. On the distant runway I noted the lights of a departing aircraft. Soon the comforting rumble of an after-burner reached me. I wondered how many guards Osan had on the far perimeter? And I wondered about the nuclear storage on Osan -- where was it and how was it protected? And then I wondered about the security of the dispersed Matador units that were located somewhere outside the Osan perimeter -- were they really secure? And what about the Mickey Mouse stuff that might still be going on -- operations of which I might never have insight -- operations that might even be going on at my own Kunsan Air Base?

In the distance, at what I presumed was the main gate to Osan Air Base, I detected a dimly lighted village. And I wondered if that village was an asset or a liability. I did not have such a built-up area outside the gate at Kunsan Air Base -- perhaps that was a benefit for which I should be happy. Momentarily, I gave thought to visiting the off-base Chicol Village but, considering the hour, gave it up -- any such visit on my part would probably be misinterpreted.

*[When I did transfer to Osan, I had the Commander of the Air Police unit take me on a night visit to the "facilities" outside the Osan gate. On the dirt road leading from the base, we passed open-air meat stalls, flies everywhere -- and worse. Then we toured some twenty whorehouses. I had "been around the block" in my life but this was a new experience. One stringy-haired, ill-kempt "mama-san" (I sensed she was on drugs) raised hell with me when I did not take off my shoes on entering her facility. These "facilities" varied from some really crummy, dirty houses to some high class affairs with, in some instances, well-endowed Caucasian ladies serving the clients -- the ladies, by physical appearance, I concluded were Russian. Some men, apparently operating on credit, left their military ID as collateral. This was the "real world" of Korea.]*

Back in the VIP quarters, I joined some transient personnel in the lounge area and asked the bartender for my usual Scotch and soda. The others in the lounge area were in civilian clothes which did not enable me to quickly determine if they were civilians or officers or of

**what service. But the conversation ran easily and I joined in. Talking was without restraint.**

**When those present learned that I was the new commander at Kunsan Air Base, there were some smiles. I knew that they knew or suspected something that I did not know -- but I did not pursue the point.**

**Eventually, our discussion centered on matters of Korean politics and I found that a couple of the persons present appeared knowledgeable.**

**President Rhee, I was informed, was in deep trouble. Apparently, Korean industry was leading the way to a new economic future and the resultant social upheavals were beyond the aged Rhee's ability to cope. From what I had observed since arriving in Korea, the theory that there was an on-going industrial advancement of consequence within the South was hard to believe -- but I listened.**

**And then I learned that there were major rumblings among the students in Korea and our intelligence system had forecast of a "Student Revolution" of significant proportions.**

**This conversation, clearly heard by the Korean bartender, was disturbing. Many of the subjects discussed had to be sensitive. And I still did not even know who my conversational associates were other than some had introduced themselves by military grade -- one was an Air Force officer serving on the UNC/USFK staff in Seoul; one was a rather braggadocio Army officer -- it appeared that he was assigned to Eighth Army; the identity of the others was in doubt but I surmised that at least one was involved in intelligence or CIA work. Each one, however, seemed to seek a position of expert knowledge among the group. Soon, all I did was listen.**

**That night, as I turned in, I tried to reflect on all I had observed and heard during the day. Many things troubled me.**

**Finally, a totally new thought entered my mind: Dogs! I had observed that there were more than a few pet dogs at Osan but I had seen none at Kunsan. It was something of a parallel to singing -- the personnel at Osan sang; the personnel at Kunsan did not.**

**I had never been in a military situation wherein the men did not have dogs -- as well as other pet creatures to include everything from rabbits to monkeys, birds and snakes. But dogs dominated the equation. From World War II, I had a lasting impression of the dog "Trey" that Ernie Pyle had written about in *Brave Men*. Trey was a major fixture in the 323rd Bombardment Group (M) in England and on into France. Trey hated to fly so to get this Great Dane from point**

A to point B, the Flight Surgeon gave him a tranquilizer. Amazingly, Trey, as huge as he was, never set off a land mine in the combat areas of Cherbourg and beyond. But there had been more pet dogs and other animals -- some so famous that they made international news.

Was this absence of dogs and singing at Kunsan a psychological reflection of more serious problems? I had no ready answer but I was deeply disturbed.

Finally, my thoughts turned to home. I thought about writing a letter to Mary to tell her about the conversation with Mike and other things. Still, deep inside, I knew that the conversation with Mike and the troubling subjects of the day were not something to relay to a distant wife. Tired, I sought some sleep -- sleep in the double bed that engulfed me -- for the moment I was isolated from the worries of Kunsan Air Base and from Korea.

*I had never been in a military unit wherein the men did not have pet dogs -- as well as other animals including even monkeys. The dog "Trey" (above), written about by Ernie Pyle in "Brave Men," was a major fixture in my World War II unit -- the 323rd Bombardment Group (M).*

As my mind began to drift away, I heard an aircraft take off -- the afterburner blasting the air. Then, mingled with some distant conversation and laughing, I heard singing coming from the lounge.

**Dimly, I listened to the converted "How Much is That Doggy in the Window" refrain of :**

***I was ordered to duty in Korea,***
***And left my true love far behind.***
***It's been so long since I've seen a roundeye,***
***That a new love I must truly find.***

***How much is that josan in the beanbag,***
***The one with the big brown eyes,***
***How much is that josan in the beanbag,***
***I'd like to try her for size.***

**Was the mood which I had been observing at Osan a reflection of the terrible conditions prevailing in Korea and a giving-up of normal elements of moral protocol? As I reflected on that thought, I recalled the verse of a song Mike had set forth for my amusement. It began with:**

***Way up on One-Eighty***
***Where the Colonels all live,***
***Sits a DV type quarters***
***Where love lessons they give.***

**And here I was in those DV quarters on Hill One-Eighty -- the focus of the ditty Mike had uttered. What had taken place in these quarters in years past? And what was the future not just on Hill One-Eighty but in all of Korea -- and especially for my Kunsan Air Base? Would once again the North Koreans strike at an unprepared military presence? And what, if anything, could I really do to alter what I was observing? Was the mountain confronting me too big to move? Was I undertaking to fight a war I could not win?**

**Disturbed by my thoughts, I got up and, once again, attempted to write a letter to Mary. But the words did not come out right. She needed no history lesson nor worries about war in Korea and beyond. Eventually, I tore up the letter and went back to bed -- a big double bed in what were alleged to be bachelor quarters.**

**Soon I was asleep.**

# DAY FOUR -- A THURSDAY

Morning came all too soon. But it was great to start the day with a hot instead of a cold shower. And then there was breakfast in the VIP quarters -- not powdered eggs but real eggs. With that, there was a choice of ham or bacon. Further, there was a half grapefruit. And everything was served by an attractive Korean girl. I felt as if I was in another world. But I had to wonder why the food at Osan was so much better than what we had at Kunsan? Something was wrong -- terribly wrong!

With breakfast over, I decided to walk down the hill to the Air Division Headquarters. En route, I could tell by the looks of the men I passed that I was a strange apparition -- apparently, at Osan, a Colonel walking was not a regular event.

My encounter with the Comptroller was hardly profitable. It seemed that every money question I asked had an answer that resided in Fifth Air Force in Japan. And, when it came to construction, about the same result emerged. The entire construction program was run out of Fifth Air Force. But, to my surprise, it was confirmed as being done through the Army Corps of Engineers -- which made it an even more distant factor. As to whether I or the 314th Air Division had any input to the budget process, it seemed remote. The argument was that, with the one year tour, the military personnel in Korea were not there long enough to understand the situation -- and, so, the staff at Fifth Air Force handled everything. Basically, it seemed that, in Korea, one was supposed to take what one received and be happy about it. I was not very happy and getting less happy by the day! I already suspected that Fifth Air Force really did not know what was going on in Korea and could hardly begin to deal with the problems of the 314th Air Division and its subordinates. Certainly, the evidence continued to mount that a visit to Korea by the Fifth Air Force staff was a rarity.

The Director of Personnel greeted me with a comment about my reporting in direct to K-8 and then to General Joyce. Obviously, there was some displeasure surrounding my action but I could tell that he did not share in that displeasure. As had been briefed to me en route to Korea, the Director confirmed that the personnel pipeline was running and no change would or could occur for 12 or more months into the future. If a person was lost for any reason -- illness, court martial, anything -- the most likely effect was a vacancy that would remain a vacancy for at least the next twelve months. It was all very depressing.

Calling for a staff car, I was taken to the VIP quarters on Hill One-Eighty to retrieve my B-4 bag and then whisked to Flight Line Operations. Akers was waiting for me. He tried to suppress a smile but could not. At his side, Sergeant Phillips was also smiling.

"Aircraft is fixed," Phillips reported. "A new thermocouple is in place and the compasses point in the same direction."

"It takes an S.O.B. and a plan," I answered.

"Yes, but are you one?" Akers asked.

I did not answer. Instead, I asked about the weather.

"From here to Kunsan, it isn't bad but we have some stuff moving in from China," Akers answered. "We might have some rain by tonight. Right now, there is a lot of scud out in the Yellow Sea. The weather mass is moving east at about ten miles an hour."

I asked Akers about the weather moving in from the Central Pacific and he informed me that, by all indications, a typhoon was forming and heading west at a good clip. For the present, it looked like it would hit the Philippines and then make landfall on the continent at Hong Kong -- but no one was certain about anything at this point.

As we boarded the Gooney Bird for the return to Kunsan, I asked Akers to take the left seat. I had a lot of thinking to do. To my delight, the rear cabin was stocked with tires.

Halfway to Kunsan, Akers tuned one of the radio compasses to the AFKN Kunsan station and we were greeted with the news and some music. I only half heard the news. I kept asking myself how I had managed to get into this situation and whether I could really do something about it in the two months I had before reporting to Division.

We began to hit some clouds and Akers, on a VFR flight plan, jogged around a few of them -- then he changed to an IFR flight plan. The weather was getting worse. Akers commented about the problem of forecasting weather when most of it came from China from where we received virtually no weather data. He added that, in Korea, most weather forecasting was mostly a guess. At Kunsan, we made an instrument let down -- the ceiling was about five hundred feet with visibility under a mile in light rain. Apparently, the weather coming in from China was moving faster than expected.

Akers hit the runway dead on and greased the Gooney onto the runway. He was a good pilot and I had to remember that when it came to the writing of his Efficiency Rating. I asked Akers how much flying time he had accumulated and it made my Form 5 accumulation look sick. But, then, I had not been in a flying job since World War II and, in the USAF and other headquarters slots I had filled, one was lucky to accumulate a hundred and fifty hours a year in the cockpit -- many persons in such assignments accumulated little over the required four hours a month for pay purposes.

After landing, I went directly to the headquarters building. Davidson was waiting for me.

"We have a problem," he stated.

"What now?"

"The prior manager of our PX, a Mr. Wright, has returned."

"So?"

"So he was kicked out for black market operations. We thought he had been fired by the exchange office in Japan but he is back here with a valid ID."

"Are we to give him his job back?"

"No."

"Well, what is he doing here?"

"I talked to Captain Wild and Captain Pastiak and they think he is here to collect on some black market debts. He has asked for base quarters -- officer quarters -- and wants a vehicle to go into the city."

"How did he get here?"

"He hitched a ride on the regular transport run out of Japan."

"Does he carry any orders?"

"We asked and he said that he didn't."

"Did he say why he was here?"

"Only some vague words about having to clean up some personal things before he returned to Australia."

"Why wasn't he jailed or, at least, fired if he was dealing in black market?"

"It's a long story. The problem seems to be that he is an Australian citizen, hired by the Fifth Air Force exchange office in Japan and working in Korea. No one could figure out the law that applied so they had to let him go free. We wanted to hold hearings here but he is not subject to the military code so Fifth took over. This all happened well over a month before you arrived. We didn't expect him to come back -- but here he is."

"All right, Davidson. This is my base and I can set some of my own laws. Tell this Wright fellow that he will get no transportation from us except the right to board a flight out. In the meantime, he is restricted to quarters -- and make that the enlisted quarters -- except for eating and, in that case, he is to take the most direct route from those quarters to the enlisted mess hall and back. Tell him he is not authorized access to the officers or enlisted clubs and, certainly, he is to have no PX privileges. Tell him if he leaves the base for any reason, he will not be authorized re-entry. Also tell him that he is to make no telephone calls. Make certain that our switchboard knows this. And tell him that, if he violates these rules, he will be placed in our jail."

"Can we do this?" Davidson asked.

"I just did. Now get the word out to this Mr. Wright and tell Captain Wild that I want strict enforcement."

"Do you want me to tell Fifth what is going on?"

"No. But let the enlisted men in the billet you put him in know that he stole their PX materials and sold it on the black market. I think that will serve to get him out of our hair quickly. And tell Captain Wild that, if anything happens in the barracks, like a fight, to look the other way."

On entering my office, I saw a sealed brown package on my desk. Noting the return, I was over-joyed. It had to be flags from the Pentagon!

Calling for Jones, I tore open the package. There were four flags -- one had a gold fringe on the edges! And there was a Pentagon telephone book!

"Tommy, take a look at this."

Tommy's eyes lighted up.

"Flags! Damn, we have flags! How did you get it done so fast?"

"Never mind the how. The only thing that matters is that we have them. And I suppose you know what to do?"

"Yes sir. We run up the colors."

"And then we are going to do something else. I saw that you have a G.I. record player sitting on a file cabinet in the outer office and I have to presume you have a record that plays reveille and retreat, among other things."

"Yes sir. But the record player doesn't work."

"Then fix it or get it fixed. We have about 100 watts coming out of almost every hootch on this base. If we have men who can run stuff like that, we must have men who can fix an old record player. Find someone who knows something about electronics and get it running. In the meantime, set reveille at 0600 hours and retreat at 1800 hours. And have Captain Wild's Air Police do the honors of raising and lowering the flag. And check to be certain that they know how to do it. Then find, or build, a staff and base for this fringed flag -- I want it behind my desk."

"Yes sir."

In a minute, Jones was back in the office.

"Sir, it's raining outside. Do you want me to run up the flag in the rain?"

"The flag won't complain if you don't run it up but I will."

"Yes sir."

And then the telephone on my desk rang. At almost the same instant Davidson rushed into my office -- his face was flushed -- he seemed agitated by something. I picked up the telephone.

"Colonel Moench here."

----------

"He's down somewhere off our base? You think it's about fifteen or twenty miles out and due west?"

----------

"And you want us to do a search because it would take too long to get an aircraft down here from Osan? How about the ROKAF helicopter that is based here? Can't the ROKAF take on the search?"

---------

"O.K. We'll go. But keep the air clear of other aircraft. I don't want a mid-air out there."

As I hung up, Davidson asked if the call came from the Osan Command Center and whether it related to a downed ROKAF F-86 in the Yellow Sea about which he had just been notified. I answered in the affirmative and asked him to take the Gooney Bird, load on some dye markers and a raft for drop, and do a search.

"Colonel, I'm not going to fly that aircraft in this weather in the condition it's in. It's getting stinking outside."

"But would you allow someone else to fly it?"

"If some other pilot is crazy enough to fly it, that's his business."

I smarted. I saw that Davidson still thought the Gooney Bird had the thermocouple and radio compass problems but that was not the issue.

"Davidson, do you have any idea what command and leadership is all about?"

Davidson said nothing -- he just looked at me.

"Davidson, a senior officer does not state that he will not fly something but someone under his authority can go fly it. Either you fly it or you ground it and prevent others from flying it. It can't be unsafe for you and still safe for some other person."

Davidson knew I was unhappy and I was. In just a few days, while he had accumulated some Brownie Points, on the whole my opinion of him had steadily fallen to where I now concluded that, in all probability, I would be forced to have him reassigned even if I had no replacement. I was going to chew out Davidson but decided to let it drop. If he didn't understand how I felt, more words would not help. I considered telling him about the aircraft repairs but thought better of it. It could be that it wasn't the aircraft but the weather that was Davidson's problem -- perhaps he was a clear weather pilot? I decided to fly the search and rescue mission myself.

"Tell Major Akers what the problem is and to join me at the flight line. He and I will do the search. Call Sergeant Phillips and have him get the aircraft ready -- to load dye markers and a raft. And, when I return, I want your Form 5 on my desk."

I felt that I had to review Davidson's flying career -- the Form 5 would tell me a lot.

Davidson blanched. Whether or not he answered, I don't recall as I simply grabbed my hat and headed out the door, leaving him standing. The chance of a successful rescue support operation was slim but it would be zero if time was wasted.

*The Armed Forces Korean Network (AFKN) transmitter and billet facility at Kunsan Air Force Base.*

# SEARCH AND RESCUE

At Operations, a check with Sergeant Butler's data indicated that the weather coming across from China was speeding up -- and worsening.

"Colonel, you are going to have a lot of low visibility out there and some rain -- and the ceiling may end up dragging on the waves."

Akers rushed in -- apparently, he had run to the Operations office. I asked him if he knew about the F-86? He said that he had been briefed by Davidson but the information he received was sketchy.

I called the Kunsan radar and asked them what their last fix was on the F-86. They confirmed that the last echo was due west at about fifteen to twenty miles.

"O.K. Akers, let's go. Do you know if Sergeant Phillips has the dye markers and raft on board?"

"I called him before I came down to Operations and I am sure that he has the stuff on board by now. Alex is a good man."

Running to the Gooney Bird, I could see that the ceiling apparently had dropped below 500 feet -- a light drizzle was falling.

"You navigate," I told Akers, "I'll fly."

We hardly had wheels up when we were in the soup. I edged the nose down until we were at about 300 feet. The windshield wipers were kicking back and forth but the rain obscured frontal vision. Vision out the side windows was fair. In that we were immediately over water on departure west from Kunsan, it was hard to tell just how much visibility we had -- gray above, gray below and gray out front -- it all came together. I asked Phillips to go to the rear and stay on interphone and be ready to drop some dye markers. And I cautioned him not only to wear a Mae West and parachute but to rope himself so that he did not accidentally fall out the open rear door.

"At this altitude, we got to be real careful, Colonel. There's some islands out ahead and we are below the radar -- no help from them." I could see that Akers was seriously concerned.

"It's your job to steer me," I answered.

Amazingly, we hit the spot on the first run. It had to be it -- a large oil slick but no debris. I yelled into the interphone for Phillips to drop a dye marker and quickly put the Gooney Bird into a standard rate turn to the left. But, as we came around full circle, there was no oil slick or dye marker to be seen. We did another full circle with no result. Then we did a square search pattern with still no result. Akers suggested that we were drifting and he pointed to some islands on the map. I pulled up enough to be certain that we cleared the island tops and headed back to the Kunsan range. Once over the range, I let down and returned to the Yellow Sea area on the same heading as we had taken on the first run. Bingo! There was the oil slick and some green dye. Once again, I put the aircraft into a standard rate left turn -- our eyes searching for a survivor -- or any debris. And, once again, we lost sight of the oil slick.

"This is crazy," I said as I pulled up to a thousand feet and headed once more back to the Kunsan range to repeat the run out.

"Why not call for the ROKAF boat?" Akers asked.

"What boat?"

"The ROKAF at Kunsan have a rescue boat they got from Uncle Sam as a part of the Military Assistance Program. It can do about twenty knots and I think they could be out of their tie up and to the slick site in about an hour -- if they have a crew standing by."

"How do I reach them?" I asked.

"Radio the tower. The tower can contact the Kunsan ROKAF."

And so I radioed the tower, gave the tower the estimated position of the oil slick, and asked that the ROKAF be notified to get their boat moving. In the meantime, we headed back out to sea on our original heading to try once more to spot a survivor. In a couple minutes and before we were half way to the slick area the tower came on.

"Colonel, the ROKAF said they can't go -- they don't have any fuel for the boat."

I looked at Akers in disbelief.

"Akers, what fuel does the boat use -- gasoline or diesel?"

"Diesel. I was on it once -- they took us fishing."

"Any idea how much fuel it burns?"

"It's a twin engine, inboard. My guess is about forty gallons an hour but I'm no marine person."

I thought a moment. I knew it was illegal -- but what the hell -- a man's life was at stake and, even if he was not an American, he was an ally who might one day be defending us. I called the tower.

"Order Major Peterson to deliver immediately four barrels of diesel to the ROKAF boat, more if he thinks it necessary, and tell them to undertake a search pattern centered on a position fifteen miles due

**west of Kunsan. Tell Major Peterson to accompany the ROKAF operation and to report to me on return."**

**I got a "Roger" from the tower. We were almost to the spot of the oil slick and, bingo, there it was again. But visibility was terrible. I was down to about fifty feet off the water trying to maintain contact and, periodically, going on instruments at that level.**

**Once more we lost the slick and once more we did the routine all over.**

**Finally, I decided that further search was not only useless but the weather was such that I could easily fly myself into the water and we gave up. A heavy rain had begun to fall. I pulled up to a thousand feet and headed back to the Kunsan range, made an instrument approach and landed. The weather was miserable.**

**Parking the aircraft, Akers commented.**

**"You still know how to do it, Colonel."**

**I sensed that, in the coming evening, there would be some bar talk about the attempted rescue and the Colonel's flying. Perhaps my "new kid" image might be improved. In the meantime, I made a note to talk to the ROKAF about the fuel situation for the rescue boat -- I had not yet met the ROKAF Commander and this was an obvious error in my priorities. I would do it tomorrow. And then I had to figure out what to do, if anything, about Davidson. But those were only two items on a very large and growing agenda. I wondered if I could get everything done that had to be done -- and I had already used up most of my first week -- only seven weeks remained and I would move on to Osan!**

**It was nearing dark when I arrived back in the office. Jones was waiting for me -- the others had quit for the night.**

**"We didn't have a flag staff for the office but I managed to get a pipe and screwed it into a hole in a wooden block. For the top, I found a fence post ball in the salvage yard. We had some silver paint. I hope it's O.K. for the time being. I'll see if I can't scrounge a real flag staff and base next time I get to Osan."**

**"Thanks, Tommy," The flag behind my desk added something to the office. "As to real scrounging, how good are you?"**

**"Don't really know. I haven't had much experience at it."**

**"Well, there's no time like the present to learn. I guess you may have seen those tires we brought back from Osan?"**

**"Yes sir. We already have some of them mounted on the trucks. The men in transportation are happy as little kittens."**

"O.K. I visited some of the warehouses at Osan and I think there may be a lot of stuff up there we could use. And I have to wonder what may be in warehouses of the Army in the Seoul area, at Inchon or, maybe, down at Pusan. Let's start at Osan. When the Gooney Bird or L-20 is free, have Major Akers arrange for a pilot to get you and Sergeant Young to Osan. Plan on spending a day or two -- we can pick you up later or you can return on the regular shuttle that passes through here to Japan. Write yourself and Sergeant Young some orders. Give the purpose as one of coordinating supply and other matters. You may need them to get billets. I'll sign them.

"At Osan, talk to the men in supply; get to know them. And visit every warehouse you can. Eyeball everything and try to figure out if there is anything there that we need. And then figure out how to scrounge."

"How do I do that?" Jones asked.

"Everybody wants something. We don't have much in the way of trading materiel here but we do have an aircraft and I bet there are people who would like to go to Japan who could get the time off but can't get the transportation. I won't mind if you trade some seats on one of our flights to Japan for some stuff we need. You make the deal and I'll back you up. But remember that *scrounging* is not *stealing*."

"Yes sir."

"And while you are scrounging, see if you and Sergeant Young can get a sofa and two lounge chairs plus a coffee table for my office. And on the next flight to Japan have the air crew purchase a set of china for me -- a couple sets -- especially coffee cups and saucers plus the stuff that goes with it -- creamer and sugar bowl. Also get some decent spoons, some napkins and the like. You might get a few dozen decent glasses for cold drinks. Just tell me how much it costs as this is a personal purchase for the office -- not a G.I. purchase."

I could see that Tommy enjoyed the growing responsibility I was placing on him. As to the office furniture, I had wanted to get rid of most of what was in place from the moment I saw it. Per my first day's order, Sergeant Young had managed to get some of it changed but more was needed. In addition to a desk and conference table, most of all I wanted a coffee table and related arrangement to bring an essential air of informality to some of the discussion -- I hated to be tied to dealing from behind a desk -- besides, it was poor protocol. To work from behind a desk was to exhibit a superior authority that did not serve many of the situations I knew I would encounter.

# THE FOURTH DAY ENDS

Once again, I had missed lunch. Remarkably, the fried chicken tasted good -- apparently, the grease pot in the kitchen had been changed. Annie was her usual, smiling self.

Some of the officers joined me for dinner. Davidson was not there. "He probably decided to stay in his hootch," I thought.

Looking around the Officers Club, it appeared that the number of josans present had decreased. I wondered if it was the weather or the new josan policy at work. Since the issuance of that policy, no one had spoken to me about it -- one way or another.

I had a couple cold beers with dinner and it all but wiped my feet from under me. I knew I was tired. Apparently the air-sea rescue flight had used up a good amount of energy. I realized that it had been mentally exhausting -- if not physically. I only hoped that the ROKAF rescue boat would come up with something.

As I finished eating, Lieutenant Jones showed up and handed me a card.

"I sort of figured that you didn't have a ration card and made one out for you."

It had not occurred to me to think about the PX rationing system in Korea. Actually, I had not yet visited the Kunsan PX -- now imprinted in my mind as a result of the Wright episode. I wondered who the current manager was -- and was he, too, engaged in black market?

Looking at the ration card, I could see that I was authorized to purchase enough booze that, if I used it all, I would be in the hospital or dead within a month. And there were a lot of other rationed items. On the surface, some of it made no sense, e.g. one radio every six months! I had to conclude that the black market operation was engaged in by many -- buy something at the PX and sell it on the local market. Hopefully, I would find time to get a briefing on the subject from Wild or Pastiak or someone.

"Shit! There was another item on my growing agenda."

Returning to the Waldorf Astoria, I took the B-4 bag out of the trunk of the car and hurried inside. The rain was coming down hard and I was soaked.

As was now the apparent custom, I saw that my mama-san had laid out the washing and ironing she had done on the top of the wooden box in the bedroom. I hung up the uniforms and placed the other items in the dresser. There were four rolls of toilet paper alongside the clothes. Somehow the word had gotten to my mama-san and a source of toilet paper had been found. I put the toilet paper in the locked wooden box. Obviously, the top of the wooden box was to be our means of communication. I wondered when the time would come when I would meet this invisible person.

Then I noticed that there were several aerosol cans on my bedside stand. Sergeant Young had done his job.

Outside the rain was now pouring down -- literally rattling on the roof and gushing off the edges. I walked around the billet to see if there was any roof leak -- I found none. Perhaps some good things did happen?

With the rain coming down in a deluge, I found myself depressed at what would now be a sea of mud. I thought about the joy of having a radio and decided that I would have to purchase one.

And then I decided to write Mary. The core of the letter was the air-sea rescue attempt. I did not tell her about the weather we were flying in or the danger of hitting an island in the low visibility. It seemed that it was just as well that she not know of those things. I also wrote about the Korean children I had observed on the Kunsan base and how little they had. Mary would probably talk to Michele and Jeff about how the children in Korea lived and how lucky they were to grow up in America. Jeff, however, was too young to understand -- he was only learning how to talk.

Eventually, I crawled under the mosquito net and sought sleep. From outside came the continuous blare of a multitude of stereo sets. In spite of the booming vibrations of the stereos, sleep seemed to come rather easily.

It was about 0130 hours when something awakened me. Lying still, my hand on my pistol, I listened. Before I want to bed, I had remembered to hit the stove to get the rats out and I felt that it wasn't the rats that had awakened me. Then I heard it again. It was the faint, staccato sound of distant machine gun fire. I picked up the telephone and called the Air Police Command Center. The duty Sergeant answered.

"What's going on?" I asked. "I can hear some machine gun fire."

"It's coming from down the coast -- to the east," the duty Sergeant replied.

"Any idea what's going on?"

"We called the police in Kunsan but the only comment they had was that they thought a coastal watch unit had discovered a landing. The weather is really bad tonight and the North Koreans often try a landing in such weather. As far as we can determine, there is nothing happening here on the base. We'll call you if something happens."

I hung up. "Call me if something happens! Shit! Call me if I'm dead!"

I imagined a North Korean unit coming ashore from the Yellow Sea and my having only one man and a dog covering a mile or so. And, in this rain, both man and dog were probably hunkered down under a poncho. I wondered what the Officers Club's Korean guards were doing -- probably sitting somewhere out of the rain. The situation was ridiculous. And the body that was taken to Seoul? Had he been a member of a North Korean infiltration party?

I picked up the telephone and asked for the Osan Command Center. A Captain came on.

"This is Colonel Moench at Kunsan. We have machine gun fire coming from down the coast to the east. Do you have any indication of anything up there?"

I could hear some background discussion and then the Captain came back on the line. They had no indication of any landings or other problems; they were going to contact UNC and ROK operations in Seoul to see if they held anything. They would call me "if they learned anything."

The machine gun fire had died down. I tried to go to sleep but it did not come easily. Now and then, I again heard distant firing but it was all single shots. I felt like calling a base alert but decided to wait -- I had yet to learn if there was even a base defense plan that amounted to anything. I wondered how often something like this happened. Perhaps this was just a routine event in the new world I occupied? The duty Sergeant in the Air Police center seemed unconcerned by it all. I decided to talk to Davidson and had the operator ring his hootch. There was no answer. That disturbed me but I let it drop -- he might be in another hootch playing cards -- or something. Possibly, for a change, he was using some initiative and might be inspecting the guard. I hoped so.

With my adrenaline running, I got up and gazed out a window that overlooked the airfield. It all seemed utterly, fantastically quiet --

almost unreal. A few vehicle headlights moved about. The ceilometer bounced off the low clouds. The base was asleep and I realized that was what I should be doing.

But I knew that a sleeping target was the best of targets. "Was Kunsan Air Base a target?" I wondered.

Finally, after spraying the mosquito tent with aerosol, I crawled in and tried to make myself comfortable. It was hot and I was sweating. No cool air emerged from the air conditioner and I got up and shut it off. The result was that the room became more quiet.

Eventually, I crawled back into the bed but, for some unknown reason, I did not readily fall asleep. Instead, the words of a song I had heard at the Osan Officers Club kept running through my mind.

## PUSAN UNIVERSITY (*To the tune of Sioux City Sue*)

We were roaming down the
countryside,
'Twas down by Pusan Bay.
We stepped into a local bar,
Just to pass the time away.

I met a gal from old Chinju,
She was a sight to view.
I asked her where she came from,
And she said, "Oh, Pusan U."

CHORUS:

Oh, Pusan U, Oh, Pusan U,
The finest school in the land,
The University that's grand.
Oh, Pusan U, Oh, Pusan U,
I hail my Alma Mater --
To you, Oh, Pusan U.

I enrolled in the great college,
Founded by Kim Pac Su.
'Twas built of honey buckets,
So they called it Pusan U.
The smell it was terrific,
But fortune saw me through,
So now I lift my glass
To the school of Pusan U.

CHORUS:

Oh, Pusan U, Oh, Pusan U,
Your course is good for engineers,
"A" frames, oxcarts pulled by
steers,
Oh, Pusan U, Oh, Pusan U,
I hail my Alma Mater --
To you, Oh, Pusan U.

I saw a girl most beautiful,
She was a sight to view,
She won a beauty contest,
She was crowned Miss Pusan U.
They spotted her in Hollywood,
Now she's a star there too.
When asked to what she owes her
fame,
She says, "Oh, Pusan U."

We have an A-1 baseball team,
We win our games straight through.
When asked were we come from,
We reply, "Oh, Pusan U."
We have a pitcher who is tops,
Our batters are tops too,
And every time we come to bat,
The crowd yells, "Pusan U."

# DAY FIVE -- A FRIDAY

When the morning alarm went off, I found myself feeling more tired than when I went to bed. Just reaching for the alarm's turn-off button was a strain. My muscles hurt. At some point I had fallen asleep but, as I awoke, the words of "Pusan U" were still running through my mind.

Somehow, I knew I was going to have to get some better rest. Part of the problem, I concluded, was that my eating habits had been terribly disrupted. I resolved to try to eat three meals a day. Further, while I was working hard, I was getting no exercise and that had to change.

Exercise! What were the men doing for exercise? Was Kunsan Air Base a case of "all work and no play" -- other than playing with josans? There was baseball but that occupied only a handful of the men. What else was there to do? Many bases of the size of Kunsan Air Base had a golf course -- Kunsan Air Base had none. Many bases the size of Kunsan Air Base had a gymnasium for basketball and other sports -- Kunsan Air Base had none. When it came to recreation for the men at Kunsan Air Base, apparently it had never been a subject on the Fifth Air Force agenda. And I had been so busy getting my feet firmly planted on the ground, I had missed the point -- so another item was added to my expanding agenda. I had noticed that a gymnasium existed at Osan Air Base but I had not seen much beyond that. I would have to be careful how I approached this subject as I knew that, politically, I could not get Kunsan Air Base ahead of Osan Air Base.

The mud outside the Waldorf Astoria was terrible and I found my shoes encased with it by the time I got into the staff car to drive to the Officers Club.

At breakfast, there was a new face -- a Captain. I introduced myself. The Captain turned out to be the Flight Surgeon back from leave in Japan. His name was Charles Baker.

Captain Baker seemed to be a pleasant fellow but rather laid back. He assured me he had had a great leave. I talked to him about leaving the base with no surgeon present and the burn incident. He said that he had asked for a relief from the Flight Surgeon at Osan but he had been advised that no one could be spared to fill in for him. I made a mental note to talk to the Osan Flight Surgeon about that.

With one-third of the Air Force population in Korea based on Kunsan Air Base and with the number of medical personnel I expected were in Osan in support of the Air Force hospital I had observed during my visit, certainly they could maintain one Flight Surgeon at Kunsan. I wondered if the Osan Flight Surgeon reported to Wing or to Division? I would have to find out as that might condition my approach to the problem.

With the breakfast over, I reminded Baker that I expected him at the morning staff meeting. He assured me that he would be there.

Following breakfast, I did a quick drive around the base trying to make up my mind on the agenda for the day. Then, approaching the headquarters, the sight of the American flag flying boosted my spirits. I wondered how the sight of the American flag impacted on the other personnel on the base.

Inside, the officers and Sergeant Butler had already assembled. But I noticed that Lt. Colonel Davidson was missing. I asked Jones about the whereabouts of Davidson. Jones seemed to know but not want to answer the question. I decided to wait and talk to him later.

Sergeant Butler was the first on the agenda with the weather briefing. The news on his area map was not good. The low pressure we had previously discussed was now a well-formed air mass and it seemed to be swinging north rather than on a course aimed at Hong Kong. Sergeant Butler's personal forecast had it coming northward over Okinawa, the East China Sea and hitting Korea dead center. He plotted its arrival in about three days. He reminded everyone that this was the first typhoon of the season.

Following Butler's weather briefing, I asked Akers if we had a published typhoon plan for the base. He said that he was not aware of one but would take a look in the Operation's safe. He explained his lack of knowledge on the subject as a result of his still being relatively new in Korea and not having had to face a typhoon before. I asked him to check the files and get back to me before the day was out.

We then talked about the gun firing of the previous night. While Wild seemed to have some knowledge of the enemy agent infiltration problem, it was all second hand from his contacts with the local Korean police. He did make the point that the infiltration always seemed to be well down the coast from Kunsan Air Base and that it seemed to take place about once every month. He was unaware of any infiltration entering the Kunsan Air Base perimeter or the perimeter of other Air Force installations in Korea.

"Now and then, the South Korean coast watchers, the local police or the ROK Army manage to kill some of the infiltrators but most of the time they seem to get away and filter into the country-side. I understand that at the DMZ it's harder for the North Koreans to get through -- but, now and then, they do."

"A hell of a comforting assessment," I concluded.

Having no intelligence officer on the staff, I scribbled out a message to the 314th Air Division and read it to the staff. I could see that the content had an impact on those present. Apparently, the issues presented opened to them a new appreciation of their surroundings.

SECRET

TO: COMMAND CENTER
314TH AIR DIVISION
OSAN, KOREA

PART ONE: GUNFIRE EAST OF KUNSAN AIR BASE LAST NIGHT. REASON UNKNOWN. LOCAL POLICE SEEM NOT TO HOLD DETAIL OF EVENT. THE SUGGESTION IS THAT AN INFILTRATION PARTY WAS SPOTTED BY A COASTAL WATCH UNIT. CAN YOU SHED LIGHT ON THIS EVENT? AND CAN YOU PROVIDE A RUN DOWN ON HISTORY OF ENEMY INFILTRATION IN THIS AREA FROM THE SEA, PRESENCE OF ENEMY AGENTS IN AREA, AND ANY ADVICE AND RECOMMENDATIONS THAT WILL FIT OUR SITUATION? FYI: CAPTAIN WILD (KUNSAN AIR POLICE) ADVISES ME THAT THIS TYPE OF INFILTRATION IS ABOUT A MONTHLY EVENT.

PART TWO: REGARDING KOREAN CORPSE FLOWN TO SEOUL FOR AUTOPSY, WOULD YOU PROVIDE FINDINGS? ESPECIALLY INTERESTED TO KNOW IF AUTOPSY REVEALED BODY TO BE THAT OF NORTH KOREAN AGENT.

COLONEL MOENCH
COMMANDING

I handed the message to Jones for dispatch.

The infiltration subject set aside, I had Akers brief on the air-sea rescue attempt of the prior day. He got a bit carried away but the briefing was still good and it served further to open up to the staff activity for which they had little or no knowledge.

The Akers briefing was followed by a report from Peterson. Per my order, he had contacted the ROKAF and, with the delivery of the four barrels of diesel, they agreed to join the search effort. However, it was several hours before they got underway. Peterson accompanied them. Peterson said that the ROKAF had advised him that the lost F-86 was from the ROKAF squadron based at Kimpo. They did not dock until 0630 hours. Peterson reported that the trip was pretty rough and, at times, they had to slow speed due to the waves. Nothing was spotted. I asked Akers and Peterson to prepare a report on the air-sea rescue attempt and send it to Osan. "But," I said, "don't mention the fuel we supplied for the ROKAF boat." I could tell that I was plowing new ground -- that the idea of sending such a report to Osan was something new.

Reflecting on the infiltration and air-sea rescue briefing items, I could detect that they served to heighten interest and give a sense of importance to the mission of the base. In my view, the idea of "team" was beginning to emerge.

When it came time for Captain Baker to make a report, he advised of the number of patients in the hospital. When he had finished, I asked if, following the morning briefing, he would give me a tour of the base hospital. I also asked him what he did in the way of inspection of the food and mess facilities on the base. He informed me that he did a "mess hall check" once in a while but, as to food, he was not a veterinarian. I told him that, regardless, I wanted him to make at least a monthly inspection of the food and mess facilities and to give me a written report. He seemed to take the matter in stride.

Finally, the meeting adjourned. I asked Jones to stay and, after the others stepped outside, to close the door.

"Tommy, where is Colonel Davidson?"

Jones fidgeted.

"Do I have to say?"

"Yes."

"He went to Seoul, sir."

"He went to Seoul for what?"

"He wasn't feeling well -- he usually goes to Seoul when he isn't feeling well."

And what's at Seoul that makes him feel better?" Suddenly, I recalled Mike's warning and, as I spoke, I sensed I knew the answer.

Again Jones fidgeted but he finally did answer.

"I think he may have a josan up there. I think you know he can't take pressure. I understand that he's got an ulcer and he drinks a lot."

"Has this *going to Seoul* been a regular event?"

"Yes. I think the Colonel you replaced just let him go whenever he wanted. I think this was a way out of a troubling situation. It's the pressure of the job. I don't think Colonel Davidson is up to it. And I hate to say this but I think the Colonel is becoming an alcoholic. I don't think men like that should be assigned to Korea -- it's too hard on them."

My Deputy possibly an alcoholic and taking off to Seoul to relax with a josan whenever he felt like it -- I was dumbfounded. I should have focused in on the problem when I noticed his hands shaking but the idea of alcoholism hadn't fully penetrated my thinking. And now, technically, there was a possible AWOL that I was looking at.

"Is he traveling on orders?"

"No sir. We normally don't write orders for travel of officers so long as they stay in Korea. Even when there is a flight to Japan, unless it is for an extended stay or for R&R, we don't write orders."

[*The informality of the operation in Korea, the idea of so much being accomplished without the presence of written orders, was in stark contrast to commands such as the Strategic Air Command were, having reviewed some 201 files of persons assigned to that command, I had concluded that orders were often written on a daily basis. In SAC it seemed that hardly a single action took place without the presence of a written order. In Korea, the writing of an order was almost an anomaly. I realized that, in part, this informality came about as a result of there being no per diem authorized in Korea.*]

My mind, I felt, was made up. Davidson probably had to go -- replacement or not. I had studied his Form 5 and I had already seen that he seemed to avoid actual instrument flying -- and now this. I knew that I would have to get approval from the Director of Personnel at Osan but, in my mind, there was little alternative. If the Wing or Division would not agree to Davidson's return to the States, I was going to ask them to take him. But I knew that I might be opening a Pandora box that could encourage others to seek a transfer home on the basis of

**job pressure. One step at a time -- I had to take things one step at a time! And, right now, the step that apparently had to be taken was to get rid of "the very good" Lt. Colonel Davidson.**

**"O.K. Tommy -- get on with your other work. I'll handle the Davidson problem. And thanks for being up front with me."**

**Jones saluted and left the room. I looked out the window and, for a minute, cursed Korea. I was beginning to sense that the Korean environment did things to men -- caused them to do things that would not develop if they had not been assigned to Korea. I was reminded of Mike's assessment of the new Wing Commander, Colonel Musgrave: In six month's he'll be messing around with a Korean josan. I wondered if Korea was already making me into a different person?**

**[*There is no question but that the behavioral profiles of American servicemen were profoundly impacted by the Korean environment.***

***There were many places in the world where, compared to the U.S., living conditions were both unorthodox and terribly sub-standard. But few of those countries were inhabited by tens of thousands of virile American military personnel on seemingly endless tours of duty.***

***Two sociological elements combined in Korea. One was the local society itself -- a population still living with the aftermath of years of Japanese dominance and exploitation. Then there was the comparatively primitive environment -- something far removed from that of the U.S. -- even far removed from that of Japan.***

***Typically, unless in combat, the American military establishment moved an American environment along with the men who served. But, in Korea the American military population was mostly supported by the leftovers of the Korean War. American servicemen did live somewhat better than the Koreans but certainly nowhere near the level of Americans at home. For most, the movement from the U.S. to the Korean environment could only be described as traumatic and the result was that despair, frustration and loneliness took over many. And a waiting remedy was often the open arms of a beautiful Korean girl conditioned to serve every man's whim and fancy. The result could be forecast. The question was how to cope with it -- if coping was really in the cards.***

***In some areas, especially in the pre-Korean War period, the commanders turned a blind eye to the emergence of live-in josans or other arrangements. Bizarre results emerged. Some persons "went native." Others undertook to establish a new life in the U.S. with their new found partner. The situations and stories that emerged were boundless and, sometimes, beyond the description of "bizarre."*]**

# THE KUNSAN MEDICAL ESTABLISHMENT

**Captain Baker had been waiting outside my office door and I joined him.**

**"Rather than going to the hospital right off, let's you and I take a stroll through the enlisted mess hall. I should have done it already but I have been on a tread mill ever since I got here a few days ago. I did go through the kitchen at the Officers Club -- that has been all. But first, I want to talk to you in the car about something."**

**When we were inside the staff car, I asked Baker about alcoholism on the base. He stated that, as far as he knew, there was none. "Booze is readily available and the men do drink a lot but, on an isolated tour, it serves to blow off steam -- sort of like the old combat whiskey that used to be passed out."***

**His assessment was logical.**

**Then I told him about Davidson and asked if he had an ulcer as described by Lieutenant Jones?**

**"I don't think he has an ulcer but he may think he has one. It may be rationalization. He has often complained to me about stomach pains but I related that to stress and treated it accordingly. I agree that Davidson has a low tolerance to stress. He holds a lot inside himself. Part of it may be the flying thing you describe -- almost fear of flying but an unwillingness to give it up. I think you may know the type. I have no capability here at Kunsan to reach a determination of ulcers -- that would have to be referred to Osan. If I thought he might have had an ulcer, I would have sent him to Osan for an appraisal. Do you want me to schedule him for an Osan examination?"**

**"No. I think the best bet is to get him off the base -- to another assignment. Perhaps in another job he might be able to perform. Obviously, he did some things right to get promoted to Lt. Colonel. One thing I have to be careful not to do is to jump to conclusions. As**

---

* Until the Korean War, it was customary to provide American soldiers and airmen in action with a free issue of candy, cigarettes, beer and "combat whiskey." Suddenly, in the midst of that war, a "beer issue" became a national controversy with temperance, church and various civic groups bombarding the Pentagon and Congress with protests against "the corruption of American youth." Bowing to such pressure, alcoholic beverages were limited to individual purchase.

Commander I have some of that stuff you call pressure and, perhaps, you better watch my ulcer development."

We both laughed as I drove away from the headquarters building.

"If you don't mind, another question before we find ourselves at the G.I. mess?"

"Yes," Baker responded.

"Earlier you made the point that you were not a veterinarian. The job of a command veterinarian is to check the food, take care of animals and more. . . ."

"I take care of the security dogs," Baker interjected. "I'm not a veterinarian but I know enough to take care of heart worms, flea problems and more."

"What about the Osan veterinarian?"

"There isn't one."

"Well, then, what about the Fifth Air Force veterinarian? Doesn't he come over here to deal with food, animals and other things?"

"Not since I've been here," Baker replied.

Mike had already briefed me about the reluctance of the Fifth Air Force staff to visit Korea but this was ridiculous. That my Flight Surgeon had to think concurrently about the treatment of "dogs and men" was reminiscent of the assertion of some World War II businesses that "dogs and military men" were not allowed on the premises. Veterinarian functions were not the duty of medical doctors. General Joyce had at one point in the initial staff meeting I had attended at Osan talked about how every person in Korea had to learn to do a half dozen jobs beyond his own but this situation was assuming absurd proportions. Already I had learned that, in the case of the petroleum fire that preceded my arrival and in the absence of Captain Baker who was on leave, Able Grossman, the Dentist, assisted by officers and medical Sergeants, had cared for burn victims. In the sense of the preposterous, what would be the next outlandish thing I would discover?

Fortunately, we were arriving at the G.I. mess.

The enlisted men's mess was a one story, sheet metal building. In that a new mess hall was being built, any semblance of repair to the existing facility had been curtailed some time ago. Stones and sand bags held down the corrugated sheet metal that formed the roof -- most of the sand bags were rotted or torn and leaking sand. Several 55 gallon oil drums located adjacent to the mess hall apparently fed an

**equal number of oil-burning stoves inside. What was visible on the outside was visible on the inside -- corrugated sheet metal. The floor inside was rough concrete; long tables with side benches served about two hundred men at a sitting -- meaning that two or more sittings were required to feed the total enlisted population. Koreans did the bulk of the cooking and serving from a cafeteria line. Clean up was also done by Koreans.**

**"Do the Koreans who work here in the mess hall get any sort of physical examination by you?" I asked Baker.**

**"When newly hired, we give them one. Then, as we get time, we do a recheck."**

**"About how often is the recheck?"**

**"About every three or four months. We don't have enough medical staff to do it more than that."**

**"And what does a medical check involve?"**

**"Mostly outward signs. We don't do chest x-rays -- we wouldn't have enough film for that. And we don't draw blood, take urine specimens, do skin tests or the like. I know it's superficial but we can only do so much."**

**"This means that our Korean workers in the mess hall could transmit all sort of diseases to our men?"**

**"That's true. Korea is not the United States. For a while we did nail scrapings but finally gave up. Almost all of the nail scrapings showed worm eggs. It's just the way people live out here. I emphasize the hell out of hand washing, particularly after going to the john, but I know it doesn't always take place. As to disease, I am worried about mosquito borne items more than stuff carried by humans. During the summer, we only get sprayed about once a month. They have a spray helicopter at Osan -- one -- and it is kept busy going from base to base. If it breaks down, we get no spray. We are overdue for a spray now but all we can do is complain. Everything depends on the spray helicopter flying -- and the priorities set by Wing."**

**"How about malaria and encephalitis?"**

**"I've got one case of encephalitis in the hospital right now."**

**"Other diseases?"**

**"You name it and we have it or have had it. Fortunately, we have a good on-base water supply. But the human refuse used to fertilize the rice paddies can generate anything. We chlorinate our own sewage before it passes to the Yellow Sea -- we don't have a real sewage treatment system -- but what we send to the Yellow Sea is a drop in the sewage bucket of this country and that body of water."**

"Swimming?"

"Not allowed except for an area on the east coast up by Kangnung -- few go there."

"Venereal disease?"

"Plenty of it. We furnish condoms, there are boxes of them at the entrance to the mess halls and in the clubs, and we freely provide *no sweat pills* but the rate continues to run over 800. We ship out the stubborn cases. We have a lot of repeaters -- some guys manage to catch something two, three or four times in a tour and that runs up the annual rates. Unfortunately, some of the old timers brag about the number of times they have caught something and it encourages the recruits not to pay attention. The common assertion of the old timers is that VD is nothing worse than a head cold."

"Do you have any good news?"

"I may surprise you but the good news here at Kunsan Air Base is drugs -- we just don't have the problem they have up at Osan, in the Seoul area and especially with the grunts serving on the DMZ. We are so isolated here at Kunsan that drugs do not give us a real problem. Other than that, I can't give you much in the way of good news other than to say that, on the whole, the men here are pretty healthy -- probably too healthy when it comes to josans -- I've heard about your new policy on that subject -- hope it works."

We had walked through the feeding area of the enlisted mess and entered the kitchen. It consisted of field equipment -- very old and much used and worn.

"We have been out here for years and we still have field kitchen equipment?"

"And that isn't the whole story," Baker added. "Wait until you see outside. The sterilizing pots are converted 55 gallon oil drums."

"Fifty-five gallon oil drums?"

"That's right. We have to use what we have. I try to have them keep the water temperature as high as possible but it's a bitch. And, if the water temperature drops, anything can happen -- especially diarrhea. Have you been hit yet?"

"No."

"You will."

"I think the difference between what I observed at the Officers Club and what we see here is too great for comfort. I am certain it causes comment among the enlisted men. Tomorrow, at the morning staff meeting, I think I will announce a policy to require the officers to eat at least one meal a week in the enlisted mess and to act on any deficiencies they see. What are your thoughts?" I asked.

"The officers won't like it but they'll do it. They may end up selecting only the days when they perceive a good menu in the enlisted mess and that could cause adverse comment from the enlisted men. We do have this new mess under construction and it tends to fend off criticism of the existing system with a promise of better things for the future. Unfortunately, the way construction is proceeding, I am certain you and I will be long gone before it is finished. One problem is that the supply system keeps losing in-coming equipment."

"Stolen or what?"

"Stolen or diverted. In Korea, who knows? Sometimes the problem is more basic -- it just isn't shipped. The mosquito net on your bed . . ."

"Yes."

"From the time of submitting an emergency requisition until we got a shipment of nets was twelve months."

"On an emergency requisition?"

"Yes. And just think what action we get on a regular requisition."

We had passed by the mess hall under construction and, without going inside, I now knew for certain that it would not be completed during my term as Commander.

"Let's go to your hospital," I suggested.

The base hospital had six beds. Captain Baker had a couple medical Sergeants and a few Korean helpers. He had one operational ambulance. There was a capability to do minor surgery -- anything major was transported to the Osan hospital. The Osan hospital did all the annual flight examinations.

"Do you treat any Koreans?" I asked.

"Only emergency cases."

The answer came so quick and so positive that I knew it was not factual and I looked hardly at Baker.

"O.K. So I do make exceptions," Baker admitted. "But I only use old or excess drugs that would otherwise have to be destroyed. Periodically, if I accumulate some excess drugs, I may make an off-base visit and seek to treat any infected prostitutes. I view it as one way to hold down the VD rate. If you don't want me to do this, I'll stop."

Shit -- what else would I learn? What Baker had just told me was probably not only illegal but unethical. I decided to avoid an answer and changed the subject.

"What's the Korean medical system like?"

"The pits. Poorly trained doctors, poor facilities, lack of medicines, you name it."

"What about the periodic physicals of Korean civilian workers that I am led to believe takes place -- the check-off on the ID papers?"

"Basically a scam -- no more. If something does turn up, such as VD or TB, the individuals may be treated but I emphasize the word *may*. Korea is not the U.S."

"When you say that the infected Koreans *may be treated*, what do you mean?"

"I mean that they may be given black market, out-dated, even watered down medication -- possibly no more than a placebo."

I shook my head in disbelief.

"What about the ROKAF on the base -- do they have a doctor?"

"Frankly, I don't know. I don't associate with the ROKAF."

"Have you ever had to deliver any babies out here?"

"Thank God, no. And I don't do abortions. Nor vasectomies. Nor eye jobs. Nor a lot of other stuff. Not that I don't get requests for such things."

"Tattoo problems?"

"Terrible. The men go to the Korean tattoo parlors and all too often get infections. I continually lecture the men not to get tattoos but it's a losing proposition."

We were now in the open ward and, one by one, Baker reviewed the cases in the beds. Finally, we stopped at a man in a restraining jacket. "Fatigue" Baker announced. He was a big black airman, well built, seemed coherent, clothes hanging nearby told me that he was a Sergeant.

"What's the problem, Sergeant?" I asked.

"Guess I couldn't take it any more, sir. I had been pulling two shifts on and one shift off for so long that I just came apart one night and shot at a shadow. Captain Wild raised holy hell with me and I guess I ended up getting a little violent. I don't remember much."

"Had you been drinking?"

"No sir. I don't drink. Anyhow, the next thing I remember is being here in the hospital in this jacket and with Doc giving me a shot that put me to sleep. The rest is great -- best I've had in a long time. Give me a couple more days and I'll be ready to go back to duty. Colonel, I'm sorry I screwed up but don't you worry none about me -- I'm a good soldier."

"You're an Air Police Sergeant?"

"That's right, sir. I was a state trooper before I signed up. Here, they had me guarding them nuclear weapons. It's an important job and I'm happy to do it. I do wish we had more men, however. I worry that a handful of guys like myself are just not enough for such a task. A good New York, Chicago or Philadelphia gang of kids could wipe us out before we got a shot off."

"I know your concern," I answered as I squeezed the Sergeant's shoulder in a friendly, understanding way. My heart went out to him, I felt sorry for him and for what had happened. I was becoming damn mad at the general situation but, worse, I now saw another problem of immense proportion. Suppose the Sergeant had fired into a nuclear weapon? As I left the Sergeant's bedside, he gave me a "thumbs up" and I could see that there were tears in his eyes. Personally, I felt like crying myself. Here was a great man, obviously a good and patriotic American, a dedicated military man, pushed by the Korean military environment to the point of exhaustion. And the reward for outstanding service to a nation could be discharge for, officially, unsavory reasons. I felt like giving him a medal. But that was not the "real world."

After Baker and I had left the hospital, I asked him about the physical and psychological examinations he made of those serving on guard duty in the nuclear area -- to include the nuclear alert aircraft area. There was none so oriented -- as he rightfully stated, he was not qualified to do a psychological examination and he held no go/no go criteria for acceptance or rejection of a person for work as a nuclear guard -- even if he had the time to perform such examination.

To the lack of fences, poor lights, insufficient guards and more, there was now added the worry of the physical and emotional status of those few who served on nuclear guard duty. In the U.S. and in other hot spots, I knew the routine -- why was it not being applied at Kunsan Air Base -- or was it not being applied in all of Korea? Was it that the supposed nuclear weapons were not nuclear weapons but that this whole thing was simply a charade -- a great cover and deception plan? Or was it, as I was beginning to suspect, the creation of a low-cost bait or trigger for the Soviets or others to snatch at? Could it be that there were those who thought that, by placing a prime, virtually undefended, target right under the noses of North Korea and Communist China, either or both countries could be lured into an operation that would trigger a war in which promotion and historical position for the protagonists could be assured -- possibly old desired strategies and aims fulfilled -- possibly the employment of nuclear weapons in accordance with a grand strategy -- possibly an annihilation of China -- and North Korea -- or even the Soviet Union? Unfortunately, while I was only a junior Colonel, I knew too much about "how the world turned."

I had a headache but, suddenly, I had something else -- a hell of a pain stabbing through my middle. I didn't need Baker to tell me what it was -- I knew. The enlisted men made a point of the local triple threat: Korea, gonorrhea and diarrhea -- and, rather obviously, I had a good case of diarrhea on-coming if not already present.

"Are you all right?" Baker asked.

"Not quite," I answered. "I think I have been hit by your Korean epidemic -- diarrhea."

Almost instantly, I broke out in a cold sweat and my hands began to shake. The pain in my middle was enormous. I knew I had to find a crapper -- and quick. But I was uncertain as to whether I was going to throw up or otherwise. Life suddenly was less than meaningful.

I hardly made the crapper when everything in me went critical and exploded.

*An Air Force mess hall. Note the sand bags holding down the corrugated metal roof and the elevated 55 gallon oil drum serving an inside heater.*

# THE ENLISTED MESS

I think I lost well over an hour running back and forth to the crapper. In spite of taking several lomotil pills, the diarrhea did not ease off. I could tell that I was dehydrating as I was thirsty as all hell. Cold coke seemed the best treatment.

With the clock creeping past 1200 hours, I resolved that, in spite of the diarrhea, I was going to eat something. Outside, the sun now scorched the wet earth and the humidity was terrible -- sweat poured out of me to the point that my shirt, both front and back, was thoroughly soaked.

As I sat in the staff car and thought about the time spent with Captain Baker, I resolved to take my own advice and have lunch at the enlisted mess rather than the Officers Club. I had already found one report in file that categorized this mess as "the worst in the entire Air Force" and it chilled me -- I had to find out for myself.

On entering the enlisted mess hall, there was an obvious stir in the building. Murmured conversations were evident at every one of the rough wooden tables. Some of the men pointed at me and made one finger gestures. I pretended not to notice.

One of the mess Sergeants spotted me and suggested I go to the head of the line. I refused and simply took a position in the moving stream of men. Those in line looked at me but no one offered to talk.

When I got to the head of the line, there was a Sergeant standing and sort of supervising things. I asked him how much the cost of the lunch was. He responded that, if I was willing to eat it, it was free. I picked up a metal tray, knife, fork and spoon and started down the cafeteria line where Koreans with large spoons slopped out the fare.

Lunch consisted of some hard hamburger patties covered with a lot of not-too-warm, thick brown gravy; dried potatoes reconstituted as mashed potatoes and served with more of the same brown gravy; boiled cabbage; bread with canned desert butter; and some Jello pudding. There was coffee and a worthless fruit punch to drink.

With my tray filled and with the hope that my churning stomach could take it, I proceeded to a table that appeared to have space available. The men slid to one side to give me room.

Seated and surveying the silent table, I asked: "O.K., who is going to start the conversation? As you know, I just got here. And, if I

**know anything, it is that I know you all have a bunch of gripes. But, if I don't know what is bothering you, I will never know what to fix or how to fix things. So what are your gripes?"**

**The men at the table continued to sit in silence -- each one glancing at the other -- each one waiting for the next person to respond. Finally, an older Sergeant answered.**

**"Sir, I don't pretend to speak for everyone but, of all the gripes we have, I think food tops the list."**

**There was a lot of nodding of heads at the table.**

**"Go on," I said.**

**"Well, just look at what we got today. And every day is about the same. Why can't our government give us decent food?"**

**"And a decent mess hall," one of the men added.**

**"And a decent kitchen," one of the other men added.**

**Again there was a nodding of heads.**

**Then, the Sergeant who had initially spoken continued.**

**"We have to eat but a lot of us think that this mess hall is what is giving us a constant dose of diarrhea -- probably worse if we only knew. I've been in North Africa and seen some bad things but that was in the middle of a war and I put up with it. I've been in the Philippines and I've served in South America. But this is the pits. Many of us have been around the block and we know that something's wrong here and, pardon my French, we, all of us, are pissed off -- all of us."**

**Again there was a nodding of heads at the table. I sought to respond.**

**"I have to agree that this food is not the best. But, among you here there have to be some ideas as to how to improve things -- begin to make things a little better. I would like to see steak for everyone -- steak a few times a week. This is my first meal at your mess but I would guess, in addition to hamburger, you are sick of hot dogs and canned tuna. But, accepting some of that, how do we make things come out better? I can recall when we were moving through France against the Germans that, for a while, we were on a constant fare of C-Rations and it was driving us up the wall. Then we got some French cooks and what they did with C-Rations was a miracle. What can we do here?"**

**There was a strained silence as each person glanced at the others. I could see that there were ideas in the group but getting the ideas out on the table could be a problem. I thought I would add a comment.**

**"And, as to mess halls, for some time after we got into France, I heated my water and cooked what food I had in my tin helmet. And**

**few of us griped -- most of us were happy to be alive. Right now, you're alive and no one is shooting at you."**

**There was a long quiet at the table and then the older Sergeant spoke again.**

**"Colonel, we are just enlisted men -- we don't know what makes the system work. We can do a lot of things -- and we can put up with things such as you describe -- but we are not being shot at. This is not war -- this is a peacetime deployment even though we know that a lot of Korean crap is happening around us. We all feel that something has to be done to correct the situation in which we find ourselves and we depend on persons such as you to get things moving."**

**"And I depend on you."**

**I allowed the thought to settle in. Then I made a suggestion.**

**"Let's try to do one thing at a time. Take, for instance, that cafeteria serving line. I can see the cooks bring out pans of food but there is nothing to keep the stuff hot and pretty soon you got cold potatoes, cold gravy and more -- just like I have on this tin platter in front of me. Bad food is one thing but cold, bad food is something else. Surely among you there are welders and other skills. I don't know what we have in supply relative to sheet metal -- I would prefer to have stainless steel but, in a storm, you can't have everything -- I don't know what we have -- maybe we have some quarter inch plate in engineering -- it doesn't matter. But couldn't you chaps find the talent to cut and weld a heating trough with some sort of oil burner on the bottom to get the water hot -- make some holding bars out of something to hold the cook's food pans on top -- and end up turning out something that kept this food hot? That would be a step forward."**

**The older Sergeant looked at the others and I could see a nodding of heads.**

**"Would you authorize the use of whatever sheet metal we could find -- even if aluminum is all there is?"**

**"You got it," was my answer. The reference to aluminum bothered me but I was not going to let it get in the way of an answer to the cold food problem.**

**Suddenly, there were smiles at the table. Some of the men did a "high five" with each other. I figured I had left myself wide open for something but I let it ride.**

**"Now, as to food." The table turned quiet. "You know the source of our food. It's mostly the Army depot at Inchon -- and, with most of it coming by rail, all too much is spoiled by the time it gets here. Hopefully, we share equally in what is available."**

"As you say, Colonel, all too much of what we get is rotten on arrival," one of the Airmen stated.

"Or stolen before it gets here," another added.

"And that's why we frequently truck the rations in from the depot instead of relying totally on rail shipments. Then we do get a little food in from Japan by air but that's not for this mess -- that's for the clubs. Of course, there are a lot of demands for the food coming in from Japan and it doesn't go very far.

"Now, I know that, unlike this mess, you pay for the food you consume in the Enlisted Club. Would it make things better if I could arrange for you to get more in the way of good steaks and some other food in from Japan for your club? Mind you, it would have to be paid for."

There was some whispered conversation at the table. Eventually, the older Sergeant spoke again.

"Colonel, the U.S. Government is supposed to pay for our rations out here. But, if it takes a little out of our pocket to get some decent stuff now and then, we'll come up with the money. But, how are we going to get it from Japan?"

"Is there someone among you who knows good meat and how to buy it?"

"Before I joined up, I used to work in a butcher shop back in my home town," an Airman at the end of the table volunteered.

"And, if I got you to Japan, do you think you could do some meat purchasing -- good meat -- not the tough stuff -- and do it at a good price?"

"I know what's good and bad meat," the Airman stated, "and I speak some Japanese -- my mother was Japanese."

"All right. We got ourselves a typhoon coming in right now but as soon as the weather clears I'm going to send our C-47 to Japan and you can go with it and buy as much meat as your club can afford and store in the reefers. And I may add a little to the pot for the Officers Club -- if you don't mind. But, it's pay as you go -- cash on the barrel head. By the way, no special stuff for the Officers Club. You make a total purchase and the officers eat the same as you do. Naturally, if you can find them and space is available on the Gooney Bird, I will not complain if you brought back a few flats of strawberries. Is it a deal?"

"We'll get the cash," the older Sergeant said.

Suddenly, those at the table were all smiles. I had made some new friends -- and it felt good.

# THE KUNSAN TYPHOON PLAN

When I got back to the headquarters, Major Akers was on hand to greet me. His face told me that his news was not good. He carried a large document.

"Sir, I looked through the safe in Operations and I found this typhoon plan but I don't think you'll like it. It looks like it's at least four years old and most of the pages are blank."

"Let me see it."

Akers was correct. I didn't like it. As far as a plan went, it was virtually worthless. Essentially, it was a lot of vague and useless words -- enough to pass an inspection with many parts "To Be Added" -- almost nothing to provide real guidance to get the base ready for a typhoon. I knew how the system worked. There was a need for a plan and the men put one together -- mostly blank pages -- and the inspectors didn't know any better -- and the square was filled. Unfortunately, those assigned to the inspector slots were often the ones who couldn't perform in the operational slots -- persons beyond promotion or "put out to pasture." That the result would be what it was could be expected.

"O.K. Akers. Have you ever been in a hurricane or typhoon before?"

"No sir."

"Have you any idea what a wind at a hundred or more miles an hour or more will do?"

"I've seen some photos but, no sir, not really."

"Did you ever stick your hand out of an aircraft window when you were flying?"

"Yes sir. It flattens the hell out of your flesh."

"Well, that may be what happens to everything here on Kunsan if we get hit by this in-coming blow -- we may be flattened. Typhoons are no joke. Typhoons almost wrecked the preparations of the Inchon landing in 1950. Two of them hit -- one right after the other. The second one named Kenzia came right up the Korea Strait with winds of 125 mph. It generated 40 foot waves. We may not have a typhoon plan but, if we expect to survive, we better decide quickly what is to be done.

"First, everything that is lying around and can be blown needs to be picked up and placed in a building or tied down. Second, if the wind hits us, these corrugated metal sheets that we have for roofs will get blown all over hell's half acre. Get some sand bags and weigh them down. Double and triple tie the aircraft to the mooring points -- better yet, get ready to fly them out to a safe area -- an area that will not be in the middle of the typhoon. If you can't fly them out, tie them down and put spoilers on the wings. Take all the vehicles you can and place them next to the stronger buildings. Get with Peterson, Polk and others and try to figure out what are the very strongest of buildings on base and set them up as emergency shelters. Stock them with C-Rations out of the war reserve. Flush and fill all water trailers we have and distribute them to the emergency shelters. Have every man put on a web belt with canteen and make sure that all canteens are full. Put out the word that, when the storm hits, water is limited to drinking and fire. Because, in spite of our work, the typhoon will probably blow a lot of stuff around, have Captain Wild set up a special security plan and tell him he can draw on all sections for any extra help he needs. Set up a guard for the emergency shelters and issue forty-fives or carbines to those persons -- with ammo. Have Doctor Baker do what he can to get ready to receive casualties at the hospital or whatever buildings survive. And assign anyone with an iota of medical knowledge to Baker. That's enough for starters. Now get moving, issue some orders and think up other things as you work."

"Yes sir."

Damn but I felt tired. I knew it was the diarrhea working on me. Again, I visited the john. Then I took another lomotil pill. Suddenly, I realized that I had not talked to Major Turnbull about the in-coming typhoon and his plan for the alert fighter aircraft. I called him and asked him to come to my office. Then I called the ROKAF Commander and asked him if he would come by. I had wanted to meet the ROKAF Commander and this was as good a time as any to get to know one another. Shortly, they both arrived and I briefed them on the in-coming typhoon and our actions -- then I asked them what their plans were. To my surprise, I learned that Major Turnbull and the ROKAF Commander, a Colonel Lee, had not met although they were based on the same airfield and flew off the same runway.

Major Turnbull had to talk around his problems because of the nuclear issues -- something allegedly not known by the ROKAF Commander. But, surely, the ROKAF Commander was not so dumb as to fail to recognize the nature of the bombs that were under the wings of the F-100s in the alert area and clearly visible from the taxiway his aircraft used. And that conclusion triggered my mind in

**another direction. Real or imagined, the Koreans had to recognize the situation but they might not recognize the intended targets -- for them, the primary threat was North Korea -- for us it was the Soviet Union. Undoubtedly, our standing nuclear alert gave the South Koreans a sense of security -- and it probably had a sobering influence on North Korea. I wished I could have read the JCS papers that were behind the existing deployment but I was not in the Pentagon.**

**From Major Turnbull, I was assured that the "bombs" could be down loaded and the aircraft flown out -- possibly back to Japan. But they would hold their alert status right until the last minute. Further, his action would depend on the direction he got from his home base. I had to wonder what direction he would take from me.**

***[I found it startling that there was no governing host-tenant agreement in this and other situations in Korea. Eventually, I would find that this was an even broader problem in PACAF.***

***Military units operating in proximity to one another need a clear understanding of command lines, authorities and responsibilities. Apparently, everything at Kunsan Air Base was the result of some informal agreement or directive of the distant past with the source and detail of such understanding lost over time. Later, as the 314th Air Division Director of Plans and Programs, given the task to establish Kimpo as an international airport, a pet project of the aging President Rhee, the lack of a meaningful baseline agreement setting forth property use lines and command arrangements proved most troublesome.***

***In South Korea, the lack of true U.S./ROK or UNC agreement on command authority was particularly troublesome and it impacted not only on the local situation but upwards to Air Forces Korea and to the CINCUNC level. It was true that, in 1950, Syngman Rhee had given operational control of the ROK military to the UNC commander. And it is true that this operational control extended to the ROKAF. But, as the years advanced, the ROK President and his military commanders moved progressively to take matters into their own hands even to the extent of mounting unilateral operations. Later, General Charles H. Bonesteel III, CINCUNC in the mid-sixties, would find it difficult to hold in check the ROK Army at the DMZ. But, already in the time frame of this account, COMAFK had to exert personal influence to restrain the ROKAF from a retaliatory attack against alleged North Korean PT boats in the Yellow Sea and, later, when President Rhee ordered the sinking of Russian ships carrying thousands of North Korean repatriates from Japan to North Korea. The means employed to achieve the desired ends were hardly***

*textbook and had no direct relationship to any command or operational control authority of COMAFK as the locus in each case was international waters -- an area outside the responsibility of COMAFK unless the rules of hot pursuit were called into play. But, in both instances, the operations, if executed, would, by way of perceived operational control of COMAFK over the ROKAF, impact on either or both the UNC command and the United States. In neither instance, did the contrived COMAFK actions to stop the attacks result from any direction via the UNC or U.S. command channels and, except for the words here printed, these events are believed to rest in that vast array of unrecorded history.*]

**Colonel Lee said that his aircraft would be flown north to Kimpo or other airfields and that the rest of his unit would hunker down and ride out the storm as best they could.**

**I asked Colonel Lee about the gun fire of the night before and he professed ignorance. He had heard it -- but that was all. I thought he was lying but I let it pass.**

**At the close of the meeting, as Colonel Lee was departing, he asked me if I could provide him some fuel for the air-sea rescue boat he operated. He pointed out that it served as protection for the Air Force as well as for the ROKAF. I told him that I had to think about it. Even though I had provided some diesel fuel for the boat in relation to the recent air-sea rescue attempt, I knew that it was illegal for me to provide fuel, or anything, to the ROKAF unless it was directed as a part of the established Military Assistance Program -- the request worried me. Lee suggested that I might want to take a fishing trip on the ROKAF boat and noted that the past Kunsan Commander enjoyed fishing. I politely declined the invitation. I had to surmise that the past Kunsan Commander did provide fuel for the ROKAF boat.**

**I had no more than settled in my chair when Wild came rushing in. I did not have to be told that we had another problem.**

**"Sir, one of my men killed himself!"**

**"An Air Policeman?"**

**"Yes sir. One of my Air Policemen. He was a new man. He came to us about a month ago from an assignment at Pusan."**

**"How did he kill himself?"**

**"He lay on an automatic and pressed the trigger. The gun kicked off several times. He was in one of the old covered bunkers and it muffled the sound -- we didn't hear it. When he didn't show up for duty, my men went looking for him and they found him in the bunker. He literally blew himself apart. There was a note."**

Wild gave it to me. The note, written on toilet paper, simply alleged that he could not put up with life. There was no other specific. "Korea again, " I thought.

"Have Davidson, if you can find him, set up a Board of Investigation -- if you can't find Davidson, ask Jones to do it. Have Jones notify Osan of the death and go about gathering up the personal effects of the deceased. Do make an inventory. I assume that Osan will notify next of kin. In the meantime, I want a memo from you and from those who knew this person -- get down on paper everything that is known about the man -- even about his family, his wife and children, if he has any -- his finances, any girl friends, everything. If he has letters or a diary in his footlocker, I want to see them. Have Jones give me his 201 file."

"I've already checked his footlocker -- no diary or letters there. I'll get memos to you on what I and others know but what we know will not be much as this chap was a real loner -- didn't talk much, didn't socialize, just sort of sat and stared most of the time. I wish we had better people assigned but we have to make do with what we get."

"Give me what information you can and do check with the Flight Surgeon and the Chaplains to see if they can add anything to the pot. I may have to write a letter to a next of kin and I will need some background."

"Yes sir."

Getting out of my chair, I walked to the office window. The hot, muggy air flowing in did not help my mood. And the view of what rested outside was hardly joyful. It was a little thing but the screens still had not been repaired -- I knew the problem -- no screen wire. Perhaps it was such a simple thing as this that caused this Air Policeman to go over the brink?

Damn, what was going to be dumped on me next! Korea was beginning to loom as a many-headed demon. And new demon heads were appearing faster than I could slay the existing heads.

I knew I needed outside help of many kinds -- financial, personnel, logistics, communications, policy, authority and more. But, less than a week on the job, I sensed that such assistance would be minimal -- if at all. Further, I was reluctant to run to the outside world for assistance. I believed in the old rule: Never ask a question unless you are prepared to accept the wrong answer -- or no answer at all.

Except for special items such as construction and finance, the option of taking the problems of Kunsan Air Base forward appeared to be an unprofitable route to follow as senior staffs, possibly even the commanders up the line unless newly assigned, would be inclined to defend the status quo and the past more than to define a new future. Further, I could already appreciate that many of the problems at Kunsan Air Base were deeply routed in distant policies and priorities -- some, such as command and air base defense policy, extending all the way back to the Joint Chiefs of Staff.

While I hated the thought, I had to conclude that, by circumstance, I was on my own.

Reflecting on the growing array of problems, I began to stack them in mental piles:

1. Those things that I would have to handle on my own with no outside assistance -- and this was the largest pile. Many of the initiatives in this pile could well end up "stepping on toes" or bordering on the illegal, if not stepping beyond, but I saw little option.

2. Those things that I could resolve by going out-of-channels and calling on distant friends. Sooner or later, I knew that this avenue of assistance would dry up and it had to be used sparingly.

3. Those things for which there was no alternative but to present them forward through command channels. Action on such issues, I knew, would be long in coming.

In the meantime, I had to hold my own and the tenant organizations together. And I had to take that which I had and make it accomplish more than its residents thought it could do. "Carrot and stick" -- I had to use both of them carefully and effectively. Still, I knew that the initiative would not always be in my hands. I suspected that, all too often, I would be *reacting* to the unforeseen rather than *acting* according to a carefully designed plan.

Suddenly, I had an idea and picked up the telephone and asked to be connected to Colonel Musgrave, the Wing Commander at Osan.

"Colonel Musgrave, John Moench here. We're beginning to batten down in preparation for the in-coming typhoon. Do you have any instructions for me?"

- - - - -

"Thank you. I'll do everything I can."

As I suspected, the Wing Commander had no thoughts on the matter. But at least I had given it the college try.

And then I realized that Wild was still standing in my office.

# THE FUEL PUMPING

It was obvious that Captain Wild had something else on his mind.

"Sir, a quick report.

"I'm getting the men lined up for fuel pumping at 0800 hours tomorrow. If the typhoon holds to its current forward movement, we should have the fuel in the base tanks before it hits. The pumping will take less than the usual time as we are down by one receiving tank. I'm told the helicopter from Osan will be in by tonight. But Osan said that, if we were delayed in the pumping, they would have to withdraw the chopper -- get it out of the path of the typhoon.

"Major Peterson has a team assembling the pipeline right now. The Koreans have spotted Peterson's team and they are starting to filter in north and south of the line and from the city of Kunsan. I think they all hope to stock up on fuel for the next winter. I'm afraid we are in for one rough one on this pumping as the number of Koreans showing up is quite large -- the camps along the pipeline are already setting up."

"How many guard/repair teams have you and Peterson set up to patrol the pipeline and effect repairs?"

"Ten."

"That's about one team per mile of pipe. Add at least another five as reserve -- match up a regular G.I. with each Air Policeman -- get Jones to place a levy for men on the other sections of the base."

I thought for a minute and then asked Wild a question.

"Wild, just how do you control the Koreans? You can't shoot them. And you can't arrest a whole population. What do you do?"

"Sir, sometimes we just have to be a little rough. The men know they are not to shoot anyone and the Koreans know we won't shoot -- although, sometimes, we shoot over their heads. So all we have left are our gun butts, our feet and our fists."

"Do your men carry billies -- do you have any billies?"

"No, to both questions."

"Have Captain Polk make you some -- good heavy ones -- long ones. If we have some black paint, use it. Black is formidable-looking. Instruct your teams to use them as necessary but aim low on the bodies -- not the heads. And try not to hit the women or the kids."

"Sir, half or more of the adult Koreans that will be at the pipeline will be women and most of them have kids."

"Well, do your best. We have to get all the fuel we can into our tanks."

I was still reviewing what I viewed as "one hell of a mess" and wondering what the ACLU or the American press would be saying if they knew about the situation when Sergeant Young came in with the morning mail. He pointed to the top item and suggested that I read it first. As I did so, my temperature went up several notches.

The letter was from an Airman Reginald Smith to his mother in West Virginia who had sent it to her Congressman with an irate cover note complaining about the Commander at Kunsan and how he was mistreating her son. In turn, the Congressman had sent the letter to the Department of Defense "for information on which to base a reply," who sent it to PACAF in Hawaii, who sent it to Fifth Air Force in Japan, who sent it to the 314th Air Division, who passed it to my Wing Commander who ordered me to reply within five working days. The letter spoke of all sort of bad things happening at Kunsan Air Base and I could see the Wing Commander relishing the communication and the apparent opportunity it presented to crucify me. What was claimed to be wrong at Kunsan? There were things such as poor food, unsanitary conditions, the use of hand grenades to chase men out of prostitute houses, to the Commander standing in the way of Airman Smith marrying a Korean girl. On the latter point, I boiled. Airman Smith alleged that the Commander was trying to keep the Korean girl for himself! The fact that the Airman's letter was dated before my arrival at Kunsan Air Base was of no comfort.

I looked at Sergeant Young in disbelief.

"You read it, didn't you?"

"Yes sir. Pretty bad, sir."

"Do you know who this Airman Reginald Smith is?"

"Yes sir. He works in Engineering. He's been out here about ten months. He's been trying to marry this Korean girl but the reports on the girl are really sorry."

"How sorry?"

"Prostitution -- real prostitution. And, at last report, VD. Plus, she's got TB and who knows what else. She's a skinny, ugly little thing. I can't see anyone wanting to take her home to mother."

"And so we have been trying to keep this Airman Smith from marrying this Korean girl?"

"For his own good, sir."

"And what about the rest of this letter -- not the food -- I know about that."

"I can't respond to that, sir."

I thought a while. Certainly, if any of my officers conducted an investigation it would look like a cover-up and the Wing Commander could get on my ass for that. I had to be careful.

"Ask Major Turnbull in the tactical fighter unit to visit with me when he gets some free time."

Sergeant Young saluted and left. It seemed only minutes and I was hardly into the day's mail when Major Turnbull showed up. I let him read the Smith letter, told him of my concern if one of my officers did the investigation, and asked him if he would do me the favor of conducting the investigation. He agreed and I asked Jones to prepare the necessary appointing orders. I wanted this thing to be official.

That out of the way, I called for Captain Wild to return. The idea of my men clubbing women and, possibly, children was bugging me. There were probably a hundred military and State Department rules against the thought I had but I remembered that after World War II the use of Koreans to police Koreans had become a political necessity.

"Wild, as to your protection of the pipeline, I have an idea. Tell me, how much fuel do we lose on a pumping?"

"That depends, sir. If they break open the line while we have the pumps running, Major Peterson says that we can lose thousands of gallons. First, we have to get the pumps stopped, then fix the line. In the meantime, even with the pumps stopped, the line will flow at a pretty good clip as the break will allow air to enter."

"And, when the pumping is over -- then what happens?"

"With our security gone, the Koreans break open almost every joint of the pipe and drain out the sections."

"Don't we purge the line with water after pumping?"

"Yes, but there's always some residual fuel in the line."

"And how much fuel is in the line when we pump? That's about ten miles of five inch line."

Quickly, we calculated the number of gallons to fill the line.

"Looking at that figure, I'd say that a few breaks in the line, when it was under pressure, would equal at least twice the full of the line when static. Am I correct?"

"Something like that, sir."

"So, in spite of our best effort, we stand to lose tens of thousands of gallons of fuel on a normal pumping -- a lot of which will just go on the ground. Well, suppose we make a deal with the Koreans in which we halve that loss and minimize the ground contamination?"

"A deal? What kind of a deal?"

"Suppose we arrange with the Mayor of Kunsan City and the village elders along the road to Kunsan to protect the pipeline with the pay off being that they can have the residual fuel for their distribution if we have no breaks during the pumping -- and we assure them that, when we are finished, the line will be left full -- not purged with water?"

"Can we do that, sir? Is that legal?"

"If we end up with more fuel in the tanks by that method, let's not ask if it's legal -- let's ask if it makes sense."

"It seems to make sense," Wild answered.

"Then do it. Tell Captain Pastiak what you are up to just in case there is a special legal item that he has to play with."

With a "Yes sir," Wild was off. Somehow, I felt as if I had solved a problem without broken bones and bloodshed. But I knew that I was setting myself up for a court-martial. Suddenly, I had a second idea and called to Wild to come back.

"I think I want to change the specifics of our plan a little. A bit ago, the ROKAF Commander hit me for some fuel for his air-sea rescue boat. How about telling him that, if he arranges with the Mayor of Kunsan City and the village elders to protect the pipeline and adds his own men to the security force, we will give him five hundred gallons -- that's ten barrels -- of diesel fuel for his boat and he can share some of the residual in the pipeline. That will get us out of the negotiation act and it will ease up on your security problem. Certainly, it is a hell of a lot better if the ROKAF have to clobber some Koreans than if we have to do it."

"It could work," Wild answered.

"Then put it into effect. But don't make a public announcement of it. We have enough trouble here."

Wild stated that he understood and departed. Although I anticipated that the word of what I had done might leak out and I might get hell for what I had ordered, I felt as if I had accomplished something and I would survive the flak. What I surely did not relish was my own Air Police beating Korean women and, possibly, Korean children. Slickies -- that was something else.

Damn, there went my stomach again. I headed for the crapper -- chills coursing through my body and a cold sweat suddenly drenching my clothes.

# DAY SIX -- A SATURDAY

The alarm went off at the usual time of 0600 hours but it was more like 0630 before I could get up the energy to sit up on the side of bed. I was weak as all hell but the severe stomach pains that had tormented me during the night seemed to have disappeared.

Struggling to the bathroom, I looked in the mirror -- I had deep, dark circles under my eyes and my face was almost the color of chalk. I splashed some cold water on my face and it seemed to perk me up. Then, my muscles aching, I maneuvered a kettle of water to the hot plate and, while it was heating, stepped under the cold shower head.

I didn't go to breakfast -- the idea of food was just too much to take. Instead, I headed for the headquarters. It was a little after eight when I got there. Major Akers was waiting for me outside.

"Had a bad time last night, sir?"

"I did but I'll make it. Hopefully, I'm over it for the time being."

"Sooner or later, we all get it -- and usually more than once. Apparently, our tender American systems can't handle all the stuff out here." Akers laughed.

"You wanted to see me about something urgent?"

"Yes sir. And it is not good news."

"So what is new and what now?" I asked.

"Sir, about the typhoon preparations, I'm afraid that we are not going to be able to sand bag the roofs and stuff."

"And why not?

"Sir, we don't have any sand bags."

A military base in a forward area with no sand bags -- I could not believe it.

"Are you certain?" I asked as incredibility dominated by thoughts.

"Absolutely, sir. I talked to Major Peterson, to Captain Polk, to just about everyone, and there are just no sand bags on this base."

"But I saw sand bags being used at Osan."

"Yes sir. And I checked Osan to see if we could get some from them but they said that they didn't have enough for their own needs."

As I went into the office for the morning staff meeting, I wondered where it would all end. I hadn't been a week on the job but it seemed that everywhere I turned I encountered more and more problems. Was there ever going to be an end? I was in no mood for continuing problems but opened the meeting with the feeling that they would come as sure as taxes and death. And, to start my day on the wrong foot, Lt. Colonel Davidson was still not present.

Also not present were Major Peterson and Captain Wild. Quickly, I learned that they had managed to get the pipeline assembled with the pumping underway at 0600 hours -- which meant that, if all went well, it could be completed by mid-afternoon. Peterson and Wild, in light of the approaching typhoon, had acted on their own to expedite the operation and had had their men working throughout the night. I was highly pleased at the obvious initiative and made a mental note to so state that fact when I prepared their Efficiency Ratings. Captain Pastiak advised that my Rube Goldberg pipeline security plan seemed to be working as, so far, there had been no break in the line. At the moment, Peterson and Wild were somewhere between the base and the port facility. The Osan helicopter had come in during the night and it was patrolling over the length of the pipeline. For once, I felt that some things were going right.

The highlight of the morning staff meeting was the weather briefing by Sergeant Butler. The typhoon was clearly on a direct course for Korea. It looked like the eye would come across the East China Sea and hit Cheju Do and then pass just to the east of Kunsan. There was a large high pressure area centered over Manchuria that might influence the typhoon to bend its northern track to the east and head it out into the Sea of Japan. No doubt, we were in for a big blow and a lot of rain. Locally, we had mostly high clouds with good visibility but it was forecast that the clouds would be building rapidly and, by nightfall, we would be getting rain from the leading edge of the typhoon. By tomorrow noon, the eye was expected to pass northward in the vicinity of Kunsan.

"What are the low and high tide times?" I asked.

"I don't have them precisely," Butler answered, "but we should have low tide somewhere around noon." Then he added as a sort of apology, "The Air Force weather system does not track tides."

Those who had not studied the tidal situation in the Yellow Sea nor the position of Kunsan Air Base on a peninsula jutting out into the sea area with the land virtually at sea level at normal high tide would not understand my concern. The Japanese had reclaimed the land on and around where the air base stood from what was, at one time, low marshes. To protect the land from the waters of the Yellow Sea, the

Japanese had erected a sea wall but, for years, this sea wall had been unattended. I had already briefly walked along some of the sea wall on a daytime inspection and knew that it was far from an effective barrier. If the typhoon hit at high tide with an on-shore wind, much of the base could be flooded. And, with no sand bags, we couldn't even protect significant facilities such as the communications center. I turned my attention to Captain Polk.

"Polk, we may have to move some water before this typhoon thing is over, what do you have in the way of pumps?"

"Nothing, sir."

"Nothing at all?" I was dumbfounded again.

"That's right, sir. Nothing at all."

No sand bags, no pumps, the drainage ditches silted shut -- the only good news was that the typhoon might come in at low tide.

"What is the peak wind expected to be when the typhoon hits here?" I asked Sergeant Butler.

"The last recce into the typhoon clocked top winds of one-twenty," he answered. "I can't see that increasing as it heads toward us and it might decrease some."

"Thank God for small favors," I thought as I addressed the assembled staff.

"As I see it, in the way of time, all we have to prepare for this typhoon is today. By tonight or tomorrow morning, we will probably be drenched with water and, God knows what in the way of wind. Let's not place our effort on other things, no matter how urgent; let's place our attention on doing whatever can be done to get ready for this typhoon. Major Akers is the coordinator of all action -- if you have ideas or questions, get them to him. I'm sure that, by now, our men all know that this typhoon is heading at us but double check. In that we might get some flooding in the lower billet and administrative areas, try to get the men to get things off the floors. Right now, I'm going to do a walk around the base with the hope that some ideas can be generated. I would like Jones and Sergeant Young to accompany me. And, because I don't know just where we may end up going, I suggest that they both put on some combat boots. While it's not raining right now, it may be pretty soon -- so bring a poncho. I'm going up to my quarters to change shoes and get my poncho and will meet you back here at headquarters in about thirty minutes."

When I returned to the headquarters building, Jones and Young were standing by. I noticed that both of them wore web belts and canteen. And both Jones and Young had hooked forty-fives on their belts. I did not comment. Certainly, they had a reason and I would let it remain that way. Sometimes, it's best not to ask questions.

"Can either of you drive a weapons carrier -- a four-by-four?"

Jones shook his head; Young assured me he could.

"O.K. Let's go to the motor pool. I'm going to switch my staff car for a weapons carrier. Sergeant Young, you drive."

There was a shortage of operational vehicles at the motor pool but the Sergeant in charge did locate an operational weapons carrier for us. Fortunately, the tires looked pretty good -- a good tread all around -- I wondered if we were going to need it.

"Let's begin at the sea wall," I instructed Young.

Departing the motor pool area, Jones advised me that the old PX Manager, Mr. Wright, had departed the base on the prior day's commuter flight.

"Good riddance," was my observation. "We don't need rubbish like that hanging around. But did he give us any trouble?"

"He cussed a lot as he got on the out-bound plane, asserted a lot about his rights and stuff like that and sort of threatened retaliation to you -- but the bottom line is that he got on the plane and left. I think we have seen the last of him," Jones stated.

*While Kunsan Air Base had no sand bags, there was a good supply of sand bags at Osan Air Base. Here we see Korean laborers building extensive sand bag retaining walls during a heavy rain storm. (USAF)*

# THE PRE-TYPHOON SITUATION

There was no road on or near the sea wall. The approach was mostly over low lying, grass-covered land. Currently, the ground was reasonably dry but I was glad we were in a weapons carrier as I expected that, shortly, the area might be impassable.

I had Sergeant Young stop at several points along the sea wall and, getting out of the weapons carrier, I walked to the top. The sea wall was reasonably thick and there was a fair amount of stone in its construction. I had to wonder from where the stone was obtained when the Japanese constructed it. I did notice that the water action had undermined the sea wall at many points and I concluded that any good in-coming wave action might well breach the system. Probably, the sea wall was within my jurisdiction and responsibility but I knew that I had no manpower or resources to do anything about it -- and I doubted if I could ever get Fifth Air Force to allocate monies to reinforce a Korean sea wall. The whole thing was just too preposterous to even remotely consider.

Beyond the sea wall, the receding tide revealed miles of slick, rolling, black mud flats. Thousands of Koreans were now distributed across those mud flats -- presumably seeking trapped fish or other edibles. To get to the distant mud flats, those persons had to walk miles through sticky, slippery mud. I knew that the process had to be well scheduled as, in not too many hours, the tide would be rushing back with the water reaching right to the base of the sea wall. Anyone caught by that in-coming tide would probably perish.

Looking at the thousands of Koreans risking their lives in such a dismal search for edibles, I was overcome. Still, I knew that this could not be one of my worries -- I had other things to worry about.

Driving to the far end of the airfield, we could view beyond the hill that dominated the approach to the runway -- and there, at the far side, was a fishing village. Normally hidden from view, we observed this village as we approached the top of the hill. With the tide out, the boats in port were all on the exposed mud flats and heeled over on their sides. The area seemed well sheltered by the adjacent hill and I suspected that it had been selected centuries ago for that reason. There was some movement of persons in the village but I could see no special preparation being done in anticipation of the on-coming typhoon.

Looking in the opposite direction, from the top of the hill there was a great view of the entire air base. I was sorry that I had not visited this spot before this date.

"What is that thing in the middle of the field?" I asked. "It looks like a landing craft." I had not noticed it before -- probably due to the high grass on the field.

"That's what I understand it is," Sergeant Young replied. "Someone told me that it was damaged in the Korean War and, later, was dragged to that spot to serve as a target for practice radar bombing by the Strategic Air Command. I understand that the boat's metal provided a good radar return to the SAC aircraft."

"Is it now used for that purpose?"

Neither Jones nor Young knew the answer. But then I saw something else.

"Isn't that a three-section sheep's foot compactor I see out there?" I pointed to what I was looking at -- in the past, it, too, had escaped my eyes.

"Yes sir," Jones answered. "It's been out there since I got here. It probably was left here by the construction unit when they built the new runway."

"Well, we can't worry about that now but when this typhoon thing is over I want Captain Polk to drag that compactor into his yard and put it on the books as *Found On Station*. If it's been out there that long, obviously it has no registered owner."

Now from the hill I could see scattered Korean houses that, although there were really no visible property lines demarcating the limits of the air base, seemed to be located on base.

"How did we end up with all those Korean houses so close to our base facilities?" I asked.

"They're not all Korean houses," Young replied.

"If they're not Korean, what are they?"

"Some of our men live in them."

"Our men live in those shacks and not in the barracks?" I found the statement unbelievable.

"Yes sir. We have a number of men who have picked up Korean companions and who have established themselves along Korean lines. Some of these men have been here for years. I am told that some may even have children. When I arrived here, I was told that they formed a sort of front line of security for the base."

**Whoa! I didn't comment. But I could see one hellacious problem. Still, what I suspected then was only the tip of the iceberg I would soon discover.**

**In the far distance, I saw the Osan helicopter making a low pass over the pipe line. And, even at the distance we were from the road that left the base for the city of Kunsan, I could distinguish Koreans gathered along the near end of the adjacent pipe line -- but just milling about or sitting.**

**Scanning the airfield, I noted that, off to the side of what used to be a cross runway, there were several aircraft hardstands -- now unused. The alert aircraft were clustered on the somewhat new, well-defined, concrete ramp adjacent to what was now the active runway. The Korean village next to the nuclear and conventional bomb storage area annoyed me but I knew it had to be accepted as a way of life.**

**Assessing the clustering of the alert aircraft and the obvious target they represented, I could not help but recall the criticism attending Pearl Harbor when the aircraft were lined up at Hickam and Wheeler. "We don't seem to learn or we don't have enough money to do it right," was my thought.**

**Looking beyond the immediate air field, I observed the light anti-aircraft gun positions on the exterior of the perimeter. But I could find no logic which supported the deployment totally to the inland side of the air field with nothing defending the seaward approach. It did not take a military genius to see that an aircraft coming in from the sea at low-level, and probably below the radar scan, could wipe out the nuclear alert aircraft on its first pass. But I was not in charge of air defense -- I had to wonder if, whoever was in charge, could go to the bathroom and find where to wipe? Was it Osan, was it the UNC, was it Fifth Air Force, who was it? Was responsibility so shredded up and passed around the table that no one was in charge? Which reminded me of another question.**

**"Have we ever, as far as you know, been officially visited by a senior UNC officer?" I asked Jones.**

**"Not to my knowledge," was his reply.**

**Trying to control my growing anger and frustration, departing the hill I asked Sergeant Young to attempt to drive on a sort of levee that marked the edge of the nearest rice paddies on the inland side of the airfield and opposite from the sea wall side. The levee was barely wide enough to accommodate the width of the weapons carrier and, from time to time, I half expected the vehicle would slide into a rice**

paddy. Sergeant Young stated that, normally, they only took a jeep with much narrower wheel base out on the rice paddy levees.

But we did manage to make it and, along the way, I observed Koreans, waist deep in water, weeding the green stand of rice. Here and there, a Korean was treading a water wheel, lifting and moving water from one field to another. We passed one American guard on duty -- that was all. He seemed surprised to see us. A few drops of rain were beginning to fall.

Eventually, we got to a regular vehicular road and drove to the front gate of the base -- the opening to the road to Kunsan City. A few Koreans were passing through the gate -- no Americans or ROKAF. I talked briefly to the guards -- they reported an uneventful posting to that point.

Before leaving the front gate, Wild drove up in a jeep. He reported that the pumping was still going on with no breaks in the line. He thought, if the situation continued, we would be done pumping in a few hours. He commented that the Koreans who were clustered along the pipe line were very docile -- apparently they had more respect for the authority of their own officials and the ROKAF than they did for Americans.

[*Those not familiar with the then scope of the theft and other problems in the ROK and the heavy-handed treatment of Korean nationals by the ROK police and military forces trying to maintain a semblance of law and order would not understand. In this environment, the U.S. military forces undertook to live by U.S. rules but it was very difficult and it was not unknown to have frustrated guards rough up repeat offenders. With knowledge of this, the U.S. State Department ordered that persons arrested would not be beaten. While this order may have cleared the conscience of far-away Washington bureaucrats, it solved nothing in the forward area where the rule might be followed to the letter -- meaning that no offender was roughed up "after he was arrested." As is so often the case, the local commanders were left with the need to grab the blade of a two-edged sword without getting cut.*]

Departing the front gate, I heard several fighters taking off. I assumed that the ROKAF commander had decided to evacuate his aircraft.

By the time we got back to headquarters, it was past noon and I asked Sergeant Young if he would mind picking up a snack of some kind for me from the Officers Club. By now, the rain was increasing.

The stack of paper in my "IN" basket was quite large and I decided to work at it. Most of it was routine. One message had come in from General Joyce at Osan stating that he wanted me to come to Osan for a staff meeting on the coming Wednesday. That would mean a flight to Osan either by the C-47 or the L-20. I wanted to get a flight off to Japan to get some food and made a note to talk to Akers to be sure that both aircraft would be in commission on the coming Wednesday -- I would use the L-20 to go to Osan.

Sergeant Young arrived with a sandwich and a coke. As I ate, I tried to figure out the sand bag problem. Something had to be done. I called Colonel Kincaid, the Director of Materiel at Osan. The story was as told to me -- they held no extra stock and it was doubted that any new stock of bags would arrive in the near future. Kincaid and I were in agreement that this was one hell of a situation.

To get sand bags, I thought of contacting the Army depot at Inchon but decided against it. Finally, I concluded that there ought to be a stock of bags somewhere in Japan and I started calling air bases there. Finally, I found a base commanded by an old friend that had a good supply of sand bags and he was willing to share them if I would give him a requisition. However, I would have to provide for the transport of the bags. The answer came easy -- as soon as the current typhoon had passed, I would make two trips to Japan -- one for sand bags and one for food. If I scheduled the first trip to pick up the sand bags and dropped off the meat purchase chap on that trip, I could then return for the food on a second trip. That would give the meat purchase chap time to get his work done -- and, in that this would be his first trip, I knew it would take time -- once he got to know the supplier in Japan, things would go much faster.

Studying my calendar, I penciled in a one day trip to Japan on the coming Tuesday with a follow-on trip for the coming Friday. This would give me the option of using the C-47 or the L-20 for the Wednesday trip to Osan for General Joyce's staff meeting. In that the loads out of Japan would be well within gross weight for the Gooney Bird, I could use the seating capacity to handle some passenger movement to Japan with a drop off on the Tuesday and a pick up on the Friday. Undoubtedly, there were some deserving persons who could use an R&R break. But, how they would be selected would be a problem. I decided that I would pass that problem to Jones -- he seemed to enjoy the tasks and authority I passed to him and he was doing better with each passing day.

**My sandwich eaten, I realized that I needed a haircut. I had seen a building with a barber pole and Sergeant Young confirmed that it was the one and only barber shop on the base.**

**En route to the barber shop, I noted that the men were working as best one could expect to get loose materials picked up. Looking in one barracks, I could see that the men had stacked items on tables, chairs and beds in anticipation of a possible flood. I worried about the wind coming in but I knew that was all I could do -- worry.**

**As I entered the barber shop, I saw the C-47 and the L-20 taking off -- I wondered where Akers had decided to take them? I had not heard any of the F-100s taking off and decided that I would check on that after getting a hair cut.**

**The hair cut was a new experience. The barber was a Korean. The cutting over, the barber asked if I wanted a shampoo. I agreed -- partly to learn what might happen. There was a small, discolored sink in the barber shop -- at one time it had been white porcelain -- but no spray nozzle. To substitute for that, the barber filled a Number 8 can with water and poured from it. And then I learned that, with the hair cut, one literally got a body massage -- head, neck, back, front and arms. It felt good and I left the barber shop feeling relaxed.**

**On the way back to headquarters, I passed the base PX and stepped inside. Immediately, a Korean civilian bowed and introduced himself stating that he was "the manager." The array of products in the exchange was extremely limited -- little more than the very basics and not enough of that. There was no toilet paper -- the manager stated that it sold out as soon as received. There was no radio available and I learned that the radios the men owned that had been blaring every night were purchased by them in Japan -- mostly from the Japanese exchanges. But the Air Force exchanges in Japan and Korea were run by Fifth Air Force -- why could the Japanese exchanges carry such items but they were not available at Kunsan? The manager did not know. I asked the manager about purchasing a tape recorder and, while he had none at the time, he stated he would get and hold one for me. I left the exchange concluding that it was really inadequate in consideration of the number of Americans being served and the range of items I saw on the shelves. Something was wrong, but I did not know what.**

**By the time I got back to the headquarters, the rain was coming down rather heavily and the wind had begun to pick up. I asked Jones to get Sergeant Butler to give me a weather update and then called Major Turnbull. He told me that he had checked with his home base**

**and they told him to ride the typhoon out in place. He said that they had "neated up" the alert area, had reinforced the tie down of the fighters and had placed spoilers on the wings. I was worried but I knew that I could not order the F-100s out.**

**Sergeant Butler's news was both good and bad. According to the last weather data that had come in, it looked as if the wind in the typhoon had decreased slightly. Further, with evening coming on and the temperature dropping, he thought the wind would hold at the decreased level last reported or might even decrease further. The rain, however, was wide spread and quite heavy. He estimated we might get in the vicinity of six to eight or more inches before the storm passed over. And then he gave me the bad news -- another typhoon had been spotted in the Pacific and was headed on the same path as the one that was about to hit us.**

**Jones had stayed during Sergeant Butler's weather briefing and I asked him if Davidson had returned -- he had not. As I sat stewing over that information, Akers came in. He seemed pleased at the preparations he had supervised. "It isn't all that great but it's the best we could in the circumstances. I shifted the C-47 and the L-20 to Kimpo. The ROKAF Eighty-Sixes also went to Kimpo. The fuel pumping is done and the Osan helicopter has left."**

**Akers had barely finished when both Peterson and Wild showed up -- I was surprised to see that they were both carrying forty-fives. Their report was good. The pumping was completed without a single break in the line. Apparently the situation was a little wild, literally a free for all, when the fuel flow was cut off and the Koreans began scavenging the residual fuel. It was a hell of a solution but it was a solution. Now I had to sweat out word of my action reaching the Wing Commander -- and a possible court-martial.**

**Night was beginning to fall. Outside, the rainfall was increasing. "Let's go get a bite to eat and get ready for the big blow," I suggested. "From here on, I think we will simply be in a hunker-down position. Jones, we haven't discussed this but, until this blow is over, double the headquarters duty staff and be sure they have a weapons carrier available in case they have to move around."**

**We were leaving for the Officers Club when Lieutenant William Short, he carried the nickname of "Short Circuit," came in -- he was the Deputy Communications Officer -- Deputy to Major Benson.**

**"Sir, our communications are down."**

**"All of them?" I asked.**

"Everything except the MARS station. Either the land lines are shorted out with the water or they may have been cut?"

"What about the nuclear alert unit?"

"They still are in communication with their home base and Fifth Air Force. Their lines run separate from ours."

Land lines cut! What is the first thing one seeks to do before an operation against a target? It is to cut off communications!

"How often do we lose communications to the outside world?"

"It's rather regular, sir. I expect that Osan has already figured out that we are not on line and they are tracing from their end. I will get a vehicle and run a line check from here. I will run a check through the alert unit to Fifth Air Force and back to Osan to be certain that we are proceeding on the same course of action. What usually happens is that the Koreans decide to cut out a piece of line either to sell it as scrap metal or to use it for rope to tie down something on their A-Frames or trucks."

"When you do a line check, do your men carry weapons?"

"No sir."

"Well, from now on, I want them to be armed. And," I turned to address Wild, "Wild, is it possible for you to send an Air Policeman, someone who knows something about rules of engagement and stuff like that, to accompany the communications repair team?"

"I can do it, but every man I send out means one less man for me to work with on security here. And," he added, "what the blazes are our rules of engagement?"

"Send a man out and let's figure out the local security problem and formal rules of engagement later."

"Yes sir."

Steadily, my opinion of Wild was improving. I could not put my finger on it but I had come to discount the earlier Enlisted Club event as some sort of anomaly. Perhaps there was some background that I did not know?

We went to the Officers Club for dinner but with a short stop at the bar before we sat down to eat. We toasted the in-coming typhoon. My diarrhea was definitely gone -- I was beginning to feel like a human being again but the feeling would be short-lived.

With dinner over, my mind again turned to the troubled subject of base defense. I still had not had the opportunity to examine what the plan set forth but I was worried about something else. No generally available plan, I knew, would normally contain negative thoughts -- such as retreat. But I also knew that such a possibility was not outside

**the bounds of the possible. And I had examined the Korean road maps and knew that any evacuation of Kunsan Air Base had to proceed via Kunsan City and then southward -- possibly to the southern coast to Yosu or across to Pusan. Air evacuation was just not realistically in the cards. Just possibly, some air evacuation might come forth via Chonju or some airfield to the south but that seemed remote considering all that might transpire in the event the UNC line deteriorated. So how could I conduct an evacuation if that became a necessity?**

**Mentally, I added up the ground transport available -- it was hardly adequate for the assigned personnel let alone rations and other support material -- and I knew that, in such event, there would be a lot of "hanger-oners" -- Koreans, casual foreigners, UN types, religious persons, etc. I tried to calculate the fuel consumption to the south coast and relate it to the number of fuel trucks we had available. The answer was not comforting.**

**And then my thoughts turned to the matter of destruction of the nuclears and other material at Kunsan Air Base -- material that could not be evacuated. Was there a Fifth Air Force plan -- any plan?**

***[A fall back/retreat scenario is not an ordinary planning routine. One plans for success -- not failure. Still, an astute planner will envisage the down side of operations. When assigned to U.S. EUCOM, one of my early tasks was, along with three other field grade officers of the other Services, to develop a unilateral plan for the defense of Europe. The bottom line was that, short of a nuclear exchange, there was not enough military force then available to defend Europe against a vigorous Soviet attack -- the best that could be orchestrated was an orderly withdrawal in the direction of Spain with a defense on the line of the Pyrenees. Several things emerged from that conclusion one of which dealt with the handling of the American civilian population in Germany and other places. For them, rules were set forth covering emergency evacuation supplies to be maintained by each person to include, if they owned a vehicle, sufficient stored fuel to reach Paris -- preferably Spain. In my own case, I had a built-in 40-gallon reserve tank in the boot of my Oldsmobile 98 convertible. Unfortunately, I knew that, in a military emergency, I would never use that vehicle. The plan was that, in such an emergency, all civilian type vehicles owned by military personnel would be turned into a common depot and the prevailing joke was that, as the military went to the combat front in six-by-sixes, they would pass the civilian population riding in the other direction in their relinquished personal vehicles. Such is war!]***

*Beyond the hill at the end of the runway, shielded by the hill, was a Korean fishing village. Here it is shown with the tide out and several of the fishing fleet resting on the mud bank. Dimly, in the distance, are some off-shore islands.*

*A Korean farmer walks a water wheel, pumping water from one rice paddy to another.*

# DAY SEVEN -- A SUNDAY AND TYPHOON NUMBER ONE

The typhoon had a name and, since it was the first of the season, I know it began with an "A." But, for me, it was simply "Typhoon Number One."

After dinner and throughout the night, on almost an hourly basis, I called either the headquarters Duty Officer or the Air Police Operations Center for a status report. The rain was coming down in "buckets" but the wind, while strong and periodically gusting, had not matured to the full force of a leveling typhoon.

Periodically, I tried to place a call to the Osan Command Center but the lines remained out. I tried to use the MARS Station but the weather was sufficiently bad that they could not get through on high frequency. I was, for all intent, "alone and far from home."

Little sleep was to be had during the night hours and, when not worrying about the typhoon, my mind turned to contemplate the vulnerability of the base to infiltration, its proximity to the enemy, the lack of a good defense capability, the communications problem, the shortage of men and materiel, my perceived problems with the Wing Commander at Osan but, most of all, the nuclear storage. Was the situation I perceived really real? Between the nuclear alert aircraft and the weapons in storage, just how many weapons did I have to worry about? I had not been furnished an inventory and I had not made one. From the beginning, that time when I met the ex-Commander of Kunsan Air Base in Japan, the inference was that all matters relating to the nuclear weapons was somehow vested in Fifth Air Force -- allegedly, it was not one of my worries. But I was worried for, certainly, there was no one visible who seemed to be worrying. And then there was the issue of control -- who had signed for these weapons? I had not! Was it that Major Turnbull, the temporary office-in-charge at the alert area, was the nuclear signatory -- the person in charge? My discussion with him did not indicate this.

The more I thought about the nuclear issues, the more were the questions that came to mind.

Why did I not have a nuclear team on the base -- the excuse that weapons needing maintenance were simply lifted out did not seem to be

**a correct answer? And why were the extensive regulations that covered every single nuclear storage and other situation of which I knew seemingly not implemented at Kunsan Air Base -- to date, I had not even seen a file of such regulations? And why, of the inspection reports I had reviewed, was there no inspection report by the nuclear teams that came out of the Air Force IG and the Atomic Weapons establishment? Was the nuclear destruct team on the base really my Major Peterson who was to act on some unauthenticated orders? Was it, as I had suspected a few days prior, that the things we were told were nuclear weapons were not weapons -- only "Silver Bullets?" And, if that was the case, what the hell was going on?**

**With that thought I came full circle to my earlier consideration of the possibility that the Kunsan operation was no more than a clever cover and deception operation or, worse, we had been set up as bait. But bait for whom? The only answer that I could come up with was Communist China. Communist China was hell bent on getting a nuclear capability and, after a cut off of Soviet assistance, having a hard time getting there. What a step forward it would be if Communist China, sitting right across the Yellow Sea from Kunsan, could be enticed to slip across and swipe a nuclear weapon or even a major nuclear arsenal and, perhaps, make it look like the operation had been conducted by North Korea! And what a coup for some if the whole operation, if conducted, would net for Communist China no nuclear weapons -- only Silver Bullets!**

**And then I reviewed my thoughts about the scenario that might have been set up to reinforce the ROK perceptions by way of a visible nuclear threat to North Korea. The standing policy was neither to confirm or deny the presence of nuclear weapons in any location but a person would have to be blind not to recognize where a nuclear capability existed. If anyone was fooled on that subject, it was only the American and foreign public -- not the military forces facing the United States.**

**[*About a year later, a briefer in PACAF casually discussed the readiness of the command to conduct nuclear operations. Some press persons in the audience picked up on the briefing and filed a story keyed to a headline: PACIFIC AIR FORCES MOVING TO NUCLEAR WAR. Almost immediately, the telephones to PACAF were jammed. Some authorities in Washington, D.C. demanded to know who had "leaked" the story. General Rosie O'Donnell's (CINCPACAF) reaction was in the "so*

**

*what" category. "Our enemies know where we have nuclear weapons and, should they not, they ought to. It will make them pay attention."*]

**It could be that the JCS viewed the nuclear alert aircraft, be the weapons real or imagined, as key in the game of threat and counter-threat. And it might be reasoned that it was too dangerous to allow persons such as myself to know the truth -- again, the existence of special security clearances and "need to know" restrictions. What a coup for someone to place a threat in South Korea that the North Koreans would view as valid when it was only a hollow shell! In terms of "cost effectiveness," the idea of a few false weapons and some aircraft standing alert was a bit "off the wall," but not without reason in consideration of other scenarios I knew were on-going.**

**Struggling with the imponderables of the situation, I kept thinking how great it would be to be able to return to the Pentagon and view the JCS papers relating to the situation. All nuclear weapons were tightly controlled from the JCS and a look at those papers would tell me instantly if the weapons at Kunsan Air Base were real or imagined. But, then again, they might not for, if a cover and deception plan had been properly orchestrated, those papers would not contain the right answer -- only an answer that supported the cover and deception plan. To get beyond such papers, I knew I needed clearances that I did not have.**

**Soon, I found myself wondering if the scheme that ran through my mind was known by the President -- the man who ultimately held the nuclear trigger?**

**Most of the night I just sat in a chair thinking -- now and then I might have dozed off for a few minutes. Periodically, I repeated to myself that "mine was not to understand why, mine was but to do or die" -- but that solved nothing.**

**And then I reflected on how simple it would have been had I been named a SAC Wing Commander having a detailed set of operational objectives to achieve -- simple things such as aircraft in commission, training programs, assigned targets, flying hours to achieve, maneuvers, etc. And with all of those items supported by good logistics, established routines and more.**

**As I reflected on this comparison, I recalled the SAC officer who reported to my office in the Pentagon and my giving him a problem to solve. "What am I supposed to do with this?" he had asked. "Think," I answered. "But in SAC we had everything spelled out for us," he replied. "So now you have to think," was my answer.**

**And "thinking" was consuming me. Unfortunately, my thinking was not producing the best of answers.**

**By morning, I had decided that, real or false and whether or not the weapons at Kunsan Air Base were my responsibility or that of Fifth Air Force, no one was going to have a picnic if they tried to get at them. But how would I carry out my decision? And would I get any support from outside sources? I thought not. Just as I was, at the moment, all alone, cut off from the outside world, I felt I would be all alone on this one.**

**With the first of the next day's light filtering through the windows, I had cataloged in my mind several actions:**

**1. I was going to get a U.S. Marine Lt. Colonel, one who had passed through the base on a routine proficiency flight and with whom I had struck up a friendship, to revisit. While, except for the U.S. Embassy guard, there was no Marine unit in Korea, he had been assigned to the CINCUNC staff in the war plans office. I would talk to him about base defense -- get his ideas as to what was needed and how he would play the game if he were in my shoes. I had a great admiration of the Marine Corps and I felt he would give me the "straight skinny." I was not a ground officer but what I was looking at was a major ground defense situation. I needed help.**

**2. I would talk to the ROK Army Commander in the Kunsan area. What we needed was, as a minimum, some informal agreement on how we could cooperate in an emergency. In particular, I wanted to know how long it would take him to reinforce my base. Naturally, I could not reveal to that Commander the real basis of my worry. Thus, I would have to build my own cover and deception plan for that encounter -- and it would have to be plausible as I would suspect he would report the meeting upward in his command line. As I thought about that cover and deception plan, I concocted a scenario in which the Chicoms would traverse the Yellow Sea and make a landing at Kunsan. Whether it was realistic or not, it would make for a lively discussion.**

**3. To get on more friendly and cooperative terms with the ROK Army Commander in the area, I thought about some special support -- the Oriental gift routine. For that purpose, as I knew the ROK Army Commander had no aircraft, I thought I would offer him some select support flights in the L-20 or the C-47 -- such as to a hunting ground -- Cheju-Do came to mind but Kangnung seemed to be an easier spot to reach without word of same reaching the Wing**

Commander -- I wondered when the birds migrated south. Perhaps there were hunting areas in Korea of which I had no knowledge?

4. Then, locally, I had to find a way to integrate the ROKAF unit into my defense scheme. I had already learned that there was no such relationship established between our units -- we just lived on the same base and that was about it. Further, I had come to learn that some of our "slicky" problems appeared to be the result of actions by the members of that unit. Whether that was the action of individuals or that of the unit, I did not know. I was reminded of the ex-Commander's words about the use of the ROKAF helicopter for slicky operations, black market and more. And I had already learned that they did not file flight plans in my operations system -- they did it all in their system. And then I recalled that the front gate was manned exclusively by my men -- what check did they make of the ROKAF going and coming? I had to find out."

5. I had to meet and know the Mayor of Kunsan. I had an inquiry that had reached me by way of Captain Wild that the Mayor wanted to have a welcoming dinner for me and I thought I would accept. I knew that protocol would embody a return event at the air base but could not come up with a plan for that. Perhaps I could fulfill that protocol need with the L-20 or C47 in the same manner as I was planning for the ROK Army Commander? Perhaps a case of booze sent to the Mayor would do the trick? I wondered if I had any protocol money to work with -- no one had mentioned it -- as soon as possible, I would have to inquire about that -- I hated myself for having failed to determine this before this date.

Suddenly, my thoughts were shattered by the morning alarm -- for a few minutes I had dozed off. Outside, the rain was falling in torrents -- sometimes coming straight down but -- when a blow of wind struck, slashing vertically at the windows -- some water was beginning to find a way through.

With a poncho on, I battled the wind and the rain, got in the staff car and drove to the Officers Club. Many of the staff and others were already there -- it looked almost like a command center operation. Quickly, I was briefed that, so far, things were going well -- a lot of water but no serious flooding -- some wind with very strong gusts but nothing of the knock-down-buildings nature. I noticed that Sergeant Butler was at the Officers Club, and, when I asked him about the weather, I discovered that he had stand-up charts at hand. Procedurally, at least, things seemed to be looking up.

I asked Butler to join me for breakfast and he seemed both pleased and honored. Akers and Wild made up the four at the table. There was no "officer" and "enlisted" element in what followed.

Sergeant Butler reviewed the weather. The communications with Osan had come on line just before his coming to brief me and the indication was that, as he had estimated, the wind had tempered somewhat. The rain forecast was still on the heavy side -- the estimate was now at least eight inches. But, considering the number of hours it was spread over, there seemed to be time for run off as opposed to flooding. Butler showed us some of his charts -- they were well done and informative. As we talked, however, there was a gust of wind that rattled the sheet metal roof of the Officers Club. It was disconcerting. A few roof leaks had already developed and pots had been placed to catch the dripping water.

We were about to leave the Officers Club for the headquarters, when I realized that it was Sunday. Jones was standing off to the side and I told him to tell the Chaplains that I recommended church service be postponed until later in the day and after we could determine what this typhoon would do. The last thing I needed was a church filled with men with the building collapsing.

Four hours later, it seemed that we would survive. By nightfall, the threat was over. We had some water on the base but the winds had not developed to the point that our structures were torn apart. I thanked God for little favors.

That evening, at the Officers Club, I noticed that the Chaplains were having dinner together -- Father Collins and Chaplain Johnson -- who I had learned was Presbyterian. I asked if I could join them and, immediately, Father Collins pulled an extra chair to the table.

I apologized to both of them for suggesting a rescheduling of Sunday services -- they both seemed to understand.

As I ate, I turned to the subject of morale and the impact of the Korean environment on the men -- I suggested that this was a subject we shared and asked for their thoughts.

"You're Protestant -- aren't you?" Father Collins asked. The way he asked the question seemed to place me in some subordinate echelon of humanity.

"I was raised German Lutheran but, as Commander, I will try to attend all religious services."

"Including Jewish services?"

"Yes."

"Then your support of religious commitments and ceremonies is a matter of protocol?"

"Does not the President of the United States attend services of many?" I asked.

Father Collins' face flushed. I decided to add some of my own personal philosophy.

"Look. Religion, all religions, serve a good end. I don't care what the religious belief is. I do know that a religious person is a better military person than a non-religious person. And, as a very practical matter, one set forth by a senior military person of our country, if something screws up, I hope the men pray to God rather than lynching the Commander. And, when it comes to prayer, how about both of you orchestrating some prayer that we don't have any more typhoons coming at us? Perhaps you can come up with a General Patton prayer?"

The Chaplains politely laughed. I doubted that either of them knew enough about military history to understand what I was saying.

"While we are on the subject of religious diversity, which one of you will brief me on the prevailing non-Christian religion in Korea? My historical knowledge needs some beefing up."

"I'll try," Chaplain Johnson replied.

"And, having attended a Sunday Protestant service, I note that there are Koreans who attend those on-base services. Which leads me to ask if either of you visit any Christian activities in Kunsan or other places, if there are any -- and, if not, why not? Certainly we all have a need to support good relations with the outside community."

"There is a Priest who operates south of here," Father Collins answered. "He was here all through the Korean War. I have an on-going relationship with him but I do not participate in his services -- he conducts them in Korean and I don't speak Korean. If you see a motorcycle on base, it will probably be him. He comes here about once a month. We keep him in booze and help him out in other ways."

*[I have to admit that the full of the story of the Catholic Priest who "operated south of Kunsan" was very troublesome. First, I had to wonder how he had managed to survive the invasion by the North Koreans -- why had they spared him when, in their drive south, they executed so many religious persons? Was there a special relationship? And, as a converse consideration, I had to wonder if he now had been accorded U.S. support in payment for serving as an information point for the U.S. or ROK counter intelligence efforts. Finally, the described*

***relationship between this Priest and my own Catholic Chaplain raised the issue of other intrigue. Could it be that the powers-to-be had recruited my Chaplain and the southern Priest as an information channel? Worse, with the apparent access to the base by the southern Priest, was there the possibility that he served as a conduit for information to the North Koreans? Suspicion is a terrible thing and, for some reason, I was uncomfortable with my Catholic Chaplain and worried by the relationship between he and the southern Priest.*]**

**Chaplain Johnson had nothing substantive to add and I thought it best not to pursue the Collins statement as I suspected I would find that the "other" support for the Priest would include fuel for his motor cycle and a whole lot more.**

**Regarding my question relating to the morale of the men and the idea of sharing thoughts -- it seemed to have vaporized. My guess was that each Chaplain had a different view of the situation "and never the twain shall meet."**

**In the conversation, I tried several times to bring the two Chaplains into the main stream of my command problems but failed. They each seemed to live in their own world and neither one was the real world I faced every day.**

**Because I believed that religious leadership could and should play an important part in the Kunsan situation, I had opened my staff meetings to that segment of the organization but I was to conclude that the Chaplain group desired no part of that responsibility. Already, I had found that Father Collins offered no comment during our staff meetings and no advice and counsel on significant issues. And I came to understand why, in other environments, the Chaplain community was not invited to participate in the day-to-day considerations of command. A formidable support I thought I had apparently was not there.**

**Nonetheless, I was determined to keep trying and suggested that, whichever Chaplain attended my morning staff meeting, he open the meeting with a short, non-denominational prayer. If this was an appropriate routine on The Hill in Washington, D.C., it ought to be appropriate in the headquarters of Kunsan Air Base.**

**Something told me that Father Collins did not like the idea.**

# DAY EIGHT -- A MONDAY

To my surprise, dawn revealed a brilliant sun although the air was terribly humid from the rain that came with Typhoon Number One.

At breakfast, Annie placed a jar of strawberry jam on the table and announced that the kitchen had some ham instead of the usual bacon or pork patties. It turned out to be canned ham and quite salty but still a welcome change from the otherwise monotonous menu. How these things arrived I did not know but I still did not feel up to asking. The coffee seemed even better than normal. And, with everyone feeling relieved that the typhoon had passed with no significant damage resulting, the mood was upbeat. Annie's comment: "Storm no big thing. Everybody much happy."

At the morning staff meeting, Davidson appeared. He made no apology, made no comment, nothing. It was as if his absence was quite routine.

Inwardly, I boiled. I had rehearsed many times how I would handle the situation but, suddenly, my plans fell into a hopper. I conducted the staff meeting as if everything was normal -- as if Davidson had never been absent from the Kunsan scene.

We did have a busy program for the staff meeting:

Butler's weather briefing told of the second typhoon now over the horizon.

Peterson reviewed the fuel pumping situation.

Benson talked about the problems of line breaks in the communications system -- apparently the Koreans had stolen some sections of wire about ten miles northeast of the base.

Wild discussed the problems of the guards during the storm. Obviously, standing guard in the middle of a typhoon was no joy.

Akers told about the preparations for the typhoon and the innovative ways some problems were solved.

Jones reviewed how the Duty Officer situation had worked out -- he recommended that a weapons carrier be placed at the disposal of the duty personnel as a norm. I agreed but Peterson indicated it may be a problem as we were really short of vehicles. I reminded Peterson that we were not talking about putting miles on the

**vehicle -- only having it available and it could be otherwise sitting in the motor pool. "It can just as well sit outside the headquarters building where it can be useful if there is an emergency."**

**Jones also said that he had managed to get the G.I. turn table to run but that the reveille and retreat recording was well scratched. I asked him to use it anyhow and, tomorrow, to try out the system. In the meantime, I told him to find a new record.**

**While we were on the subject, I asked Polk if he could find some pipe and, by successively inserting smaller pipes into larger pipes and doing some welding, build us a metal flag pole -- something that was straight -- and place it in a concrete support base. I suggested we have a burning of the crooked, tree trunk flag pole that was in place in front of the headquarters. Everyone laughed and there was a suggestion that we have a "flag pole" barbecue.**

**With the thought of "barbecue" on the table, I asked: Why not? Could we have an officer/enlisted picnic? There were many glances around the room. Sergeants Young and Butler were in the room and, out of politeness, no officer/enlisted status problem, if there was one, emerged. Again, I asked: Why not? The conclusion was that a picnic would be organized within the next two or three weeks. Friday was the day of the week selected. There was a discussion of the type of drinks to be served at the picnic but no decision was then made. A committee of officers and enlisted persons was established. I promised that, if they worked fast and needed some stuff from Japan, I would try to get it. My promises were getting me ever deeper in trouble but I could see that the mood of the officers and men was changing.**

**And then we got down to some serious business.**

**I asked Peterson about the alleged tractor and draw mower. It turned out that we did have a tractor but most of the teeth were broken on the draw mower and it would no longer cut. I explored the possibility of manufacturing new teeth but I was assured that we did not have the right metal to do it. And, so, I was left with a problem. In the meantime, the idiot stick program was beginning to produce some results.**

**Disturbed about the "broken teeth on the mower" problem, we discussed the causes and it turned out to be "all the stuff that was still on the field from the Korean War." To solve that, we discussed a pick up campaign which, I was informed, had been tried in the past "but a lot of stuff was still out there." The final solution that emerged was that we would set up a Saturday or Sunday afternoon as a pick up campaign with some trucks and about a dozen volunteers per**

truck. For a reward, I promised to set up the winner team, the one that collected the most junk, with an over-and-back R&R trip to Japan when our C-47 did a supply run. It would only be a one or two day trip but it was better than none at all. They would get one day charged as leave and with orders that would get them billets. Jones was told to cut the orders for the winners -- I would sign them. No funding was to be authorized -- only transportation. If there was more than a dozen volunteers per truck, they would have to choose membership by lot. Officers were not allowed to be team members. Because we had only a limited number of six-by-six trucks for the team pick ups, it was determined that we would have no more than ten teams competing. And, as to ground rules, it was stated that the landing craft, the sheep's foot compactor, the F-100s, my staff car, the ROKAF F-86s and neither conventional nor nuclear bombs were on-limits for this exercise. There was a laugh all around the room. I could tell that the mood was not only relaxed but cooperation was beginning to replace lethargy and rebellion.

As the staff meeting wound down, Jones placed a sheet of paper on my desk. On it was a set of numbers. Jones was grinning from ear to ear.

"I figured it out, sir. Now that I know how to do it, I'll get the combinations changed on the other safes. I hope the numbers I picked are O.K.? Who do you want to have access to your safe?"

"How about yourself, naturally my Deputy, the Majors on the staff and Captains Wild and Pastiak. Put the combination in a sealed envelope in the Operations safe."

The staff meeting had closed on a high note. Officers and men were discussing problems and talking about solutions. But then I had to face the Davidson situation. I asked him to stay.

When we were alone, I asked Davidson about his health. I told him that I did not appreciate his departing the scene without talking to me and that I considered his action as tantamount to AWOL. I did not go into the issue of "fear of flying" as I could see that his hands had begun to shake. Finally, I asked him, if he were in my position, what he would do in reverse circumstances.

With every situation there is a story and I listened to that of Davidson. But, when he was through telling me of his life's problems, I repeated my question and told him that, as far as I was concerned, I had lost confidence in him.

Davidson ended up asking me if I would give him permission to look for another job in Korea. I agreed but told him that he had only

**the week to find a solution. After he left the office, I called the Director of Personnel at Osan and explained the situation. To my surprise, the Director stated that they had in-coming a Lt. Colonel who seemed to have his head screwed on tight and that he would assign him to me as a replacement. Further, he would issue orders transferring Davidson to the Osan Wing as a temporary solution.**

**[*I never knew what happened to Davidson. He was not the man for the job and, in a way, I felt sorry for him. Undoubtedly, he would have survived, perhaps been promoted, in other environments but, as was so often the case, the Korean environment was terrible for any who had what might be a border line tolerance to stress.*]**

**With the Davidson situation off my mind, I decided to attempt a partial cure of the grass problem and, with communications now on-line again, I called an old friend currently stationed in Japan -- he commanded an air transport unit.**

**"Jake, this is John Moench. I'm in Korea -- Kunsan Air Base. I'm the Commander over here and I need some help."**

**----------**

**"That's right. Kunsan Air Base in Korea."**

**----------**

**"No, I did not step on too many toes. At least, not yet."**

**----------**

**"Right. I need help. Can you purchase a civilian lawn mower for me in your vicinity -- something like a 24 inch or 30 inch rotary model -- four cycle? And can you get me a dozen blades to go with it?"**

**----------**

**"O.K. Whatever it costs. Just get it to me and, if you don't have anything coming this way, put it on a bomber. We do have some B-57 Canberras that land here now and then. I'll write a personal check to you as soon as I know what the bill is."**

**----------**

**"Yes, it's damn important and urgent. And thanks. Should you ever want to see what the *Riviera of Korea* looks like, take a trip over here. But don't plan to spend the night as we ain't got no beds."**

**[*About a year later, Kunsan Air Base would receive its first government purchased lawn mowers.*]**

As I hung up the telephone, I had a sense of special accomplishment. Hopefully, within the next few days, Kunsan Air Base would have its first lawn mower. And a lot of other good things were beginning to happen.

And then Peterson walked in.

"Sir, we have a lost convoy in trouble."

"And what the hell are you telling me?" I asked. "Has the convoy been ambushed?"

"No, not that. What has happened is that a supply convoy to Inchon got caught in the typhoon, hit a washed out bridge, took a detour on back roads and trails and got lost. In the process, they blew enough truck tires on the bad roads to now be dead in the water. They managed to get to a telephone in a city and get a call through to us. The problem is the city they told us they were near -- there are some six cities by the same name."

For a few minutes, I just held my head in my hands. How could all this be happening?

"Didn't the convoy carry spares and other equipment?"

"They carried some spare tires, some maintenance equipment and some maintenance personnel. As I understand the call, they simply used up all their tires."

"Can we drop them mounted spares -- do we have drop equipment -- parachutes?"

"Sir, we have done that in the past -- not with parachutes -- we just free fall the items. We have to hit pretty close to target -- but it can be done. On the rims and inflated, unless they land flat, the tires can bounce and roll to beat all hell but it can be done."

"Well, you and Akers plot out the locations of these same-city names and take the L-20 and find our convoy. I assume they have food, PX and other stuff on board and we need it. Get some tires ready to drop. When you get back, brief me on the result."

And then the telephone rang. It was a call from the Osan Operations Center. There was an aircraft down in the vicinity of Kunsan. They had approximate coordinates. I was to get an Air Police cordon around the crash site as soon as possible; my men were not to examine the wreckage; nor was I to inspect the wreckage. If there were any survivors, I was to care for them but, to the extent possible, keep them isolated from Americans and Koreans until they could be evacuated. There was to be no report on the crash and press coverage was to be avoided. No photos were to be taken. Shortly, I could expect a special team to arrive to take over and process the wreckage. Why

**the procedure? I was told that I did not possess the essential security clearance to be given the answer!**

**The words that I uttered in response are not here printable. I was already concerned about security clearances and here was now another issue. I was the senior Air Force officer in much of Korea, I had two installations under my command, I was supposedly sitting on a major nuclear installation but, somehow, I was not significant enough to know what was going on around me -- *I did not possess the essential clearances*! Could it be that I did not even have the clearances to know what was going on on my own base?**

***[Progressively, the military system, highly influenced by covert and intelligence operations, to include operations beyond the military sphere such as that of the CIA, has been dominated by a system of special clearances that transgress all command and control lines. An example in the general time frame of this illustrative account was the story revealed to me by a later staff officer. In this case, the staff officer was to brief the Chief of Staff of the Air Force but, to do so, the Vice chief of Staff had to be excused as he did not hold the necessary security clearances.***

***Without commenting directly on the Kunsan Air Base situation, some time later I found myself in the awkward situation wherein I discovered that one of my subordinate officers possessed a specially conferred clearance and instructions for a unique operation for which I was to have no knowledge. He even possessed his own security pad and a private safe. To put it bluntly, every time this officer was goofing off allegedly it was to perform his specially-assigned job.***

***For any commander or staff leader to act wisely and in conformance to any grand strategy, he needs a breadth of information. Lacking such information, the commander's or staff officer's actions may trigger undesired results. The "no win" dilemma is that of "action" or "inaction." And, all to often, a commander's or staff officer's action will be followed by a "why did you do that" criticism. On the other hand, a commander's or staff officer's inaction can well be followed by a "why didn't you do something" criticism.***

***My own philosophy was "to do something" and let the chips fall. However, unless asked, only selectively, would I inform the upper echelons of some of my activity -- most did not wish to know for, by knowing, they assumed responsibility.]***

# DAY EIGHT CLEAN UP

By early afternoon, the lost truck convoy had been located by the L-20 search and spare tires had been dropped. It was expected that the convoy would arrive at the base by evening.

The aircraft that crashed proved to be an unmarked B-57 Canberra that apparently was flown by Chinese Nationalist pilots. The supposition was that it had flown into Communist China territory on an intelligence gathering mission -- probably to obtain voice and electronic intercepts along with photo coverage -- the crew was dead. It appeared that the aircraft had been hit by aerial gunfire -- I suspected MIGs. The whole thing was very "hush hush" and everyone was briefed to forget anything and everything they might have seen or heard. I smelled a CIA "Mickey Mouse" operation but said nothing. I had too many other things to worry about.

On Kunsan Air Base, the winds of Typhoon Number One had blown a lot of stuff around but by nightfall most of it had been picked up -- damage to buildings consisted of a few sections of corrugated metal blown off roofs.

There was one problem. Apparently, in the height of the storm, a number of one hundred pound general purpose bombs had been stolen from the conventional bomb dump. How many were stolen was not clear but it was obvious that one of the bomb stacks was missing some units.

I talked to Wild about the loss of the bombs and he stated that this theft of conventional bombs did occur "once in a while" but not very often. A guard was stationed in the general area of the bombs but, with the rain, visibility had been minimal. Wild said that he had talked to the guard and was convinced that there was no collusion in regard to the theft. As to who stole the bombs, the immediate answer was the Korean fishermen.

"They take the bombs and use them as is or they melt out the insides and manufacture smaller explosives. The things are used for fishing. They know that an underwater explosion will stun the fish and they will come to the surface -- literally to be scooped up. I would expect that, in a day or two, you will hear the thump of explosions off shore."

"Don't these fishermen know the danger attending any fooling with explosives?" I asked.

"They've been doing it for so long that they are experts."

"Can't we raid the fishing village to get back the bombs?"

"Needles in a hay stack and what is our off-base authority?"

"You mean that we just sit here and take it?"

"That's about what it amounts to. If we went into the fishing village at the end of the runway, the odds are that the bombs may already be aboard fishing boats that are in port or at sea. And we don't even own a row boat on this base so how do we get to their fishing boats? It's a losing proposition."

"So what keeps them from stealing a nuclear weapon?"

"Colonel, I'll be damned if I know." Wild was most serious. "I understand that, up north, in the Matadors, a slicky gang penetrated the wires and actually got their hands on a nuclear -- and then left. This information may not be in the official record but my information is pretty solid. As to those of us here in Kunsan, you know what we have to protect the nuclears, the alert aircraft -- and everything else. If someone really wanted to get the stuff, I think that they could do it any night of the week. Worry about it -- I worry to beat all hell. But what can I do but the best I can do with what we have?"

Suddenly, Wild and I were on the same wave length. I knew there was little point in getting all over his butt. The problem was much larger. And, somehow, I had to find a way to deal with it.

As we talked, a staff car drove up to the headquarters building. Within minutes, I heard Jones let out a yell. It was a new staff car -- the one promised by Colonel Kincaid, the Director of Materiel at Osan. And it was a beauty -- a big, blue station wagon -- and brand new!

The new car was dirty from the drive down from Osan and I asked Jones to get it washed. He delighted at my giving him the keys -- I expected he would do some driving around the base. Within the hour, I had a new, shiny, blue station wagon in front of the headquarters building and the men were lining up to look at it -- soon photos were being taken. With the new staff vehicle, there came a sense of pride that their new Commander could get things done. I could see it in the faces of the men -- there were smiles, some "thumbs up," and more of the salutes were now freely given. I had started to succeed -- but I knew that I still had a long way to go and the number of days remaining before I transferred to Osan was diminishing.

After writing a letter home, I turned in early. But I was not to have a good night's sleep.

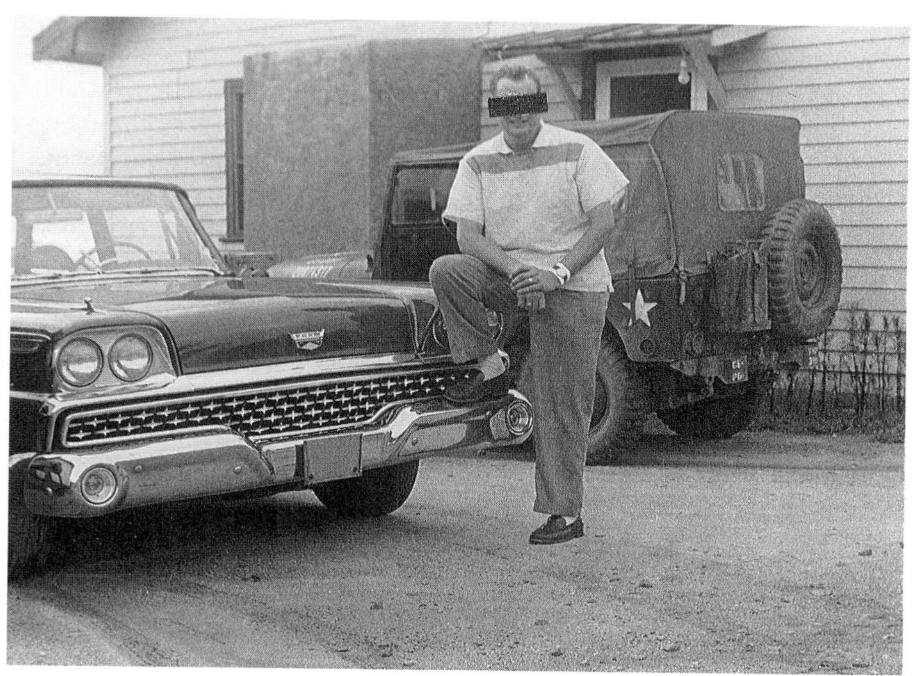

*The arrival of the new staff car was of such significance that many of the men had a photo taken with it. In the above photo, an individual in civilian clothes poses with the vehicle. The white band on the left wrist is paper napkin under the leather wrist watch band -- an attempt to reduce irritation from excessive sweating.*

I think it was about 0230 in the morning that the BRRRRRT of a full clip on automatic fire awakened me with a terrible start. This was not fire from "down the coast" -- it was close in fire that had to be right on my base.

I grabbed the telephone and asked for the Air Police Command Center. A duty Sergeant answered.

"I just heard the shots. What's up?"

"Don't know, sir," was the answer. "We heard them and we have the reaction team moving out to find out who fired."

"Just why in hell don't I have radios," I thought. "I'm sitting on a nuclear base, or I think I am sitting on a nuclear base, and surrounded by all sort of enemies from that of Communist China down to individual slickies, and I don't have a single radio for communication. This is all totally crazy."

I got up, dressed, opened the wooden box in the bedroom and retrieved a holster for my thirty-eight, and then drove down to the Air

**Police Command Center. Wild was there when I arrived. He was dressed in civilian attire -- probably a quick dress job -- he had slipped on a shoulder holster and a Thompson was cradled in his arm."**

**"So, Wild, what do you know?"**

**"Nothing yet, sir. The team is out. We only have one team. I wish we had more than one but that's the way the ball bounces."**

**As we talked, from the distance came three well-spaced shots.**

**"They've found the source of the shooting," Wild announced to me. "I think I can tell from the shots which post it came from. Do you want to go out with me to check it out?"**

**"My pleasure," I answered as I swung open my thirty-eight to check the chambers. Somehow, my appearing with a holstered thirty-eight made an impression on the Air Police who observed it -- one can detect such things. And my willingness to go out to the problem site instead of sitting back while others took risks was an additional plus mark for me.**

**Wild was correct as to the location of the problem. When we arrived at the spot, we learned that a relatively new recruit in the Air Police unit, one who had come from a disbanded communications unit but who was a country boy who had quickly learned to be dog handler, had stumbled onto over thirty slickies entering the base. This was more than what one person could handle. In desperation, his dog on full alert, he had fired a full clip into the air. The slickies, shocked by their discovery and not knowing whether the guard would, with the next clip, seek to kill them all and, further, fearful of the alerted German Shepherd that was tugging at his leash and ready to tear the slickies apart, were all willingly and fearfully spread-eagled. As to the new recruit, he was scared as all hell.**

**The Air Police reaction team took the slickies into custody but Wild assured me that, as soon as they were turned over to local authorities the following morning, they would be loose and probably coming back on base to steal.**

**"It's a never ending cycle," Wild stated. "We catch them; we turn them over to the local authorities; they buy their way out; then they undertake their prior slicky operation; we catch them again; and the cycle goes on and on. We have captured some of these guys so often that we know them by first names."**

**"So what can we do?" I asked.**

**"What I'd like to do is what the Turks do up on the DMZ. If they catch a slicky, they tie the S.O.B. to their front gate and let him dry out for a few days. And they don't have much trouble with the**

bastards. Us -- we treat them as if this was the United States and all that happens is that we get them back. Colonel, if you have a suggestion on how better to do our job, I'd like to hear it. My men are awfully tired of the situation."

I didn't have an acceptable answer to the slicky problem but took another route.

"What about the Airman who caught the slickies tonight -- what happens to him?"

"Nothing," Wild answered. "He did his job."

"And damn well, I would say."

"Yes. He must have been scared shitless."

"Well, I think that calls for something, don't you?"

"I don't understand."

"Well try. When a man does a poor job, I intend to kick butt. When a man does an especially good job, I want the base and others to know it. Write up that Airman for an Air Force Commendation ribbon and let me hand carry it to Osan. And, when we get it approved, I want to pin it on the Airman at a formation of your men. Brief Jones on this and tell him that when the Airman gets this commendation, I want photos and a story for Stars and Stripes and for the kid's home town newspaper. Which reminds me -- who does PR on this base?"

"No one that I know of, sir."

"Does the base have a camera?"

"I have a G.I. camera in the Air Police Center but I think that the only other cameras on the base are those that the individuals own."

So now I had something else about which to talk to Jones. With the broadening work I was laying on Jones, I decided he had to be named my Executive Officer.

As I watched the captured slicky boys being herded toward the main base area, hands clasped over their heads, I had to wonder about the base jail -- was it big enough?

"Can you stuff that many bodies in our jail?" I asked Wild.

"That and more," he replied. "But they may not be able to sit down. Haven't you seen our jail?"

"No. Where is it?"

"It's behind the Air Police Command Center. It's really a big box made out of PSP welded together. It can get hot as hell when the sun is out and equally cold in winter. Believe me, no one wants to get locked up in it for very long."

I decided that I needed to inspect my PSP jail house -- but it would have to be another day.

***Some fifty feet separated the nuclear weapon storage and this scene. Depicted here is a sort of fence -- in other areas there would only be a roll of concertina, if that. The fence shown, as good as it may appear, had holes in it large enough for persons to crawl through.***

***And then there were the surrounding hootches. It was found that in this one a group of prostitutes operated. The young boy was the salesman.***

# DAY NINE -- A TUESDAY

The morning staff meetings had already developed into a routine. And, with each day, the function had become better and the participation more professional. Persons were not only beginning to understand the operation of the base but they were beginning to better understand their own responsibilities.

I briefed the staff on the sand bag solution and asked Akers to get the C-47 airborne to Japan. Jones said he would handle the selection of persons for R&R in Japan. I told Akers that I wanted to take the L-20 to Osan the next day and get a checkout en route. I hoped to get back before nightfall but suggested to Akers that he pack a bag. I asked Major Trunbull to come with me to Osan and use the day to visit the command center and get acquainted with Division operations personnel. He was pleased at the invitation.

The weather briefing from Sergeant Butler indicated that, true to initial projections, Typhoon Number Two was following the same course as Typhoon Number One. But I was relaxed knowing that a plane load of sand bags would soon be on Kunsan Air Base.

Polk said that he had a new flag pole almost finished and that, if he could scrounge some gravel from the ROKAF, he would have it raised within the next day or so. Apparently, the ROKAF had a crusher they had received under the Military Assistance Program and, periodically, they worked a nearby hill. He said that he did have a pallet of bagged cement in his supply. I asked Polk about using some materials from the Army Engineer construction projects -- he advised that they were out of materials and all their concrete pour was on hold.

Progress on the clean up crews was advancing and Jones reported that they would probably set the date for the competition as the Saturday after that immediately coming. He noted that some teams were already scouting the area for the best clean up potential -- the areas with the most trash.

In driving to the headquarters, I had noted that ROKAF trucks were picking up the trash and garbage at the clubs and other locations. When I asked the staff what was going on, I was informed that the ROKAF had won the right to pick up this material and that the payment for that went into the base recreation fund. The staff further informed me that the ROKAF had a trash and garbage sorting facility

**right outside the main gate. "They never throw anything away," Peterson added.**

**As I reflected on that statement, I decided it was time for me to visit that facility and also take a look at the road into town and Kunsan City itself. I asked Wild to do the honors of driving me in. I suggested the new staff car but he urged me to use a weapons carrier. "The road into Kunsan is just bad news for a staff car," he said. "The potholes could break an axle and I am certain we have no replacement parts."**

**The morning staff meeting closed, Wild and I took off for Kunsan City. I noticed that Wild, as well as carrying a forty-five, had placed a carbine in the vehicle's gun rack.**

**The ROKAF trash and garbage sorting facility outside the main gate was really a rubbish heap on which some hundred Koreans, mostly women and children, picked and sorted. I got out of the weapons carrier to observe close up what was going on. Basically, all wood was cleaned and sorted by size and type; nails were removed, straightened and sorted; paper and cardboard was separated, stacked and bundled; metal cans went into another stack -- a lot of metal from beer and other cans ended up as materials for the Korean toy manufacturers; 55 gallon drums had the tops and bottoms chiseled out and the sides were flattened by pounding -- I was told that the metal was, among things, formed into bus bodies; cloth was piled into groups according to the material; glass was sorted by color, smashed and placed in piles -- it was a most efficient operation -- and, by the time the sorting was done, virtually nothing was left in the sense of true, discardable trash. As to garbage, I was stunned to see that select elements were apparently removed for human consumption. Observing the operation, I concluded that I would be a millionaire if I could just get one day's trash from New York City to this site.***

**But there was a serious aspect to the garbage situation.**

**"Who inspects the garbage?" I asked.**

**Wild looked at me in disbelief.**

**"What do you mean -- inspect the garbage -- it's garbage?"**

**I could see that I had to give a lesson.**

**"Did you ever hear of the worker in a German camp who daily wheeled out a load of manure. The guards kept probing the manure for hidden items but found nothing. The key was not the manure -- the worker was stealing wheelbarrows."**

---

* The sale of garbage was so significant that recorded history would tell of the number of barrels sold each month. (Source: HRA files.)

"We don't have that problem -- we inventory the barrels and we get them back."

"But what's inside the garbage? Garbage, just like manure, is a perfect cover for almost anything. I expect we lose a lot of flatware in the mess halls and clubs . . ."

"We do."

"Well, assign someone to check the garbage. You check the grass going off the base on the A-frames -- check what's under the garbage -- probe the barrels. You may be surprised what turns up."

Wild shook his head as he took in what I had said.

"Sometimes the obvious is not obvious," he concluded.

Proceeding toward Kunsan City, I could see our disassembled pipeline along the side of the road. The Koreans had done a thorough job. Only infrequently, were two or more sections still intact. I was surprised that, as far as I could determine, the Koreans had stolen no pipe or any of the connectors. I concluded that they did not want to discourage the movement of fuel by pipeline -- if movement was by railroad tank car they might lose the current source of product.*

Further up the road to Kunsan City, we passed through a small village and I asked Wild to stop. Leaning against one of the straw-roofed, mud houses were blocks of concrete about four feet square and all of a foot thick. I sensed that I was the only one who owned such concrete. On inspection and with little doubt, I was looking at sections of hardstand from Kunsan Air Base that had been carefully cut into squares and hauled off. I marveled at the skill and time involved in the work. Later, Captain Wild and I traveled around the old hardstand area and found where the concrete had been cut away. With each piece of concrete weighing well over a thousand pounds, we wondered how they had been taken off the base with no one observing it. We learned that the four-by-four concrete slabs were being sold for use in the floors of Korean houses.

Just beyond the village, we encountered a ROK Army road block and check point. Although we were waved through, I noticed that Wild had unsnapped the flap on his forty-five. His explanation: "In Korea, one never knows."

Still further up the road, Captain Wild pointed out where a Korean farmer had found a free source of electricity to run a water pump for his rice paddies -- this in lieu of the foot operated water wheel. What the farmer did was throw wires over the passing electric

---

* Within a year, to combat pilferage, the movement of fuel was switched to rail. (Source: HRA files.)

**feeder lines, thereby making a contact. Fortunately, the voltage in the feeder line was comparative to the winding on the motors running his water pump. "Sometimes the system backfires," Wild stated, "and the farmer gets electrocuted."**

**In some of the fields, cattle were pulling crude farm implements. Horses were not observed but some carts were being pulled by something between a horse and a shaggy-haired pony -- the carts were all constructed from the frames and axles of destroyed military vehicles. The tires of the carts were obviously military discards.**

**As we approached Kunsan City, the rice paddies gave way to gardens and I noticed that, in each garden, there was a sort of raised shack. When I asked Wild about these many shacks, the resultant answer was most intriguing and it provided some insight into the rampant slicky problem.**

**"In Korea," Wild stated, "there seems to be the philosophy that no one should possess more than he needs and can take care of. According to that philosophy, if you have more than you can protect and take care of, the next person who has the capacity to protect and take care of it has the right to take it from you. Thus, the person who has a garden is forced to build a watch tower to protect his planted crops. If he fails to build and man such a tower, his neighbors have the right to take his product."**

**When we arrived in the city, Wild showed me what were two "On Limits" facilities -- places were the men of the base could come. We did not enter -- we just drove by.**

**"The problem," Wild explained, "is that the sanitary conditions in the city are simply terrible -- no clean water, outside and open benjos, total filth almost everywhere. These two places have assured us that they will use paper cups. As to what they serve, I think it is mostly stuff stolen from us."**

**Observing that raw sewage flowed in shallow, slime-covered ditches alongside the road, I had to agree with Wild's assessment of the sanitary situation -- it was disgusting. Then, noting fly covered meat hanging in open-air roadside stalls, I asked Wild about refrigeration.**

**"Virtually none. The On-Limits clubs have managed to get some old household refrigerators but that is all. There is a small ice plant in Kunsan City but the water they use is contaminated. Ice is mostly used by the fish industry -- not by the civilians. We prohibit Americans from consuming ice off base -- or water -- or food."**

The roadside stalls reminded me of North Africa and the Middle East. And I recalled the time I became deathly ill in the back country of Turkey when I had been forced to eat at the fly-covered roadside stands.

"With no refrigeration, how do the Koreans manage food storage?" I asked.

"Mostly, they don't," Wild answered. "Rice is no problem. Vegetables are sold fresh -- or nearly fresh. The same goes for fish but some fish is salted and dried. The prime thing is kimchi. If you get a chance, take a look at the big, concrete kimchi pits on the ROK military installations. They usually have several pits working. But don't sample any of the military kimchi unless you want to get sick as hell."

I was storing more information on Korea and Kunsan City in my mind when we drove by the fuel storage tanks in the port area. Wild pointed out to me the tanks that belonged to us and the tanks that serviced Kunsan City. There was no military guard at the fuel tank area.

"We just can't cover everything," was Wild's answer to my question.

On the way back to Kunsan Air Base, Wild repeated that the Mayor of Kunsan wanted to invite me to a dinner -- a sort of get-acquainted dinner. In addition to me, the Mayor wished to have the ROKAF commander and some of his staff as well as some of my own staff as guests.

"Tell him that the third Saturday from now is acceptable," I said.

"Have you ever been to a Korean party?" Wild asked.

"No, but I have been to events in Europe, the Middle East and more. I can get along."

I noted that Wild did not argue -- he only smiled. I felt that there was something I did not know but I was not going to ask.

Before we reached the main gate at Kunsan Air Base, the temperature had risen considerably. And with the rise in temperature, the stench from the rice paddies rose appreciably. I was reminded of Bob Hope's comment: We know what it is, but what have they done to it?

On entering Kunsan Air Base, we passed a number of squatting Koreans cutting and stacking grass. "The grass cutters," Wild observed as we passed them.

"And probably all of them are slickies," I added.

"To a degree," Wild answered. "One thing they like are the colored reflector lights such as are used along the taxiways. We have given up trying to replace them. In the villages, they break up the glass and turn it into jewelry. They will put things such as that in the bundles of grass and it is hard to find the stuff."

"What do you know about spies and espionage technique?" I asked.

"Nothing, sir. Do you think some of these grass cutters are spies?"

"I can't say but let me tell you how our system can take a patriotic foreign person and turn him into an espionage agent for our country and without the person knowing it."

Obviously, Wild's interest was aroused.

"I'm listening, Colonel."

"O.K. I'll fuzz this story a bit so as not to reveal an operation that might still be on-going. I tell it to you to broaden your security perspective.

"In this hypothetical case, the U.S. needs information on an enemy foreign country but we can't get our agents into the territory -- their security is just too good. So we undertake to get information from persons of other nations who do have access to that enemy country. To get these foreign persons to work for us, we create a sub rosa operation in the country where we want to recruit our agents. The nature of our sub rosa operation, obviously manned by persons of the nationality of the country, is something local to that country -- it may be a wholesale supply house, a shipping company, anything that makes sense. Then our personnel, with the outward cloak of being locals, recruit individuals entering the target country but under the guise that these individuals are recruited by and reporting to their own country. The trick is to play on the loyalty of that person to his own country. But the true facts are that these individuals are reporting to us and not to their mother country."

"You mean that the North Koreans, the Soviets or the Chinese Commies could have people such as these grass cutters obtaining information for them with the thought that they were obtaining information for their own country -- the ROK?"

Wild shook his head as the information I gave him settled in.

"Christ, Colonel, how in hell could we get a handle on something like that?"

"Probably we can't. But we have people whose job it is to find out those things. I only hope that they know what they are doing."

"Do you think they do?"

"Sometimes I wonder."

Wild turned quiet. I knew I had raised his level of concern and I hoped that I had not revealed too much "special clearance" information to him. I thought about telling him about foreign moles in the U.S. but decided that his plate was already full.

I did considerable thinking on the way back to Kunsan Air Base. I was only into my job for a week and, already, my agenda overflowed. What would it be in two, three or four weeks? The thought was mind-boggling. Truly, I was "up to my ass in alligators" and I could well be missing the big things with so many small things bugging me. On the other hand, perhaps I was approaching the situation totally wrong. Perhaps I should take it easy, over-look all the things that bothered me, relax and enjoy life and let the problems pile up for the next commander to solve. Was that not what some of my predecessors must have done? And was that not what others in Korea might now be doing? Even those at Fifth Air Force?

Reflecting on the situation, I recalled the statement of a senior Air Force officer to "never become so objective you lose sight of the world in which you live." Had I lost sight of the world in which I was now living?

Stepping into the headquarters building, Tommy was waiting for me. He had a large photo in his hand.

"You'll enjoy this, Colonel. We found it in an old file. It's a photo of Base Operations when the 3rd Bombardment Wing was here. The sign in front says that K-8 is *The Best Base in Korea*."

I looked at the photo with mixed emotion. The Base Operations building was apparently new as the stucco finish had not yet been painted. Small trees had been planted in front of the building, there were walkways and a small fence to keep persons on them. Two proud, happy men stood in front of the Base Operations sign. What, in so few short years, had happened at Kunsan Air Base -- *The Best Base in Korea* -- the Riviera of Korea?

Laughingly, I suggested to Tommy that the base must have sunk a bit over the years as the sign in the photo cited the elevation as 33 feet while our flight charts listed it at 29 feet.

*K-8 Base Operations, 3rd Bombardment Wing photo on the following page.*
*Courtesy of Colonel H. R. White, USAF (Ret).*

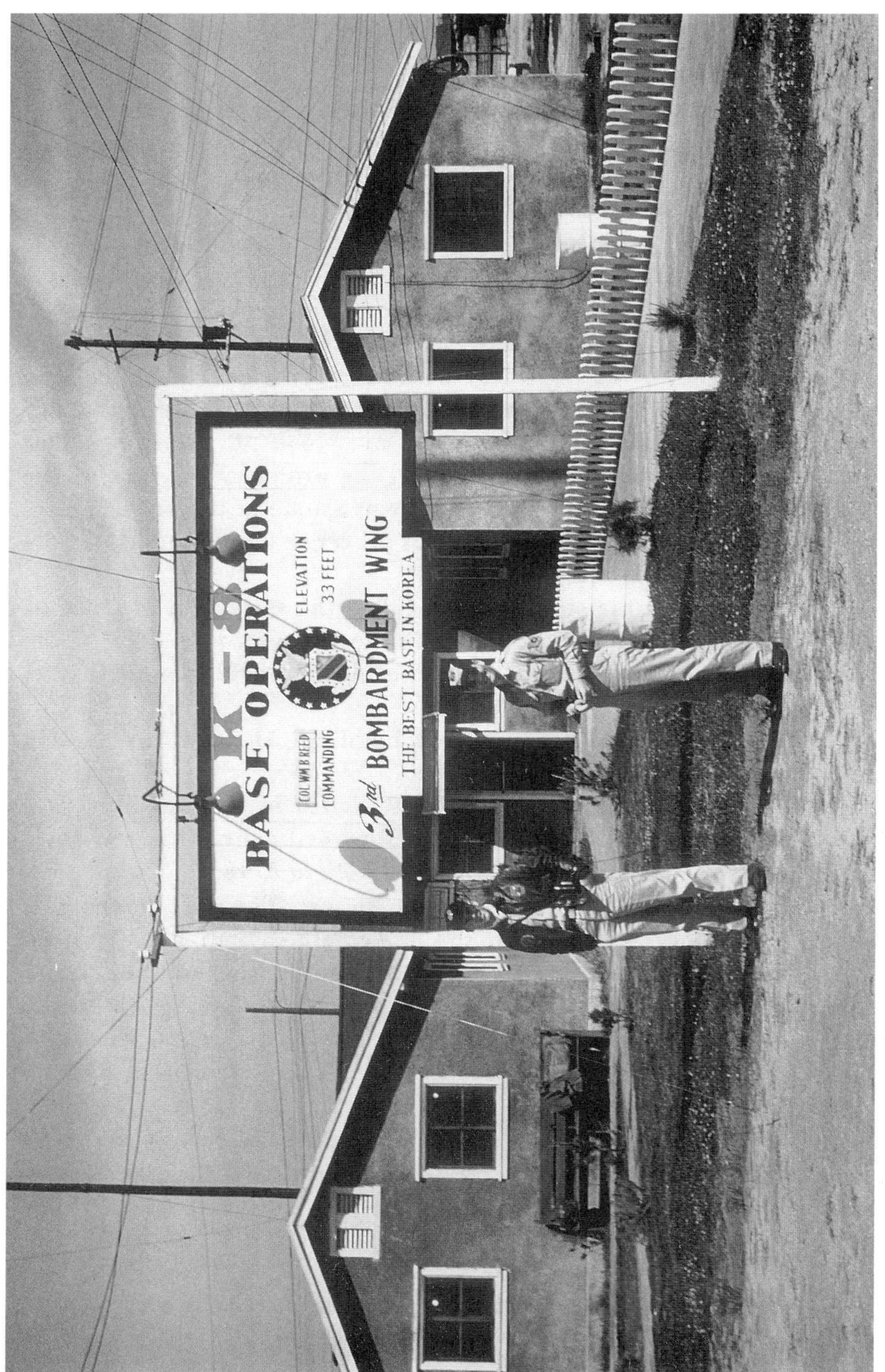
K-8
BASE OPERATIONS
COL WM B REED
COMMANDING
ELEVATION
33 FEET
3rd BOMBARDMENT WING
THE BEST BASE IN KOREA

# THE HOOTCH INSPECTION PLAN

No matter how I looked at it, Kunsan Air Base was a mess. And, probably, the biggest element of that mess was how the men lived. To date, I had not inspected any of the barracks and was reluctant to start -- it smacked too much of a boot camp -- or a cadet routine. Yet, this was a military organization -- or was supposed to be one.

But the officers were to set the example for the enlisted men. And I already had the sense that most of the officers quarters were dumps outfitted with little more than beds and 100 watt amplifiers. Further, as far as I could determine, much like the Waldorf Astoria, housekeeping was relegated to a mama-san. But if my mama-san could allow my quarters to develop into a trash heap -- as it was on the first day I arrived -- then many of the officers quarters might be the same kind of trash heap. I resolved that the coming Saturday I would inspect the officers quarters as a prelude to inspecting the enlisted quarters on a following Saturday. Once I had inspected the officers quarters, the pressure would be on the enlisted men to clean up their act -- at least that is what I hoped would happen.

On arriving at the headquarters, I called in Jones and told him of my plans. He was quite honest in his appraisal. "The officers won't like it," he stated.

"Probably not," was my reply, "but I'm going to do it. Your job is to get the word out and tell them the inspection will be standby starting at 0900 hours on Saturday. And, by the way, what is the status of Davidson?"

"He's departed the base, sir. He left on today's commuter run to Osan."

Jones had no additional comment and I did not ask for any. I thought, however, a point had been made that I would not stand for certain things among the officers.

"What's the status of the base briefing?"

"It's looking pretty good," Jones replied. "Would you like me to run it by you?"

"You mean that you would want to handle the whole thing -- including questions?"

"Yes sir."

More and more, I was coming to appreciate that I had a "Number One" Second Lieutenant working for me and, in the next few days, I was determined to name him Executive Officer.

"Bring it in."

The briefing was good. Obviously Jones and the staff had spent some midnight oil to get it done. It was organized so that an unclassified and a Top Secret briefing could be presented without altering the orderly sequence. Clearly, there was enough detail to satisfy most visitors, and the art work, although no more than grease pencil, was quite satisfactory. I posed some test questions to Tommy and, to my surprise, he had an answer for most of them -- and a good answer. Wherein Jones lacked a ready answer, we discussed the issue. Jones was eager to learn and the discussions proved to be quite lively.

"I've got to go to Osan tomorrow morning but, if I'm back in time for our staff meeting on Thursday, I would like you to present the briefing to our full staff. I think you and the staff did a great job." And, with that comment, I could see Jones standing straighter and taller.

"And now I've got something to ask you."

"Yes sir."

"Recall when we were out on the hill at the end of the runway and you pointed out the hootches on the field in which you said some of our men lived?"

"Yes sir."

"And you stated that there were men here who had stayed in Korea for some years and who actually had set up housekeeping?"

"Yes sir."

"Well, can you give me a list of all men who have extended beyond the one-year tour; and annotate those you believe to have set up housekeeping in the hootches. Do it quietly -- no one but you and I to know what you are doing. Understand?"

"Yes sir."

I didn't know where this information would take me but I suspected it would not be a happy ending. Only time would tell. "Going native" was not a new phenomena -- in fast moving combat, it did not occur but, when the men were based in an area over a period of time, it happened in Africa, in the Pacific islands, in Asia and more.

"Oh, and another thing. Regarding my trip to Osan tomorrow, how about you and Sergeant Young tagging along and beginning your scrounging work. I'll probably be up there the full day -- may stay over night. Pack a bag."

"Yes sir."

"And, while you're scrounging, visit the Osan Public Relations office. Tell them that I've appointed you as the Kunsan Public Relations Officer and that I ordered you to get a G.I. camera and film. I know Wild has one but we could use another one. If they won't sign one over to you on a permanent basis, tell them to loan one to you. Tell them that we have some significant events up-coming that you have been ordered to cover. And, if they balk, tell them that, as an alternative, I want one of their staff to be temporarily assigned to Kunsan. I'm sure that will bring them around."

I winked at Jones -- he understood the game plan.

"Oh yes, have Major Akers report."

"Yes sir."

When Akers arrived, I told him that, rather than flying with me to Osan, I would like him to stay at Kunsan and, with Davidson gone, act as Deputy Commander in my absence. "You never know what will come up," I told him, "and someone needs authority to act. We will be getting in a Lt. Colonel to replace Davidson but it may be a week or so before he arrives so have Jones write an order making you Acting Deputy Commander."

I hesitated for a few seconds to see if Akers had a comment about the departure of Davidson or his taking on the job of acting Deputy Commander but there was none so I continued.

"As to the L-20 checkout, who do you recommend take me up to Osan and do the check ride?"

"I have a Lieutenant Preston assigned to me who is a good pilot and he can do the job."

"O.K. Alert Preston that I want an 0900 take off -- we'll leave right after the morning staff meeting."

"Yes sir. And by the way, Colonel, the C-47 is back from Japan with a full load of sand bags -- the cabin was full -- bales of them." Akers smiled. Inwardly, I felt as if I had won again. But I was going to be wrong.

That evening, I wrote a long letter to Mary. I told her about the sand bag fiasco -- made a joke out of it. And I told her that I would be going to Osan in the morning for my first staff meeting at the Air Division. I then described Kunsan City to her.

The letter sealed and readied for mailing, I began making notes to guide my thoughts at the Osan staff meeting.

Working on my game plan for the Osan staff meeting, the thoughts I had while driving back from Kunsan city kept bugging me.

Was I pushing too hard? Should I adopt a more "lay back" attitude? How aggressive did General Joyce want me to be? And could I maintain good relations with the majority of the Air Division and Wing staff persons at Osan if they saw me only as a pushy trouble-maker?

I had always driven myself hard. For me, there was never a goal less than that of excellence. My view was that, unless "excellence" was held as the objective, even "mediocrity" would not be achieved. But I had moved into an environment wherein mediocrity was probably too high a goal and, certainly, excellence was hard to discover.

Again, those words of that seasoned Air Force commander haunted me:

*NEVER BECOME SO OBJECTIVE YOU LOSE SIGHT OF THE WORLD IN WHICH YOU LIVE.*

Was I losing sight of reality? Was I trying to win a game that could not be won?

I did not sleep well.

*Located next to the single railroad track that serviced Kunsan Air Base was this American's "home away from home." The argument that the men living in these ramshackle Korean style hootches on the base perimeter served as a forward defense element just did not wash. I viewed what I saw simply as men "going native" and I knew that I had to do something about the situation -- but what?*

# DAY TEN AT OSAN -- A WEDNESDAY

We were airborne at 0900 hours. Aboard the L-20, in addition to myself, there was Preston, Turnbull, Jones and Sergeant Young.

The L-20 was little more than a current version of the old UC-64 I had periodically flown in Europe in War Two. With narrow, conventional landing gear, I could see that it might have a tendency to ground loop in a cross wind. As I recall, the L-20 flew and stalled at just about the same speed. But it was a good work horse. Preston coached me through takeoff, in flight he reviewed the characteristics of the aircraft and, at Osan, I shot a pretty good landing.

Once on the ground at Osan, everyone scattered to do his own thing. There was a staff car waiting to take me to Division headquarters and I asked Turnbull to join me. At the headquarters, I introduced Turnbull to Barbara, General Joyce's secretary, and asked her to arrange for a visit by Turnbull to the command center and an introduction to some of the operations staff. She agreed.

In that I was early for the scheduled staff meeting, I used the time to visit with my Air War College friend, Colonel Jack Hubbard. My focus was the nuclear weapons at Kunsan. My concern was that, if they were not real but only dummy Silver Bullets, I would find that the whole thing might be covered by a security clearance that I did not possess. The question was how I could raise the subject without raising it, discuss it without discussing it -- and I had to face the fact that the operation, if it was what I thought it might be, may not even be known to the Director of Operations. I decided that the best approach to the problem was to discuss the matter of nuclear inspections.

"Jack, have you had a chance to review the inspection reports in the command -- especially those elements impacting on operations -- such as the nuclear items?"

"I have glanced at some of the inspection reports," he replied. "Why do you ask?"

"Well, I've gone over the recent inspection reports covering Kunsan Air Base and, for one thing, either the base was run a hell of a lot better than what I now find to be true or the inspectors were not worth a dime. What is the inspector staff here at Division?"

"You mean Kunsan got off clean on the inspections and you're complaining?"

"Not quite that. It's good not to have a bad inspection report and all the hassle that goes with it but I can see that the inspectors really missed or walked around some big things -- and it worries me some."

"Like what?"

"Well, for one thing, when I arrived at Kunsan I found that all my trucks were running on one tire -- and there was more. I can't imagine an inspector visiting a base and not writing up stuff like that. I've got some of these things fixed but the system worries me. Who are the Division inspectors?"

"We've got a Colonel in charge -- he's new just like the rest of us. I think he has one officer assigned to him. For the rest of the job, he has a few civil servants. I understand that the civil servant concept developed as a result of the one-year tour with Fifth Air Force concluding that more permanent local expertise and stability was needed so they hired some civilians to do the inspections. On the surface, it seems to make sense."

"Any idea what their security clearances are?"

"None whatsoever. That's not my job. I've got enough to do trying to run operations."

I figured that I had pursued the question as far as I could take it for the moment. Further, the time for the staff meeting was at hand. Jack led me to where the meeting would take place.

General Joyce was not in the meeting room when we arrived and that gave me time to meet the staff. Quickly I learned that much of the Division staff "double-hatted" as Wing staff -- this included Personnel and Materiel but not Operations. The Inspector appeared to work out of Division but I was not certain. Communications and Electronics was headed by a Lt. Colonel. Division Intelligence was handled by a junior officer and I could see that he was mostly a relay center -- apparently the real center for intelligence was Fifth Air Force -- and that told me what the problem was for I had already sensed that the Fifth Air Force focus embraced little in the way of Korean happenings.

At the gathering was a Lt. Colonel George Buck who was the Commander at Kimpo Air Base -- which I learned was little more than an air terminal operation. Colonel Al Jenkins, who had picked up the ROKAF Military Advisory Group job in Seoul, was present. His command line ran not to General Joyce but to the U.S. Ambassador in Seoul. But his support came from Wing.

By the time I had made the rounds, General Joyce and the Wing Commander, Colonel Musgrave, walked in. General Joyce asked if I had met everyone and I assured him that I had.

The meeting started with a run down on the weather. The briefer gave an overview of the recent typhoon and noted that there was a second one working its way in the direction of Korea. I was surprised that no one seemed concerned about the weather situation.

The next briefing covered intelligence with the information almost a parallel of what I had been exposed to at Fifth Air Force -- one could get about as much information by reading a newspaper.

With the weather and intelligence briefers excused from the room, General Joyce welcomed the new faces at the table and gave the assembly a pep talk. Basically, it centered on the big job to be done and his reliance on everyone to do his part. Then he went around the table asking each person to comment on his job, the problems, etc. Eventually, he came to me.

"General," I began, "I have now been at Kunsan for just over a week. It has been a revelation and I have to wonder if everyone here really wants to listen to my bleeding?"

"John, to the extent you are bleeding, we want to know it. Let's hear it. Of course, we can't do your work for you but to the extent it's our job here to get something done I want my staff and Wing to do it. So talk to us."

"General, it's hard for me really to know where to begin. Osan and Kunsan, while they are only about thirty minutes apart by air, are almost in two different worlds. Here at Osan, you have some reasonably good food -- at Kunsan we have lousy food. Until, on my last visit here, I obtained assistance from Colonel Kincaid, the Kunsan trucks were all running on one tire. When I arrived at Kunsan, they didn't even have a flag to fly -- now one is flying. I'm trying to get things fixed at Kunsan as fast as I can but I know I shall need assistance. And, in getting things fixed, I may take some shortcuts that will disturb some persons."

"You won't disturb me," General Joyce interjected with a big friendly smile on his face. I noted that the Wing Commander winced at that response. I continued.

"There's no need for me to hang up a lot of dirty linen at this meeting but, before I return to Kunsan tonight, or tomorrow, I will be talking to your staff. Hopefully, the staff will have answers to some of my problems."

I sat down and studied the faces at the table. I could see that each person was wondering what I would raise privately with them and each was moving in the direction of covering his own butt. It was going to be an interesting day. General Joyce now took the floor.

"John, before you leave for Kunsan, stop by my office and tell me how things went. And, by the way, I plan to be down to your base on this coming Monday. I'm going to take an orientation swing through all the Air Force bases and facilities in Korea. I won't be able to spend a lot of time. Figure out a routine for my staff and me -- something that will cover about two hours."

"Yes sir." Privately, I was disturbed. Two hours was hardly enough time to get at the real problems -- but it was a start.

Those in the room rose as General Joyce prepared to leave. The Wing Commander followed him out. Then, suddenly, a few in the room turned on me.

"What the hell are your trying to do, put us on report," one said.

"If you have some gripes about something, why don't you come directly to me instead of going to General Joyce," another commented.

I knew that I had screwed up the routine. Now the problem was going to be whether I could survive in the atmosphere I had created.

My first stop was with the Director of Personnel. I really had nothing to unload on him other than the general personnel shortage situation which we both understood. I asked him about Lt. Colonel Davidson and he told me that, in light of the time he had already spent in Korea, he had decided to move him back to the U.S. He had become aware of Davidson's Seoul apartment and it seemed that a quick move to the U.S. was the best solution to break that up. As to his drinking, the Director of Personnel hoped that, as a result of the change, it might be solved. "If not, the Air Force has a problem to handle but it can be handled better back in the States than over here." I agreed.

My next stop was with the Director of Materiel, Colonel Kincaid. I decided that I would not pursue the war reserve item at the present time -- my focus was more on current issues. I told Kincaid that we had completed a pumping of fuel. He was surprised that we had done it without incurring a break in the line. I did not tell him how that had been achieved. But, on the matter of fuel, I pointed out that we had lost a tank as a result of the fire that took place before my arrival. He stated that he recognized the problem and would work to get a new tank installed at Kunsan. "We have some bolted tanks at

**other locations, tanks left over from the Korean War, and the best answer may be to disassemble one and move it to Kunsan." My thought, however, was that the bolted tank was the source of the last fire -- due to age they leaked and were not repairable. "All my tanks are leaking and there is no fix at hand." I urged a welded tank. "Perhaps we can take the drilled sections of a bolted tank, cut them down and give you a welded tank," he suggested. "I'll look into it."**

**I then told Kincaid how I had solved the sand bag problem. We both had a laugh over the problem and my solution.**

**Kincaid then asked me about the truck tire situation and whether I liked my new staff car. To both questions, I gave an upbeat answer. But then I began to focus on the mess hall problem -- the condition of equipment. Kincaid promised that he would look into it.**

**On the matter of construction, Kincaid stated that he had no real role. "In fact, the 314th Division really has no significant role. The whole thing is run from Fifth Air Force." I told him about the sorry ramp in front of operations and alluded to more problems. Then I raised a question. "If no one in the 314th Air Division is directly responsible for construction and rehab, does that mean that I have authority to deal directly with the staff at Fifth Air Force?" Kincaid saw my problem. "Let me do some investigating and I'll talk to you when I get down to Kunsan with the General."**

**We shook hands and I left to go to the office of the Inspector. But, before I got there I realized it was noon and I decided to go to the Officers Club for lunch -- hopefully I would meet and have a productive talk with Mike. And I was in luck. As I left the headquarters building, Mike and some secretaries were on their way to lunch. I yelled to Mike and we ended up having lunch together.**

**"I guess you know about Colonel Davidson?" I asked.**

**"Yes. And I told you some of the story. One thing about Korea, if anyone has a problem that might be contained in the States or some other assignments, send them to Korea and it will surface. I've seen it happen time and time again. You just wait. Have you been faced with drug problems yet?"**

**"Not yet and, for Christ's sake, don't tell me I have that too. My Doc says that its no big thing at Kunsan."**

**"You've got a little of it. But we've got more of it here at Osan. Wait until you see the village outside our gate. At least where you are it's miles to Kunsan City -- no outside cluster of whorehouses and other activity.**

"The in-coming men here are always briefed about the drug problem. In the local community, it's legal outside the gate and the men can get it cheap -- dirty but cheap. And, sooner or later, if they partake, they will get caught. And, when they get caught, the people who sold it to them will testify against them. Here, what is legal for the Koreans is illegal for us. And, before long, you will be sitting on court-martial boards, as President since you are a Colonel, and you will be giving people a dishonorable discharge and sending them to jail. It's not a pleasant scene but it is an unavoidable scene. And you will hate yourself for what you will have to do."

Mike was all-knowing and smart. She already knew about the staff meeting and, again, advised me that I was developing one hell of a pissed off Wing Commander who was going to work overtime "to get me." "Of all his hates, you have become his number one hate," Mike advised, "and he is going to bust his ass until he can box you in. Believe me -- I know what goes on."

Mike then told me about how the ROKAF had recently given her an instrument check ride in order to keep her flying qualifications up to speed. And there had been a big event in the local community for "Mike-san." Apparently, Mike supported one of the local orphanages.

Mike had a way of getting carried away with her vast store of Korean knowledge and it was a chore to get her back to the mundane things that bothered me -- but we eventually got there -- mostly as a result of the water.

I was about to take a drink of the water on the table when I recalled Davidson's comment about "hair in the water." Holding my glass of water up to the light, it looked horrible -- not one or two hairs but scores of them -- some all of two inches in length. I grimaced and Mike saw it.

"Sickening, isn't it?" she suggested. "If you drink coffee, you can't see them. But that's not the half of it. Sometimes, the filters don't work and the screens in the drinking fountains get clogged with everything from bugs to small fish. My advice: Don't drink water -- drink booze."

I had to agree. The visible hairs in the water were enough to turn away the best of stomachs. But there was so much about Korea that was sickening that I was becoming immune -- perhaps my conversion to an "old man on the block" had begun. Disturbed at my thoughts, I decided to raise the subject of the IG inspection of Kunsan.

"Mike, I've got a big concern about the IG inspections that have gone on at Kunsan. There are reports in file but they are all but meaningless. What has been going on?"

"Hell, that's easy," Mike answered. "No one really cares what goes on out here. But the system needs a report -- so the inspector makes out a report. It's not what the report says -- it's the fact that an inspection and a report was made. Probably no one reads what the report says. Due to the lack of resources and a general feeling of helplessness, this whole place degenerated into a party town and, as I told you, until they moved some aircraft out here to stand alert, the Air Force was getting out of the country. And the object was to get out without spending any money. There wasn't a dime spent on housing or anything. The U.S. Army wanted to stay at the DMZ -- it was their thing and almost an essential to promotion -- those Army types who did not serve in Korea just did not get promoted. But the Air Force wanted to get the hell off the peninsula and the opposite was true -- those Air Force types assigned to Korea were lost souls. And the good old U.S. Navy was way over the horizon trying to be sea dogs in their own environment. You got here just after this whole situation reversed and it's a bitch."

I looked at my watch. It was almost 1400 hours and I had a lot of work to do. I told Mike that I had to run, called for the check and we left for the headquarters. As we walked back, Mike suggested that I come by the "girl's hootch" after work for a drink. She told me that they had a bar and that a good number of the officers would be there. I decided to do it and left word at Operations for Preston, Turnbull, Jones and Young that we would spend the night -- I did not like the idea of flying back to Kunsan at night in the L-20.

My next stop in the headquarters of the 314th Air Division was the Office of the Inspector. The greeting I received was ice cold. And the more I discussed the situation at Kunsan Air Base the more I realized that I had an enemy for what I was setting forth was a failure of the inspection system to define the problems. And, translated, this meant that his office had failed to perform. And, by extension, he was not performing although he was still new to the job. It was sort of a "no win" situation.

With additional, tight-lipped review, it was decided that he would send an inspector to Kunsan "to look into things." And it was further agreed that this inspector would visit Kunsan within the next two weeks. The Colonel stated that he would send me a message on the exact dates. For my part, I urged that the inspector spend the night.

**The Colonel advised that they did not normally do that due to the Kunsan housing shortage. My answer was that I would get him a billet. Already, I had an idea as to what that billet would be -- it would not be in officer's quarters.**

**I then went to the officer in charge of Communications and Electronics. He was a nice chap -- what I would call "a real spark chaser." We discussed the communications to Kunsan and I told him that the idea of having only land lines to communicate with a nuclear base was unacceptable. I urged he establish a program to get a microwave link established as soon as possible. He was sympathetic and said that he would propose it to Fifth Air Force but he stated that, in general, money for improvements in the communications system was hard to come by and that Fifth Air Force was not very sympathetic when it came to funding improvements in Korea. We also discussed the radar situation -- which was lousy as the system was based on much out-dated equipment that was being passed to the ROKAF under the Military Assistance Program. The limited number of radars available left great gaps in the coverage and there was no back up. To get better coverage, I suggested that the radar at Kunsan ought to be moved to the top of the hill at the end of the runway but the argument against that was that roads would have to be built, there would have to be additional communications lines, then there would be an increase in security and, most important, the U.S. would have to pay for the relocation of a lot of Korean graves.**

**I ended the day with Jack. I thanked him for giving me some latitude in the use of the C-47. In turn, he commented that he was having a hard time dealing with the Wing Commander. We discussed the radar and other military scenarios but arrived at no good conclusion. As we left his office, I mentioned that Mike had asked me to come by for a drink and he indicated that, after he cleaned up, he would be there. Apparently, the girls' hootch was sort of an operations office meeting place.**

**When I got to the girl's hootch, I found that Mike had decided to put on a sukiyaki dinner for everyone. There were about a half dozen "Operations" girls there. Mike owned several electric frying pans and, at a low table in the common room of the hootch, she had prepared all the essentials. She stated that she always managed to finagle some food stuff from the exchange and commissary at Seoul and that her Korean friends on the outside helped her to get decent fresh vegetables. To the side of the room, I could see that she had acquired a case of Japanese sake -- and I soon found a small Japanese cup of hot**

sake in my hand. It was a great and friendly evening and so radically different than anything that took place at Kunsan that I thought I was in another world. I had to wonder what my officers and men would think if they observed me enjoying myself in the surroundings -- and especially with some American girls -- some "round eyes."

Adding to the delight of the evening, the officer in charge of Communications and Electronics arrived with a guitar and proceeded to lead in singing. Soon, I learned of an array of new military songs. Again, I had to draw a comparison between Osan and the Kunsan Air Base environment where I found no singing taking place.

I had intended to talk to the Intelligence Officer the next morning but discarded the idea. Actually, probably the result of the pleasant evening social put on by Mike, I overslept and, on awakening, realized that I had to get going to get back to Kunsan. I did go by General Joyce's office but he had gone to Seoul -- apparently something to do with the U.S. Ambassador. At the flight line, Preston, Turnbull, Jones and Young were waiting for me and, after filing a clearance, we headed back to Kunsan Air Base.

Turnbull thanked me for getting him to Osan. "Having some understanding of the 314th Division is important and I'm going to recommend that my replacement get to Osan." I agreed and told him that we would provide transportation.

On the way back to Kunsan, Jones and Young asked if I could get our Gooney Bird to Osan the next day. They had scrounged some furniture for my office, a new air conditioner for the Waldorf Astoria and a refrigerator. We had to get the C-47 to Japan for the food pick up but I thought it could be managed on the day following. Preston said that the C-47 was due for a 100 hour inspection but that it could be fudged a bit. Suddenly, I felt that we were beginning to work together for a common cause and that the men were enjoying the success that came from achievement -- regardless of how that achievement was realized. Still, I knew that there was a host of basic problems to be solved and that my time was rapidly running out. I was pleased that my men were becoming more aggressive in problem solving but I knew that there was a limit to what we could do on our own.

I had already come to realize that there was a virtual wall between Korea and Japan and it was in Japan that most of what happened in Korea was controlled. That left me with the option of changing Japan or going around it. But, if I went around Japan to call on friends back in the Pentagon and other locations, I was going to upset many an apple cart and, sooner or later, bring damnation on my

**head. Was the answer to roll over and play dead? That was not my way of doing things but I knew that I had to play my cards very carefully.**

**[*Shortly after arriving in Osan, Jack Hubbard called me aside and told me that I was making many enemies by virtue of using the senior Air Force contacts I had. "You are considered a name dropper," he stated, "and you are pissing off everyone who doesn't have your connections." Following that comment, I "pulled in my horns" and tried my best to get along with many things I found hard to stomach. But, now and then, discreetly, I still called on my friends for help.*]**

***When it came to property development, the grave situation in Korea was a nightmare. Graves were everywhere -- except for the Korean War military cemeteries, there was no "cemetery" in the conventional American or European sense. As in the above photo, grave mounds were virtually on every hill or rise of ground -- even in valleys. The result was that, as soon as some land use was discussed, the Korean families presented monumental demands to agree to the movement of the grave sites of their ancestors. Money for this was hard to obtain. There were many graves scattered on the hill on which I suggested the Kunsan radar be placed and it would not be moved to that site..***

# DAY ELEVEN -- A THURSDAY
# RETURN TO KUNSAN

Bolstered by the sense of accomplishment and even though Jones had not been able to acquire a camera from the Osan Public Relations office, the flight back from Osan was a stimulating event. Success breeds success and we were beginning to succeed. But I knew that the road ahead would not be easy -- there was just too much to do -- too many problems to address. Nonetheless I felt as if we were getting somewhere. Time, however, was rapidly running out -- at least for me.

Soon, the Kunsan Air Base came up on the horizon. The air was smooth and visibility was excellent. As I let down, I noticed that some of the house tops in the villages we flew over looked red and I commented to Preston about it.

"It's the peppers," he stated. "They are beginning to harvest them. They put them in large, circular, reed baskets and place them on the roof tops to dry. They are hot as hell. It's part of what makes kimchi what kimchi is."

I shuddered at the thought. Little did I know that soon I would be exposed to what was viewed as a national food of Korea.

The Kunsan runway coming up, I called for landing instructions. It was a direct run in and, after a short float, settled on the runway and taxied to the macadam ramp in front of Operations. Waiting to meet us was Major Akers. I could see that my Acting Deputy Commander shouldered problems even before I got out of the aircraft.

"What's up?" I asked.

"Sir, I hate to tell you but we have had a tower problem."

"What's wrong with the tower? It was operating all right when we came in."

"But it hasn't been," Akers replied.

Through my mind went communications and other difficulties but not what I was about to learn.

"Sir, the men who were manning the control tower got drunk on duty -- totally drunk. And we had aircraft coming in and taking off on their own -- unable to communicate with the tower. It's a wonder we did not have an accident. The first thing we knew of the problem was an Army liaison pilot who came in and said that he had flown by

**the tower, was unable to raise it and then observed that the persons in the tower seemed to be sleeping. Obviously he did a rather close fly-by."**

**I found it difficult to believe what was being said but I constrained myself and listened.**

**"Anyhow, I went to the tower and found that the personnel in it had passed out. They were so drunk that they had to be carried down the tower ladders -- and that was a chore. Captain Wild has them locked in the jail. I did not take further action as I knew you were coming in and I thought, actually I hoped, you would take care of the situation."**

**Holy Moses! Who would have thought that something like this could happen? Fortunately, there was no aircraft accident as a result. If an accident had occurred, I could imagine myself trying to explain the situation to the Wing Commander.**

**"I'm going to my office. Get everyone who has any association with these persons to my office right now. I want some down to earth conversation."**

**"Yes sir."**

**Several persons, officer and enlisted, showed up in my office.**

**"All right. Can anyone tell me why this happened?"**

**No one wanted to speak and I asked again.**

**"This is serious. We are playing Russian roulette. What the hell is going on?"**

**Still no one volunteered an answer. Finally, Akers spoke.**

**"Sir, I think it is Korea. Korea just breaks down good people. The men in the tower were four and five stripers. The road to four and five stripes is not easy. They had to have done the right things to get to where they are. And then they came to Kunsan. And Kunsan is one pit of a hole. And I think they just came apart. We can blame them, but we also have to blame the situation."**

**I saw that there was a nodding of heads in the assembled audience but I had to respond.**

**"O.K. So Kunsan is viewed as the pit of a hole. Does that mean that everyone gets plastered and endangers the life of everyone else? And the answer to that has to be a great big NO! Certainly, we have problems here. I recognize some but certainly don't know all of them. But problems are something to be solved -- not something to be drowned in a bottle of booze. I look to each of you to help me solve the problems of this base -- not to go about getting plastered. And I will not tolerate the route of the bottle as a solution to anything. I am**

**certain that the men who were in the tower may have been known to you, may even have been your friends, and you feel sympathetic toward them. But how would you feel if you had to write a letter to a widow or child if they had caused a fatality on landing or takeoff? Think about this now and when you go about your own jobs. As to the men who were hauled out of the tower, they are through working on this base! And, yes, I will prefer charges against them and I trust that they will be out of here on the next available flight. I just don't have time for the likes of them. And, if you have any questions, I will try to answer them. If not, you are all dismissed."**

**There was no question. The men left the room. I was shattered. Drunken personnel -- passed out men in the control tower. Unheard of! But it had happened on Kunsan Air Base -- on my air base. And what next? No doubt the Wing Commander would get wind of this and use it to his advantage. Suddenly, I realized that I had virtually no front and no rear -- surrounding me on all sides were enemies -- lots of enemies.**

**Alone in the office, I walked to a window and looked out. There, I found myself searching for what might be the next catastrophe. I was in a foul mood. Were these problems always happening or were they the result of my presence -- was I the cause of what was transpiring?**

**There was a slight noise behind me. Turning, I found Miss Lee bringing in a hot cup of coffee. I sensed that she knew I needed it. To date, we had never really talked and, to take my mind off the morning's catastrophe, I asked her to sit down and tell me about her family.**

**I soon learned that Miss Lee's father and mother had been killed by the North Koreans. She had the equivalent of a high school education, this from a convent in the area where she had learned English, and she had worked for the Air Force for several years. She had one brother in the ROK Army and one brother in the ROKAF. She lived in Kunsan City in a two-bedroom house along with some ten other members of her family. She rode the Korean bus to and from Kunsan Air Base. For her family, she was the major wage earner.**

**For the first time since arriving at Kunsan Air Base, I scrutinized Miss Lee carefully. Her clothes were well attended, modest and clean; her hands and finger nails were clean; her hair was well groomed; she had a good set of teeth; and she did not smell of kimchi.**

**I began to feel that, under the burdens of Kunsan Air Base, I might have misjudged Miss Lee as a possible security risk. I ended up telling her about Mary and our two children. And then I asked her a**

**question about the Korean children I had observed on the base -- their schooling and more.**

**"They get schooling from the family," was the answer.**

**And, with that knowledge, I found myself telling Miss Lee about the schooling system in America, the advantages the American children had and more. Miss Lee's response was that she would have liked to have grown up in America.**

**And then my mind was triggered and I decided on something and called for Captain Polk.**

**Miss Lee went back to doing the things she did. I had a new appreciation of Miss Lee -- perhaps she was not a security risk.**

***Korean kids were great -- happy, unconcerned about the primitive surroundings in which they found themselves. Here, four very young boys are captured on film -- two of these boys are carrying "A" frames and out for a day's work. In America, laws would prohibit what is here shown. But, when it came to Korea, what is here shown is mostly the good part.***

**The conversation with Miss Lee had the effect of cooling me down. But I was still mad at the world and wondering about myself. Could I have, in some way, prevented the tower incident?**

I turned to the paper stack on my desk. Half way through the paper drill, Captain Polk arrived. I asked him about the new flag pole. He assured me that it would be installed before General Joyce arrived on Monday.

"Jesse, I have a new job for you."

"And what is that?"

"Do you have much pipe in the yard?"

"A fair amount but most of it is old salvage stuff and some of it is rusted."

"Perhaps you have what is needed," I answered. "Do you recall what a kid's swing set looks like?"

"Sure. I grew up on them."

"And could you build some out of the pipe you have -- do you have enough acetylene and oxygen?"

"Enough."

"Well, if you can, would you build two double swing sets. I would like to give them to the on-base ROKAF for use by their children. From what I can see, about all they have to play with is old tires."

"Consider it done, Colonel."

I have to admit that I was taken back by the gung-ho reply -- but it buoyed the hell out of my spirits. And then Captain Wild walked in the office door.

"Colonel, we have a problem out by the hill at the end of the runway -- out by the fishing village."

Another problem! Was there never an end?

"And what is it?" I asked.

"The villagers have discovered some buried drums and they are digging to beat all hell. What should I do?"

"What are in the drums?"

"I think it's a tar substance."

"Well, let's go see. Do you have a four-wheeler outside?"

"I've got a jeep."

"Fine. Let's go."

When we arrived at the hill site, there were all of a hundred Koreans digging furiously and hauling out 55 gallon drums. I inspected a few. Apparently the drums contained tar that had been used in the construction of the old runways, taxiways and roads. Undoubtedly, the engineers, finding they had an excess and in the old military tradition of burying problems, simply dug a hole and buried the drums. Now, as a result of the rains of the last typhoon, the tops of

**the drums had been exposed and the villagers were well on the way to reaping a bonanza.**

**"Colonel, what do you think we should do?" Wild asked.**

**"I think we ought to step back and let this happen. We didn't know these things were here. They found them. Let them keep them. Do you have any idea what they will use this stuff for?"**

**"I think they will use it for the bottoms of their boats."**

**"Well, wish them good fishing."**

**"Yes sir."**

**I perceived that Wild had some other idea but I was not going to explore it. As we left the area, a bearded person who I sensed was the chief or an elder of the village, a Korean in a white robe and black, wide-brimmed hat, saluted and bowed several times. I think he understood what had happened. Perhaps I had developed a friend?**

**That evening, when I arrived at the Waldorf Astoria, there were several footlockers in my room. The surface shipment of clothing and other items I had assembled before leaving for Korea had arrived. I eagerly opened the footlockers as if they were Christmas presents from home. In one locker was my 12 gauge Browning automatic and the thirty-ought-six -- plus some boxes of ammunition. I felt as if I had some new friends. I started to place the guns in my bedroom box but, after reviewing the situation, decided that I would deposit them with Wild and have them kept in the Air Police Command Center.**

**That night, I wrote a long letter to Mary telling her about the receipt of the footlockers, about my plan to have some swings built for the ROKAF children on the base and more. With the receipt of the footlockers, my mood had improved to the point that I forgot to bang on the stove before I went to bed and, just as I was dozing off, the noise commenced.**

**With a curse, I got up and hit the side of the stove. The scramble of rats began and soon all was quiet and I went back to sleep.**

**Then, in what seemed like minutes, they were back. Again, I went through the routine but, again, they came back.**

**Eventually, I was fed up and made a mental note to talk to Jones in the morning on a plan of action.**

**When I finally fell asleep, I do not know. But I do know that it was not a good sleep.**

# DAY TWELVE -- A FRIDAY FORECAST OF ASSASSINATION

I spotted Jones as I entered the Officers Club and asked him to join me for breakfast.

"Tommy, there is something that I want you to do as a matter of urgency."

"Yes?"

"I want you to make up a bulletin to announce that we have a Pied Piper Program starting immediately and the person who kills the most rats will get a $25.00 bond and a seven day R&R leave to Japan. The program is to start as soon as you post the bulletin and end at midnight Sunday. The proof of the killing of a rat will be the presentation of a rat tail. Pick a place for the count -- some place out in the open and where there is a pit in which we can bury the tails. I'll pay for the $25.00 bond. Do state that the use of guns to kill the rats is not authorized."

"The Chaplains will be unhappy with the program extending into Sunday -- it may cut down on church attendance."

"I thought about that but my greater focus is the coming visit of General Joyce on Monday. I'd like to have some of these rats cleaned out by then. And, if they kill enough, I may get some sleep at night."

"The rats have been hitting your quarters again?"

"Not again -- constantly. And I'm getting tired of it. You'll get it done?"

"No problem, sir. But work from now until Sunday night may be interrupted as the men will probably goof off to hunt rats."

"Tell the officers to live with it. It's only three days. We'll recover."

"Yes sir. But I have a problem, sir."

"And what is it?"

"Our mimeograph machine, sir. It's over twenty years old and it has broken down again. It's been *red-tagged* but we have no replacement. My men are trying to get it fixed but we have no spare parts."

"Well, do your best."

A twenty-year old mimeograph machine? My God? On the other hand, the assigned C-47 we had was even older. I decided to change the subject.

"I haven't heard reveille yet."

"No sir. I am still having trouble with the turntable. It's really an old job -- built some time before the Korean War. I thought I had it fixed but I was wrong. I hope to have it fixed in a day or two. I rewound the motor but I don't think I was smart enough to get the right speed out of it. We just don't have the right wire -- or anything. If the old rubber belts that run the thing fail, we are dead in the water as there are none around."

I wanted to comment but didn't.

After Jones and I finished breakfast we went to the headquarters. The staff meeting was short. The tower operators had sobered up but were still in jail. They did not belong to me -- they belonged to the Fifth Air Force communications service. So, with the close of the staff meeting, I asked Jones to get me their commander on the line. After I explained what had happened, the commander asked for a recommendation. It was simple -- get the culprits off Kunsan, demote them and send replacements on the next flight to Korea. After some grumbling about personnel shortages, he agreed.

I had just laid down the telephone when I heard the loud, straight pipe exhaust of an arriving vehicle. Looking out, I saw a red foreign sports car, a convertible, with U.S. plates on it. A young man in civilian clothes got out and sauntered to the front of the headquarters. In a few minutes, Tommy came in to announce that I had a special visitor. "I think he's from Counter Intelligence or something like that. He says his name is *Mr. Olson*. He does carry DOD civilian ID. I have seen him at the Officers Club a couple of times but did not know who he was. He's arrogant as all hell."

"Well send him in and we'll find out who he is and what he wants. And stay in the office."

In seconds, Tommy ushered in Mr. Olson. He was a youngster with a pimply face and hair that was too long -- he looked like a "hippy."

Mr. Olson flashed an ID in front of me and stated that he was with Counter Intelligence. He said his area of responsibility was from Kunsan south. He added that he had been on a mission well to the south and just returned to the Kunsan area; he had heard that I had reported in and wanted to present himself to me. He went on to assert that he had officer privileges and would, from time to time, bring

**Koreans on base, some of them girls. But he assured me that all his associations were in the line of work.**

**I doubted it and asked Mr. Olson if he was a civilian, an enlisted man or an officer.**

**"I can't answer that, sir. As I showed you, I carry civilian identification. We are not allowed to identify ourselves beyond that. Regulations."**

**"And so you are Counter Intelligence. That car you drive would advertise you in neon lights. No Korean drives anything like it. I thought you guys operated in a clandestine manner -- not as show dogs." I just did not like this Mr. Olson. "Who is your boss at Osan?"**

**[*Universally, the disguised personae here illustrated by "Mr. Olson" were disliked by the officer group and even the NCO group. These individuals, always alleging superior authority and demanding officer accouterments and wide-ranging support, failed to realize the negative impression they made on others. While their work may have been significant, the individuals involved were not generally respected.*]**

**"I can't answer that, sir. Regulations."**

**This guy sounded like the transportation officer at Maxwell Air Force Base -- regulations/regulations/regulations! Wars could not be fought with regulations! Somewhere there had to be common sense. I was angry.**

**"Well, did you come here just to tell me that someone gave you officer privileges and you wanted to use those privileges to entertain josans at the Officers Club or did you have something else to say?"**

**Mr. Olson's face turned red. I knew I had hit a tender spot in his make-up and that the "girl" stuff was not all that legitimate.**

**"I do have some information for you but it should be in private."**

**"You can tell me anything you want with Lieutenant Jones in the office. He's got the same security clearances I have. And, by the way, I don't know what your clearances are so get that boss of yours, whoever he is, to send me a message telling me."**

**Mr. Olson fidgeted but did not answer. Finally, he gave in to my demand to allow Jones to remain and proceeded to tell me what the additional information was that he sought to pass to me.**

**"Sir, I really would prefer not to tell you this but you are on an assassination list of a South Korean political group. This group hopes to create a political problem for the Rhee regime by killing one or more**

American commanders. Your name is on the hit list. I had previously informed your Captain Wild about this but ordered him not to disclose the information to anyone."

Suddenly, I recalled the appearance of forty-fives on Jones and Young during the pre-typhoon trip around the base. Wild probably had told some others to take care of me. And then there was the periodic appearance of a carbine. Obviously, I was being looked after. I would have to talk to Wild and Jones about this. I did not appreciate someone such as Olson "ordering" my personnel to do anything -- it subverted the whole command concept.

"So what am I supposed to do? And how is it that they are going to kill me?"

"Hard to tell, sir. But from what we have learned about this group we think that they would want to do it long range and that most likely means a rifle -- probably a scoped rifle."

"Are you certain there is no tie to North Korea?"

"As far as we can determine, there is none. But the depth of North Korean infiltration in the ROK is always a question."

"And would not a North Korean assassin desire that his undertaking be covered to appear to be the work of a South Korean?"

"Very possible."

"Thus, your Mickey Mouse friends could have been duped into assessing this threat as coming from South Korea."

"It's possible."

"What about General Joyce -- is he on the list?"

"Yes sir."

"And what are you guys doing to provide some protection? Or do you just lay this on me and go find a josan to interrogate?"

Again Mr. Olson flushed red.

"Sir, I am only one person with a lot of area to cover. If I get specific information, I will try to get it to you or your Captain Wild."

"And is there anything else you want to tell me?"

"No sir."

"Well, have a nice day. But don't start using this base for girlie entertainment. Make certain that the business you conduct here is real business or I will have your butt."

Red-faced, Olson left my office. From the sound of his vehicle departing, the tires spinning, I knew he was pissed -- but I did not care.

I turned to Jones. The confrontation with Olson and the thought of assassination had left me testy.

**"O.K. Tommy. You knew about this and that is why you sported a forty-five the other day. Am I correct?"**

**"Yes sir. I also keep a forty-five in my desk -- as does Sergeant Young. Sergeant Young also has a carbine available -- you may have noticed. Captain Wild briefed us that there was a problem but he did not go into the detail Mr. Olson did."**

**"Well, next time you learn something like this don't keep it to yourself -- brief me. Right now, however, we have a bigger problem than keeping me alive. Get Wild in here on the double."**

**It took about fifteen minutes for Jones to locate Wild and get him to the office. When he arrived, his face was flushed. Obviously, he had been running.**

**"Wild, I just got some interesting information from a Mr. Olson."**

**"Tommy told me, sir."**

**"Well, let's talk about General Joyce. He's going to be in here Monday. We can worry about me later."**

**"Yes sir."**

**"Well, what are your thoughts? How do we look out for General Joyce? If he's going to get zapped, I don't want it to happen here. Not that I want it to happen any place. When you have a plan, brief me on it."**

**Without waiting for a reply, I turned to Jones.**

***[The non-military public does not understand that assassination is a very real option in any confrontational environment. Years prior, I had read many studies on assassination when attending the Air Command and Staff College at Maxwell AFB and the subject was actively discussed in seminars -- particularly as an alternative to higher casualty options. At the time, I recalled the conclusion of one study which asserted that selective assassination was a "refinement" of the techniques of achieving political and military objectives.***

***The history of assassination is quite extensive and, with modern methods, it's application has been broadened. Shortly before the time of this account, Ukrainian Nationalist Leader Stefan Bandera in Munich was assassinated by a Soviet agent using a method suggestive of suicide.***

***Logic would tell me that a North Korean plan for assassination would be carried out by removed persons, e.g. a South Korean dissident. A more removed assassin would be an American but I doubted that such would be the case.]***

"Tommy, we haven't discussed the handling of General Joyce's visit -- more importantly, how now do we handle the security for that visit. Call General Joyce's secretary -- her name is Barbara -- and find out who will be traveling with the General, the time of arrival and the time of departure. Then, this afternoon, meet with me to lay out a plan. You can assume that whoever comes with the General will tag along so don't try to develop any side trips for anyone. If the General is planning to have lunch here, my inclination would be to feed the party in the enlisted mess but let's wait to see what the timing is."

After Wild and Jones left, I just sat staring at the ceiling. As if sensing something was bothering me, Sergeant Young had Miss Lee bring me a coke.

I had not yet been two weeks on the job but so much had happened that it seemed much longer. And, if so much had happened in the few days I had been at Kunsan Air Base, what was about to hit me in the coming days -- would the future simply be more of the past?

The previous Commander of Kunsan Air Base who I had met in Japan did not convey to me the diverse problems with which I had already been faced. Was it a case that he also faced these problems but did not wish to tell me? Or was it a case that his technique was such that these problems did not surface? As I reflected on this question, I concluded that the motivation of the past Commander to depart early from Kunsan Air Base may have been a desire to not be present when the new 314th Air Division Commander, General Joyce, entered on the scene. Most likely, the past Air Division Commander knew of the problems and accepted them as a norm while General Joyce would find the existence of these problems as unacceptable. Thus, if the past Commander of Kunsan Air Base had continued on, he would have been placed in the position of explaining to General Joyce why, over the prior year, he had allowed the situation with which I was now confronted to exist. That the existing situation may have been beyond his control would probably have been lost in the ensuing examination. The easy way out for this Commander was to be transferred from Kunsan Air Base before General Joyce arrived and learned of the situation. And the smart way out of the chance meeting I had with this Commander would be to tell me that everything was great with the fallout being that, if I found it otherwise, the fault would rest with me and not with him. That conclusion, right or wrong, did not leave me in a good mood.

# THE VISIT PLAN

At lunch there was considerable discussion regarding the Pied Piper Program and a number of the men were placing bets as to how many rats it would take to capture the prize. For my part, my mind was on the coming visit of General Joyce. The assassination information had placed a whole new twist on the issue and, before lunch was over, I reaffirmed to Wild and Jones that we needed a planning session. Both were at my office when I arrived. I invited them in and closed the door.

"Do either of you have a large scale map of the base?" I asked.

Jones said he had one in his desk and darted out to get it.

Spreading the map on the conference table, we began to consider options.

"The General is supposed to arrive at 1300 hours and depart at 1530 hours," Jones stated. "His Secretary says that he is bringing with him the Wing Commander, the Director of Operations and the Director of Materiel. He will have his Executive Officer with him -- a Captain. They're coming down in the General's C-47."

"O.K. Let's not make this visit complicated by working in a visit to the ROKAF. If we get him to the ROKAF, they will want to give him some coffee, brief him and God knows what. We just don't have time for that. So don't even let the ROKAF know that he's coming.

"When they arrive, I want to bring them straight to this office. And, Tommy, I want you to give the visiting party our base briefing -- the Top Secret version -- and do a good job of it. Also, borrow Captain Wild's camera and check out one of your men on its operation. Have your man at the aircraft when the General steps out and have him shoot pictures during the visit -- but not in the office during the base briefing. After the visit is over and the photos are developed, I want you to put together a book of photos, to which we will add select photos covering base facilities and problems, and send it to the General as a reminder of the visit and our problems.

"As to what happens after the base briefing, we have to consider that the General and the Director of Operations will want to visit the alert area so we have to get Major Turnbull in on the planning. For my part, I would like the General to see the G.I. mess hall, the burned fuel tank for which I have already asked for a replacement, the war reserve materiel, the nuclear storage area and the hospital. I want to keep him out of the enlisted barracks as I have not yet had time to do an inspection. If the General comes up with something special for the program, we will just have to fit it in.

"Now, with respect to movement and security, what do you have in mind?"

"I suggest your staff car and a couple jeeps for transportation," Jones answered.

"And I'd like to have an Air Policeman driving each of the jeeps," Wild added.

"And how about overall security?" I asked. "How about putting the dogs on the perimeter?"

"That will tire the dogs and we will not be able to use them that night," Wild stated.

"That's O.K. The Koreans are used to our having the dogs on night duty. They will not know of the switch until it's all over and, by then, the dogs will be back on nights."

"I could reinforce the guard element during the General's visit but I may have to compensate with a reduction on the next shift."

"Do it," I ordered.

"How about side boys?" Jones asked.

"No, I think that would be too much and it could imply that we have more bodies than we really have. I'll be there to greet the General as he steps off the aircraft. I assume that the Wing Commander and the General's Executive Officer will tag along close to the General so I will take them in my staff car. For escort of the others, get Akers and Peterson involved -- have them split into two jeeps and ride with their counterparts. Tommy, you stay here in the headquarters and be ready to brief. Wild, I don't want you close to the group -- you stay in the Air Police center or move about the base as needed.

"Tommy, when the group arrives for the briefing, I want a round of cokes or some other cold drink -- no coffee. But don't have Miss Lee do the serving -- pick a couple men from your office for that job -- and tell them they are to get the serving done and move out of the office ASAP -- make sure they have hair cuts and clean uniforms. And have Sergeant Young make certain that no one is close to the office during the briefing."

I thought for a while and then suggested we plan the travel route for the visit. Using the map Tommy had brought in, we sketched out the sequence to be followed and the roads to be used. The jeeps would follow my staff car. When that scheme of things was worked out, I asked Captain Wild if he had any binoculars available. He did have several.

"O.K. I want you to station one Air Policeman on that hill at the end of the runway and have him keep a watch on the base for any unusual activity."

"But what good would that do, Colonel?" Wild asked. "Without a radio, what could he do if he saw something?"

"I thought of that and all I can come up with is a Rube Goldberg idea. Give him a flare gun and some yellow and red flares. If he sees a questionable thing happen, have him fire a yellow flare. If he sees something really dangerous taking place, have him fire a red flare. Have a member of your reaction team with a jeep stationed at the hill with the observer. His job will be to drive from the hill to let us know what caused the flares to be fired. That would leave the observer in place to watch succeeding developments. I think the observer and the reaction team should be armed with rifles -- loan my scoped rifle to the hill observer -- it's damn accurate but make sure he knows how to use it -- have him do a test firing on the range before he takes it out."

"Anything else?" Wild asked.

"Yes. Uniforms and equipment. Make sure that the Air Police look like police. Use arm bands on the ones who drive. When we are in the headquarters, don't allow the drivers to sit in the vehicles -- have them stand at the entrance and return to the vehicles as the party leaves for the field trip."

"Yes sir."

"All right. Tommy, once more for good luck, please run through the base briefing for me."

That night I made certain that my pistol was loaded and under my pillow. What a hell of a way to live! I wanted to write to Mary but the assassination news, compounded by my thoughts relating to General Joyce's visit, kept my mind busy. I knew that the General's visit gave me one of those "only one time to make a first impression" challenges and I was worried that I might goof up the whole thing.

When, two weeks prior, I had passed through Japan, I had acquired a rather large book covering Korean history through the period of the Korean war and somewhat beyond. Added to the books I had carried from the States, I had a small library. I had devoured the first books during the flight over but I never had found the time to accomplish some real study. Now, with the impending visit of General Joyce, I felt compelled to add to my knowledge. I had no idea what general questions might come up during the General's visit nor an idea as to his historical knowledge but I wanted to be prepared. And so, prior to going to bed, I read for several hours. The result was unsettling.

Adding weight to my prior knowledge, Korean history was an account of severe violence -- even violence among Koreans themselves. And, if I could believe what I read, during the Korean War mass executions by both the North and the South took place. The American press, however, featured mostly the actions of the North Koreans -- and then the Chinese Communists. Particularly disturbing was a photo showing roped South Korean civilians being led away to execution. I had already been exposed to the "North Korean Village" at the edge of Kunsan City but it was obvious that other divisions existed in the South. And I knew from the scant intelligence reports I had obtained that there was considerable dissidence in the South aimed mostly at the Rhee regime. All of this created a very unsettling surrounding environment -- an environment in which the alleged assassination scheme was made especially believable. The nature of the whole scheme of things was unsettling. I already was aware of the scope of ROK Army road blocks and check points and I wondered what really happened when the passing parties were not U.S. personnel. Coupled with North Korean infiltration and with seemingly many of the infiltrators not apprehended, I had to conclude that there was sympathy for the infiltrators present in the South. And, to me, that spelled trouble of a major variety. I wondered how Osan viewed this situation -- if at all? So far, I had not encountered dialogue on the subject and I had to wonder why?

That night, as many nights before, I did not sleep well.

[*For the year I spent in Korea, no U.S. Commander was assassinated. I never did learn what the group was that was supposed to have planned the assassination about which I was briefed. Eventually, but not while I was the Kunsan Commander, President Rhee was overthrown and that may have removed the threat. Or the threat was not real -- only conceived to give me a bad time. But, in the meantime, I had to treat the information provided to me as factual. For some reason that I have long forgotten, I never did discuss the assassination threat with the Commanding General of the 314th Air Division.*]

# DAY THIRTEEN -- A SATURDAY

Since it was Saturday, there was no morning staff meeting -- the officers went straight from breakfast at the Officers Club and then back to their billets.

The 0900 hours inspection of the officer's quarters went slowly. I had forgotten to stipulate the uniform of the day but everyone was in Class A. The uniforms looked good, shoes were shined, hair had been cut and the quarters themselves were in reasonable order. The condition of the buildings, however, was sorry -- all were in need of maintenance, the heating systems were an accident about to happen, only a few of the billets had a telephone, some of the men cooked in the billets using hot plates, bathing facilities were on the order of my own -- terrible. I made some light comment as I went from one set of quarters to another.

In most of the billets, four officers were housed. The prevailing hobby seemed to be stereo and, in each billet, often more than one set was present. Now and then I made an observation but nothing serious. I reminded those who commanded sections that the next item on the schedule would be an inspection of their assigned enlisted quarters. There was considerable comment about the Pied Piper Program and I learned that, some time ago, a similar program had been instituted but with the men authorized the use of guns. I was informed that the exercise sounded like a war. Akers and one of the junior pilot officers was not present -- I had excused them so that they could take the Gooney Bird to Japan for a food purchase.

When the walk-through of the officer's quarters was over, I had mixed emotions. I had hesitated to schedule this inspection as I found it degrading for the officers. But I knew that, if I subjected the officers to the inspection as a first point, there would be less resistance when the enlisted quarters were inspected. I wished I had things scheduled so that I would be comfortable taking General Joyce through an enlisted billet but I could only do so much in the time I had and I had already done quite a bit in now less than two weeks.

Fortunately, I still had the rest of Saturday and all of Sunday to get ready for the arrival of General Joyce.

When I finished the inspection of the officer's quarters it was almost 1100 hours. Peterson had told me that, it being a Saturday

**night, there would be Korean entertainment at the Officers Club. Special Services, he said, scheduled Officers Club entertainment every second week. On one week the entertainment would be for the officers and the next week for the enlisted men. Periodically, a movie would be shown in the clubs -- there was no movie theater on the base in spite of the number of men.**

**With no radio in my quarters, I was mostly unaware of what could be received on the air waves. When flying, I had listened to AFKN Kunsan and, with the inspection of the officer's billets over, I asked Jones to take me to that broadcast facility. It was a small Quonset and I found that two men rotated to operate the turntables and read the news and events reports that were received from the USFK and the Fifth Air Force public relations offices -- operations ran from 0500 to 0100. If, during operating hours, the assigned personnel needed relief, they had a volunteer list of aspiring disc jockeys to draw upon. Apparently there was no shortage of persons who liked to be "on the radio." I was pleased to note that there was a good inventory of records.**

**Discussing the welfare of the men with Jones, it was confirmed that there was a Red Cross representative, an American lady, on the base. I was surprised that I had not seen her. Tommy stated that she spent most of her time with the enlisted men -- "sort of a mother figure" was how Jones described her. The other American woman on the base, the recreation specialist, I had seen. She appeared to be more masculine than feminine. Apparently, the recreation specialist, much as the Red Cross lady, associated primarily with the enlisted men. I had learned that there was a small library in what was loosely termed a recreation center but the books were few and worn. There were two old ping pong tables in the recreation center. Periodically, the recreation specialist organized a bingo game. And there was a hobby shop of sorts but it offered little more than leather tooling using some cheap kits brought in from the States.**

**As Jones and I continued walking, I noticed that Polk already had one swing set operating for the Korean children and they were having a ball. The swings were so popular that the children were standing in line for a turn. I wondered what their parents thought of all this. Tommy did tell me that the ROKAF commander was extremely pleased and that he wanted to come by to thank me. "There will be a small gift for you," Tommy stated. It would turn out to be a wooden box on which was inscribed the emblem of the ROKAF unit.**

When Tommy and I finally got to the office, I was pleased as could be. A sofa, two chairs and a coffee table were in place. Sergeant Young was grinning for ear to ear. We still had the old table and chairs but they had been moved to the side of the room. If only Jones had been able to get me some china, glasses and other support items from Japan, the setting would have been complete. "Just in case, do have coffee cups, sugar and condensed milk on hand when General Joyce is here on Monday. And have Miss Lee make up two pots of coffee. Get the serving stuff from the Officers Club."

In the distance, I could hear aircraft taking off. Apparently the tactical fighter unit was rotating.

Tommy had on my desk the list of men who had extended in Korea with the list annotated to show me which ones lived in the perimeter hootches. I was surprised to see that most of these men on extension were in the Air Police unit. Somehow, that did not seem right -- I smelled a proverbial rat but did not know what it was.

For the moment, I had something else on my mind: nuclear weapons. I asked Tommy to have Peterson come to my office. In about a quarter hour he arrived.

"Steve, let's talk about nuclear weapons. Between those on the alert fighters and those in the igloos, what's our inventory?"

The number Steve cited sent shivers through me. While the weapons were all "tactical nuclear," each was over one megaton. Collectively, there was on Kunsan Air Base enough nuclear capability to destroy North Korea several times over. And, I concluded, there must be as many or more nuclear weapons at Osan Air Base -- and then there were the Matadors. But how could the United States have this many nuclear weapons at Kunsan Air Base with such little protection? I was thoroughly puzzled.

"Steve, let's take a drive out to the nuclear storage area. Do you have keys to the igloos?"

Peterson stated that the keys were in the Operations safe and I excused him to get them. He stated that a second set of keys were in the hands of Major Turnbull.

Because the concrete igloos had not been completed, the nuclear weapons not hung on aircraft were stored in some Quonset huts. Peterson stated that one spare weapon was held on the alert pad.

With the security guards standing by, Peterson opened the first hut. Inside, a canvas cover hid the weapon.

"Pull off the cover, I want to look at this thing."

The cover removed, the weapon looked real. There were the usual access panels, the placards and more. But I had no way of knowing if there was a core inside the weapon.

"The nuclear destruct items -- the shaped charges?"

Peterson pointed to the side of the Quonset hut.

The whole thing was chilling. Then, as Peterson replaced the padlocks on the Quonset hut, I raised a question.

"Steve, do you know what a *Broken Arrow* is?"

He did not. Obviously, something major was missing in the scenario and, once again, I began to suspect that what I had looked at was not a real nuclear weapon -- only a Silver Bullet.

Departing the nuclear storage area, I decided to drive around the base and look more closely at the perimeter hootches that were occupied by my men. They were sordid shacks. I was reminded of the song:

*Hot floors and sake*
*And wild, wild women,*
*They'll drive you crazy*
*They'll drive you insane.*

Apparently these men had found the Korean way of life to their liking and they had "gone native." But I found that very difficult to understand. Still, I was "the new kid on the block." I had to give myself time to adjust. One thing I resolved and that was to keep General Joyce from seeing these home-away-from-home shacks.

By 1700 hours I called it quits. While I was deeply troubled by the nuclear situation, the day had gone fairly well and I was ready for whatever was to be the Korean entertainment at the Officers Club. Within the hour, I was at the bar and trading stories with the officers. Most of them seemed relaxed. Wild was wearing a forty-five and it bothered me to see him drinking but I had learned that he did not do it to excess -- and I understood why the holstered gun -- that damned assassination thing. I looked around -- no one else carried a gun. And, suddenly, I began to worry. In the event of a raid on the base, how fast could guns and ammo be handed out? I knew that we were not in a combat scenario but how far were we from such a thing? Finally, I set the problem aside and sat down to eat.

The entertainment consisted of a Korean dance troop. The show embraced both American and Korean dance routines. The dancers were quite good. There were a few josans in the club and one of the officers had as his guest a Korean family -- husband and wife along with two cute children -- all in traditional Korean dress. I wondered how the family relationship had come about but did not pursue the question.

Before going to bed, I again inventoried the recreational options at Kunsan Air Base. First, there was the matter of the josans. Then there were the two On Limits but still terrible clubs in Kunsan City. On base there was baseball and the limited facilities in the recreation center. Movies were shown in the clubs. Special Services did provide periodic entertainment -- an example of what I had just seen. At times, I had seen a volley ball net in use. And, except for booze, that was mostly it. There was not even an outside basketball court, no tennis court, no golf course, no pool tables, no swimming pool -- Kunsan Air Base had been shorted but I knew that the few weeks I had remaining as Commander would not allow me the opportunity to fix the situation.

My sleep that night was again troubled. I faced an enormous and expanding problem and I seemed to face it all alone.

*A Special Services Korean dance troop performs at the "Bottom of the Mark" Officers Club. The orchestra and dance troop were brought in by six-by-six truck and housed in a special Quonset hut -- under guard. Forgive the young lady at the right for being out-of-step -- she was new to the routine.*

# *THE MARRIAGE ISSUE*

***Mix up a bunch of virile young men with attractive young women and the result can be forecast. This was Korea. Healthy young men sent to a distant land for isolated tours soon found Korean companions.***

***Marriage counseling by the Chaplains was a primary occupation in Korea. For commanders, it often was a secondary occupation as the commander had the job of rendering advice and counsel that, in normal circumstances, would come from the family.***

***To bridge the chasm from paddy life to that of America, at Osan a schooling program for prospective Korean partners was established. Taught were such things as sanitation, electricity, telephone, use of household appliances, customs and more. Unfortunately, the program served even more to excite the idea of acquiring an American husband in order to move out of the paddies and into the "good life" of America.***

***The following abridged news article of a later period reveals the all-too-often tragedy of the resultant partnerships.***

## Brothels Flourishing

New York -- Just north of the village's prosperous downtown is a storefront that flourished without a shingle or a name.

The next door neighbors were naturally suspicious about the store's shy occupants: the male customers who arrived with furtive glances and left with tousled hair; the Korean women who labored at odd hours in scanty cocktail dresses.

"Hookers," smirked one person after police raided the store for a second time.

The trade -- brothels that accept Mastercard and offer reasonable rates.

Disguised as barbershops and doctors' offices, the brothels are largely staffed by Korean women who share a troubled history of broken marriages to U.S. soldiers and bleak job prospects as untrained, single, foreign women in this country.

"It's a lucrative business," said a Korean sociology professor who has studied Asian crime. "It's a trend, a phenomenon that is not only true of New York, but also Philadelphia, Washington, D.C., Chicago and Boston -- and it is growing.

"They go into it because they think they can work for a few years and earn enough money to start a new life," a Korean minister stated. "But happy endings are rare."

# DAY FOURTEEN -- A SUNDAY

After breakfast I decided to go again to the Protestant service -- I would attend a Catholic service on another Sunday.

As Commander, it was appropriate, actually necessary, that I seat myself on a front pew. I wondered what the day's service would be like. But I did not have long to wait.

Within minutes a group of Korean children were ushered into the church and lined up in the front. Chaplain Johnson introduced them as coming from a local Korean orphanage. The children stood in front of the church and, in fractured English, served as a supporting choir. There was a piano and an enlisted man, who I later determined worked for the Chaplain, handled the keys.

There was some "preaching" in the service and, at the final moment, a prayer was said in which God was asked to give the new Commander guidance. I hoped God was listening as I needed a lot of help.

With the church service over, I drove to the Officers Club for lunch.

At lunch, Annie told me that they had a "big fish happy problem." Apparently, the fishing village that had reaped the harvest of drums of tar sought to repay the bonanza and had brought a fish "for the Number One Colonel." I told Annie to have the cooks bake it and put it on the bar as hors d'oeuvres. Annie did not understand the term so I added: Small pieces to eat. That was understood and Annie smiled in a knowing way.

On leaving the club, I noted that a baseball game was in progress. I was still disturbed that men were playing baseball full time while others might work double shifts on guard duty. But I had not found an easy way to deal with the situation I had inherited.

Getting out of the staff car, I walked to the baseball diamond and then I saw something that I had missed before -- apparently the tall grass, now cut, had shielded these items from view. It was trenches, a lot of them, not on the diamond but in adjacent areas. Undoubtedly, they had been dug during the Korean War. The sides were constructed mostly of sand-filled, discarded oil drums. In some cases, bushes and small pine trees had begun to sprout from the trenches. I walked over to one and peered in -- military junk! I had a new job on my list --

clean up the junk and tear out these trenches -- fill and regrade them -- but that could take equipment that I might not have. Perhaps the clean up program scheduled for the coming Saturday would get some of the military junk picked up. To rip out the imbedded 55 gallon drums, I really needed a back hoe but I did not own one.

I drove back to my quarters and wrote a letter to Mary. The core of the letter was the church service and the Korean orphans. The new air conditioner kept my bedroom cool but the rest of the billet was hot. I had obtained a supply of beer for the new refrigerator and popped a bottle open. Then I went outside. Men carrying clubs were scurrying around, poking under buildings, looking everywhere. The Pied Piper Program was in full swing. That evening the winner would be proclaimed -- his bag was over 200 rats -- but there was a yell of "foul ball" as the winner was an Air Policeman who had used his dog to assist in catching the rats. I had ordered "no guns" but the use of dogs had escaped me. Live and learn! If we had another Pied Piper program, I would have to restrict the use of dogs. In the meantime, we were minus a lot of rats. That night, none would come down my chimney.

The evening was spent alone in the billet. Outside, there was the usual blare of stereos. Now and then, I heard an aircraft. For a while, I reflected on the Korean orphans at the church service. I wondered if any of the units on the base sponsored an orphan or an orphanage. I had observed what such an effort did for the men in War Two and I wondered if that lesson had been applied in Korea. I resolved to talk to the Chaplains about it.

But my mind was focused more on something else -- base infiltration -- even an attack on the base. I went through many scenarios from major operations against the base to minor infiltration. With each scenario, even with some warning, the base came out the loser. I had Air Police; I had other men. Hopefully, I had a defense plan of some sort. But I could see that nothing had much of a chance of working. And what was I going to do about it? As the Commander, I had a responsibility to defend my command -- but how?

As I dozed off for the night, I resolved that, once General Joyce had departed, base defense was going to take a top priority. But my mind would not wait. During my sleep, my mind kept turning on the matter of base defense.

# DAY FIFTEEN -- A MONDAY AND GENERAL JOYCE ARRIVES

Except for the weather, all attention at the morning staff meeting was focused on the scheduled arrival of General Joyce at 1300 hours. Regarding weather, the news was good -- Sergeant Butler reported that the on-coming typhoon had slowed in its forward movement and it looked like it would not hit Korea, assuming that was the eventual course, for at least another week.

One could have set his watch by General Joyce's arrival. At precisely 1300 hours, the wheels of his C-47 smoked on the runway. A few minutes later, he was parked in front of Operations. I greeted him as he came down the aircraft steps. He was followed by the Wing Commander, Colonel Musgrave, and the Division Directors of Operations and Materiel. Bringing up the rear was his Executive Officer -- a Captain. Off to the side, Jones' airman's camera flashed.

Quickly, I shepherded General Joyce and Colonel Musgrave, along with the Executive Officer, into the staff car. As planned, the Director of Operations, Colonel Jack Hubbard, and the Director of Materiel, Colonel Walter Kincaid, were greeted by Majors Akers and Peterson and driven in jeeps.

General Joyce seemed in a good mood -- he commented that the last time he had been to Kunsan it was to shoot touch and go landings -- no more. He had never gone through the base proper. The Wing Commander mostly just stared out a window -- I sensed a deep hostility.

On the way to the headquarters, the Wing Commander did ask why the grass on the base was so poorly trimmed -- in some places not at all. It was a beautiful opening. I explained the lawn mower situation and repeated the advice I had received that the Wing had excused the base from cutting grass -- a situation I personally could not tolerate. I told the Wing Commander that, on my arrival two weeks prior, not a blade of grass had been cut except when it grew high enough to be harvested by the Koreans; my then direction for the building of idiot sticks; and my new determination to get a grass cutting capability come hell or high water . I then asked him if he could send me some lawn mowers from Osan. The Wing Commander's following silence told me

**that I would not receive any. I had made my point. I noticed that General Joyce smiled.**

**Approaching the headquarters, I reminded General Joyce that, on my arrival at the base, there was no more than an old tree trunk imbedded in front of the headquarters with no flag flying in that none was possessed by the base and now we had a metal flag pole and I had managed to get flags -- not from normal supply but flown to me by friends in the Pentagon. The point was not missed by the Wing Commander.**

**Inside the headquarters, I shepherded the visitors into my office. I introduced Lieutenant Jones and Sergeant Young to the General and the others. Some enlisted men from Jones' office brought in cold drinks and the visitors seemed comfortable with that -- there was no request for coffee -- probably as the temperature was already pretty high and rising. There was no air conditioner in my office but I noticed that someone had located a fan and it was churning away -- probably someone's personal property.**

**Jones, at first nervous but then settling down, did a good job on the base briefing and he was complimented by General Joyce. At the close of the briefing, Jones displayed a base map on which we had traced our proposed travels through the base. I asked for General Joyce's agreement to the program and it was given.**

**As we drove around the base, I used the time to pursue several questions:**

**First -- what was my mission statement? I stated that I could not find one. The General said that he would order one drawn. I concluded that meant I would have to formulate one when I transferred to Division.**

**Second -- what was the Status of Forces stipulation that governed my relations with the ROKAF on the base? I stated that I could find nothing in the base files on the subject. Neither the General or the Wing Commander had anything to offer. Again, I assumed that job would fall to me on transfer to the Division.**

**Third -- I noted that we were in the mosquito season and that I had been at Kunsan for two weeks with no spray being accomplished. I repeated the worries of my Flight Surgeon and asked for an early spray. General Joyce directed the Wing Commander to get the spray helicopter to Kunsan ASAP. I could see that the Wing Commander was miffed but the helicopter did appear the next day.**

**Fourth -- we talked about base vulnerability but I got no where. It sort of came down to my doing the best I could.**

**Fifth -- I stated that my staff advised me that Taegu was under my command jurisdiction but I could find no order or directive to that effect. I had not visited Taegu but intended to go there the current week. I noted how important it was for me to know what my job was and right now I had nothing concrete on the subject. This was a Wing responsibility and the Wing Commander knew it.**

**Sixth -- I noted that my unit was designated a "Squadron." Reviewing the responsibilities, the manpower and more, and then providing some comparative values in the sense of other organizations, I urged that it be designated as a "Group." Having been in the Pentagon and knowing the system, I pointed out how easy that could be accomplished. General Joyce seemed to agree with my analysis and suggestion. The Wing Commander said nothing but some days later a message arrived stating that the Kunsan unit was a "Group" and that the "Squadron" designation has resulted from a typographical error.**

**[*Many current records state that from 1954 to 1971 the unit at Kunsan Air Base was the 6175th Air Base "Wing." This is not correct. In the transition from the period of history of the 3rd Bombardment Wing at Kunsan Air base, on September 1, 1954 the 6170th Air Base Group took over. On April 8, 1956, this unit was redesignated a Squadron. At some point in 1959, the "6170" numerical designation was changed to "6175" and, for a period, the record is unclear as to whether it was first named a squadron or a group. Much later, after being a group, it would be designated a wing.*]**

**General Joyce was particularly concerned about the enlisted mess situation. As planned, we stopped at that facility and did a "walk through." I told the General that Colonel Kincaid and I had done some review of the situation and we were working on it. He agreed that, regardless of the new mess hall under construction, things needed to be improved as soon as possible.**

**We also did a walk through of the nuclear alert area. I could see by the General's interest that this operation was close to his heart. I literally had to drag him away to keep the schedule moving. I wanted to raise with him my nuclear concerns but the time never seemed right and I decided to "let it ride."**

**While touring the base, General Joyce took pleasure in viewing some men playing baseball. "Good sport," he stated. "It gives the men an outlet for pent up energy. But you ought to spruce up the**

**diamond." I told him about the grass-hidden Korean War trenches that I had discovered around the field and my plan to cover and grade them. He approved and added that the Commanding General of Fifth Air Force was very sports-minded and had directed that the Division recruit a football team to compete with the Japan-based units. He then asked if I had any ex-football players I could transfer to Osan for the team. I wanted to but did not tell the General how difficult I found it to support baseball when I did not have enough men to defend the perimeter or do other essential work.**

**Walking to the aircraft at the close of the visit, the Wing Commander pulled me aside and chastised me for not telling him more about what I needed -- procedurally and logistically. I thought I had. In any event, while General Joyce would again visit the base before my time to transfer to Division took place, this would be the last visit I would get from the Wing Commander. For me, I came to believe that this was a good development.**

**When General Joyce boarded his aircraft we shook hands and, as he did during out first meeting, he assured me that if I needed help "just to let him know." I saw that the Wing Commander overheard the comment and it was clear that he winced at the thought of my having a direct channel to the General. I already had accepted the idea that the Wing Commander was an enemy with whom I would have to live.**

**At the scheduled time, General Joyce's Gooney Bird lifted off Kunsan Air Base. I breathed a sigh of relief. There had been no assassination attempt -- no flares had popped from the hill. To the side, a smiling Captain Wild gave me a "thumbs up." I congratulated the men who made the visit a success. I shuddered to think what this event would have been like had it taken place two weeks prior.**

**"And now we have some work to do," I stated. I had already concluded that I was not going to get essential directives or support out of the Wing. And I further concluded that asking questions would not normally produce results -- it was already obvious that Kunsan had been orphaned and that most of the past and some of the current upper echelon in Korea and on into the Fifth Air Force in Japan had other pressing interests and priorities. The best course of action was to do what I had to do in any way I could do it and to move out until I found someone coming the other way.** ***Command, I decided, flowed to the person who took it -- and I was going to take it.*** **In the two weeks I had been at Kunsan, I had made some progress but the remaining work to be done was mind-boggling. Still, as huge as my projected work schedule already was, little did I know what still lay ahead of me.**

# DAY SIXTEEN -- A TUESDAY

Driving to the headquarters from the Officers Club, I had noticed a single-engine Army liaison aircraft circling the field. A short time later, Jones came in and announced that a Marine Lt. Colonel was outside and wanted to see me. I was overjoyed. My call to one Lt. Colonel Paul Buckner at UNC had paid off. Perhaps I would now have ideas on base defense that would be better than anything I could devise by myself.

Seated on my office couch and with Miss Lee serving us a cup of coffee, Lt. Colonel Buckner and I ran through the base defense situation I faced. We were soon on a "Paul" and "John" basis. Paul seemed delighted to have been asked for advice and he was most frank and out-going -- I got the impression that he was somewhat of an outcast at the Army-dominated UNC headquarters.

Paul had done some intelligence checking in the UNC staff before visiting me and he provided me with an overview of the known North Korean landings in the areas proximate the Kunsan Air Base. The information was frightening as all hell and I had to wonder why such information did not come to me from the Air Division or Fifth Air Force. Paul also stated that he had circled the field to obtain an impression of the surroundings. His overall comment: John, you are a sitting duck out here on this peninsula. I agreed but the question was what to do about it?

To understand the problem better, Paul and I took a drive around the base, to the sea wall, to the eastern rice paddy area, to the nuclear and alert areas and, finally, to the top of the hill at the end of the runway. There we dismounted and scanned the distant airfield.

"So what do you think?" I asked.

"If I was given the task of defending this base, I think I would want at least a battalion to be anywhere near comfortable. You've got about ten miles of perimeter to defend -- in combat, a division rarely defends more than a fifteen to twenty mile front but is usually facing off against other divisions. Here, it's hard to tell the size enemy force you should be prepared to defend against.

"In terms of avenues of approach, you have them all -- 360 degrees of them and by way of any one I could bring up a company, even several companies, unnoticed. And, if they were discovered, the best you would have is one man in a perimeter defense post with a back up of perhaps a half dozen men who might not even get into position in time to do anything positive. Literally, I could be in the center of your base and in control before you could move. It would be a piece of cake.

"The land approach to your base is wide open -- the sea approach is even worse. The tide is out right now but those half dozen junks that I see laying on their sides on the mud could, when the tide was in, have brought a major force right on your doorstep and, even if you discovered it before you were hit, what could you do about it? Nothing, as far as I can see.

"But I sense that I would not have to come in your land or your sea back doors -- I could come in your front door with a transport aircraft filled with a combat team and tear you apart before you knew what was going on. To do that, all I would need to do is come in from the sea when your radar was down (possibly even when your radar was up), stay below the scan of other radars, call in as a friendly, and land. And, just to scare the hell out of you, are you aware of how easy one could, on the open market, get a C-46 or C-47 or some other aircraft in U.S. or ROK service and, from all outward appearance, with just a little paint, your men would be convinced it was a friendly? Are you aware of how your Strategic Air Command tests air bases on this score?"

"Paul, I am as aware as anyone. And I know that we regularly land aircraft here for which there is no flight plan on record. When I complain about this, the answer I get is simply that this is Korea and that's how it is in Korea. As we look at this base, right now I've got about forty to fifty men with guns scattered from hell to breakfast. I think a teen age gang could penetrate the perimeter any time of the day or night. My problem is, with no increase in personnel, what in the hell can I do about it?"

Paul scanned the base and after a long silence responded.

"Frankly, I can't see very much that you can do. One thing, those scattered hootches that seem to be on or right next to your base perimeter -- can you find some way to move them back -- those hootches are a direct avenue to your insides -- I could hide a significant attack formation in any one of them."

When I explained to Paul that some of the hootches to which he had reference were occupied by Americans, his answer was: You have got to be kidding?

And then there was the Korean village that was in grenade throwing distance of the nuclear storage site.

"I can't move a whole village," was my answer.

Did I own an armored personnel carrier -- I did not.

How many heavy guns did I have -- one fifty caliber machine gun.

Mortars -- none.

*"Those hootches that seem to be on or right next to your base perimeter -- can you find some way to move them back -- those hootches are a direct avenue to your insides -- I could hide an attack formation in any one of them." Depicted about is a typical complex of perimeter "hootches." Rice paddies and a drainage canal are in the background; hillside graves are in the foreground. Note the absence of intervening fence or concertina.*

What about the ROK anti-aircraft gun positions -- why was there none facing the sea approach? My answer was simply that that was the way I inherited the situation. I knew it was wrong but I doubted if I was going to be able to maneuver a change. Apparently, these were the positions occupied at the end of the Korean War and no one did a study of what really was needed. Further, air defense, especially anti-aircraft defense, was out of my jurisdiction.

"And that takes me to the UNC and USFK headquarters. From what you observe in Seoul, is there any concern in those staffs about the defense situation here at Kunsan?" I asked.

"As far as I can determine," Paul answered, "not the slightest. The focus of both the UNC and USFK staffs is the DMZ and the ground

**battle. The situation south of the DMZ is left up to the ROK to handle. As far as CINCUNC/COMUSFK is concerned, both the U.S. Navy and the U.S. Air Force are in some other world. They want air and naval support but how it all comes about is beyond their thinking."**

**"But, by JCS direction, the unified commander, U.S. Forces Korea or CINCUNC, is responsible for defense outside the perimeter of my base -- I am supposed to be limited to security inside that perimeter. Still, as you noted, when I look outside my perimeter all I see are open doorways."**

**"The stated argument in Seoul is that your and other bases are best defended by having troops on the DMZ. You know the scenario," Paul added. "A good portion of the ground forces are justified on the basis of providing air base defense but the ground commanders always want their forces deployed some place else."**

**And so the conversation went with each question and answer bringing a deeper frown to Paul and heightened worry on my part. Finally, we drove back to the headquarters.**

**"Can you scrounge for me a couple fifties with field tripods," I asked.**

**"What would you do with them?"**

**"Well, I haven't a clue as to what my base defense system looks like but it probably is in the same state of shambles in which I find everything else. With some fifties, and a better supply of boxed field ammo, as a start I would like to organize a couple on-call reaction teams from the general base population -- about twenty men each and all trained on the use of the fifty. This would at least give me a capability to throw in any direction as augmentation to my Air Police."**

**"It's a start," Paul answered. "As to getting you the fifties, it may take some doing but I think I can find a way to loan you the guns and give you an ammunition draw out of the Army. What I may do is devise an augmentation exercise to reinforce your base and then, accidentally, leave a couple guns behind. In the meantime, I think I want to get back to Seoul where at least I have some half-assed ground divisions filled with KATUSAs and a few pieces of artillery sitting between myself and the North Koreans."**

**We went by the Officers Club for something to eat. Soon, the conversation turned to the matter of food and I told Paul of some of my food problems.**

**"Let me think about that," Paul responded. "It might be that I can find a way to help you get out of the hole in which you find yourself. Frankly, I don't find a shortage of food up where I am but I**

**am in the headquarters and may not know the real story. Anyhow, if I come up with an idea, I'll give you a call."**

**I then drove Paul back to his aircraft, we shook hands, and he was off to the north.**

**One small step -- I had taken one small step -- but I knew that many more would have to follow.**

**In dealing with base defense, I could readily see my problem -- the majority of the Air Force persons with whom I had to work were pilots far removed from matters of ground battle. On the other hand, I had already spent much time working on the particulars of the ground battle in Europe and other places; I had spent time with U.S. and foreign ground troops on maneuvers; I understood ground attack scenarios and more. This was an advantage but it was also an albatross -- I knew too much. And, knowing too much, I saw all too many problems that my compatriots would not see.**

**And I knew that many of my judgments respecting the ground defense situation would be viewed as without consequence. Many might think that I was just "crying wolf" to bring attention to myself. To achieve a better base defense, I recognized that the road ahead was not going to be easy traveling.**

***[Bringing in a Marine Corps officer as an advisor was a greater plus than I initially realized. Progressively, when matters of base defense came up and I was able to fall back on words such as Lt. Colonel Bucker's assessment that he would not be comfortable defending the base short of having a battalion at his disposal, I silenced much adverse comment. The basic problem I faced was the same as that which eventually was encountered in South Vietnam.***

***According to "Roles and Missions" policy, the ground forces were supposed to provide defense outside the perimeter of an air base -- technically, the Air Force was responsible only for on-base security. But, in Korea, the Army was on the DMZ -- and that was a long distance from Kunsan Air Base. In South Vietnam, the Army, although justifying a large number of battalions for the purpose of providing air base defense, under USMACV direction gave priority to offensive operations. (In both instances, the unified commander solved the air base defense problem by relegating it primarily to "local national forces" -- which, in the case of Kunsan Air Base, were non-existent.) As a result in the case of South Vietnam, the Air Force developed an extensive ground defense capability to include armored personnel carriers, light tanks, sensors, mine fields, bunkers, heavy weapons, night vision capability, and gun ships. In the***

*time frame of this account, no comparative action emerged in Korea with the result that Kunsan Air Base, and other Air Force installations, were left as "sitting ducks." In the policy jargon of the time, and onward, the failure to provide for external defense of air bases was termed "an acceptable risk." The unexplained miracle was that the North Koreans (or others) did not exploit the situation. This was not the case in South Vietnam.*]

*"The land approach to your base is wide open -- the sea approach is even worse. The tide is out right now but those half dozen or more junks that I see laying on their sides on the mud could, when the tide was in, have brought a major force right on your doorstep and, even if you discovered it before you were hit, what could you do about it? Nothing, as far as I can see." At the left in the above photo, a lone Air Force officer goes down to inspect the area -- a Korean lady is seen at the right. There was no real perimeter movement restriction for the Koreans nor any monitoring capability present in the Kunsan Air Base Air Police organization -- to a very large extent, there was not even a line marking the "perimeter" of the base and, to the extent a perimeter existed in any record, the Koreans had, by encroachment, occupied more and more of the land -- hundreds of acres. It was, as Lt. Colonel Buckner stated, "wide open."*

# DAY SIXTEEN MOVES ON

With Paul Buckner on his way back to Seoul, I sought to review the base defense plan and had Akers bring the document to me. But I soon found that the afternoon was fully occupied with administrative work and, before I reached the bottom of the stack of papers that awaited me, it was dinner time. Placing the base defense plan in my office safe, I went to the Officers Club.

The mood in the club was relaxed but I was not. At the bar, Wild talked to me about the danger of moving about the base unarmed and I could see that he was seriously worried about my base tour with Paul as neither of us had carried a weapon. "Let me know when you want to move out of the central base area and I'll have some men around," Wild suggested. "There is no need to trust to luck."

While I appreciated the thought, I did not like the idea -- if I agreed to the concept, I would be trapped, imprisoned on my own base. And I was not going to be restricted to movement with body guards.

That night, I had dinner with Joe Pastiak. Periodically, I had used him as a sounding board -- seeking his advice and counsel but, mostly, it was on minor events. Now, things were getting more serious. But I could not reveal to him the detail and depth of the problems that faced me. So, skirting the real facts, we talked a lot. I think Joe sensed much of my problems and his advice was sobering and constructive. To me, Joe's head was "screwed on tight" and I liked the discussion -- a discussion I could not seem to orchestrate with many of the others on my staff.

While I had many problems on my mind, of the subjects I discussed with Joe, the matter of morality, logic, professional responsibility and trustworthiness dominated. We both recognized that the Korean environment placed unusual temptations in front of individuals as well as heaping on them unaccustomed responsibilities and a terrible environment. Further, often, simple foolhardiness entered the equation. In that context, Joe laughingly revealed to me the story of the G.I. who, during the night, seeking to locate a leak in a fuel line, used a match to illuminate the area. Igniting the fumes, the pipeline in the area blew up. Fortunately, the match-lighting individual survived.

**In response, I asked Joe if he knew about the G.I. who got the valves screwed up at Osan Air Base and ended up pumping fuel into the water system instead of the reverse? I told him that, following that event, the Osan Air Base had installed signs that read: IN CASE OF FIRE, DO NOT USE WATER.**

**And then we went on to compare all manner of notes on ludicrous happenings in Korea. At times, there were tears in our eyes as the ridiculousness of the Korean situation was revealed.**

**With dinner over and somewhat relaxed as a result of the conversation with Joe, I went back to my office, pulled the base defense plan from the safe and began reading. As I did, the lightheartedness of the evening evaporated.**

**The plan had been written years prior. There was nothing in it regarding the singular defense problem that worried me -- a direct, specially focused attack on the air base. Instead, the plan was really an overall war plan triggered by the North Koreans coming across the DMZ en masse on virtually a line. It was asserted that the Chinese Communists may or may not be attacking in concert -- but they may join the battle later -- as was the case of the Korean War. There would be accompanying air attacks from the north but they would be repelled by the ROKAF and U.S. tactical and air defense aircraft moved in from Japan and Okinawa and from U.S. Navy carriers. After that, there would be a flow of ground and air units from Hawaii and the U.S. mainland. Bombing attacks of the North Korean forces and their supply and communications system would be mounted jointly by the ROKAF, USAF and USN units. Command and control would be under the United Nations Command umbrella but, if that failed, there would be a joint U.S./Korea command arrangement -- obviously with the U.S. in the lead. But the matter of air operations was fuzzy -- apparently a lot of control of the air battle was supposed to emerge from Fifth Air Force in Japan and/or by way of CINCPAC in Hawaii. Still, set forth in the plan was a concern that Fifth Air Force might not be able to operate from Japan -- the Japanese were only allies of convenience -- that being: Japanese convenience.**

**Enemy forces were listed in reasonable but frightening detail. There was, however, a paucity of information covering the scope of friendly forces other than those already in Korea. If the North Koreans penetrated the DMZ and were able to move south, it was suggested that Kunsan Air Base would be abandoned with the personnel and key equipment evacuated. There was a map in the plan showing some of the roads leading eventually to Pusan -- few routings made much sense.**

**It was the Korean War all over again. There was a title page for nuclear operations but the following pages were all blank -- just fillers. The logistics and communications sections of the plan were meaningless. There was no usual Annex in the plan dealing with cover and deception; the intelligence plan segment was worthless; the only "base defense" language dealt with an increase in perimeter guards and the issuance of guns; in overview, it was a planning shambles.**

**On concluding my reading of the plan, I had only one thought: What a hell of a way to contemplate the running of a war!**

**[*Years later, as the J51 in CINCPAC and then, still later, as the DCS/ Plans in PACAF, I would have the opportunity to fine tune some of the planning for the defense of Korea. But it was an uphill battle with those who did the basic planning in the JCS. Most operational persons wanted to sit back until something developed and then figure out the details. The idea of pre-planned movements, specific targets and target folders, etc. was, for most, in the "too hard to do now" locker. However, some progress was made and, with the advent of computer support, there was a steady advance in the planning system. Notwithstanding, there is always something in the woodpile that can upset the best of planning. I learned that when, at one point as the situation in Korea worsened, General Nazarro, who was CINCPACAF, asked me to bring our plan for the defense of Korea to his office for review. To my total shock, when I asked my subordinate war plans office in PACAF to send me a copy of that plan, I was told that it had been destroyed by the person in charge "because it had not been used lately." To this day, that event is a common joke among those of my staff who survive and it truly exemplifies that historical assessment that "the best laid plans of mice and men can often go awry."*]**

**The base defense plan set aside, I found myself staring at the ceiling. What to do? I could not plan for all of Korea but, to do a proper job, I needed to find a way for my base to fit into a meaningful whole -- and there was no such meaningful whole. In fact, I did not hold an overall Korea plan from which to work. Undoubtedly, those in charge of war planning thought that Kunsan was too insecure and far removed or insignificant a facility to give it much in the way of baseline intelligence and planning information.**

**On the issue of base defense, I knew I was caught by policy that, on the surface, limited my jurisdiction, and supposedly my concern, to matters inside my perimeter. Theoretically, the area outside my**

**perimeter was defended by others -- army forces on land and naval forces at sea. At least that is what policy said but that was a specious portrayal -- the creation of a paper defense behind which those not at Kunsan Air Base could hide. At Kunsan Air Base, no one could hide.**

**Emblazoned in my mind was Giulio Douhet's assessment that, "it is easier and more effective to destroy the enemy's aerial power by destroying his nests and eggs on the ground than to hunt his flying birds in the air." Obviously, such destruction could occur prior to or after the initiation of hostilities. Yet, even in the case of hostilities, the war plan I had read did not envisage this event. Was it a case that the prior Korean War history and the absence of attack on airfields had lulled everyone into a false sense of security? But the North Koreans periodically attacked across the DMZ and regularly infiltrated South Korea. And, certainly, the North Koreans would be aware of the virtually defenseless air base at Kunsan. Why was it that the North Koreans expended manpower on cross-DMZ operations against well-defended positions when so lucrative a target as Kunsan Air Base was almost wide open to attack?* I had no answer but in my mind I could envisage a North Korean strategy intended to tie down the ground forces on the DMZ thereby precluding the development of an air base defense posture and setting up Kunsan and other air bases for later attack. Unfortunately, I knew that getting my own or other resources to defend against a postulated external attack was not in the cards.**

**I was, again, struck by that feeling of being all alone -- alone on a peninsula jutting into the Yellow Sea with Communist China over the proximate western horizon and North Korean infiltration surrounding me -- and all those to whom I thought I could turn for advice and assistance probably having cocktails or playing golf.**

**As I locked my safe and closed my office for the night, I was deeply troubled. I tried to write a letter to Mary but the words did not flow. In bed, sleep did not come. Finally, at about 0200 hours, I got up, dressed and drove to the Air Police Command Center.**

**My arrival at the Center caused considerable commotion. Captain Wild had been on duty during the day and his senior Sergeant was now in charge. The reaction team was playing cards when I entered. Attention was called. Putting the men at ease, I asked the senior Sergeant to accompany me on an inspection of the guard.**

---

* Some years later, in the 1967-69 time frame, significant North Korean infiltration, attacks and fire fights in the vicinity of the 2nd and 7th Infantry Divisions on the DMZ would number a half hundred but still no similar enemy action was taken against an air base in South Korea.

"Right now?" he asked.

"Right now," was my answer.

Shaking his head in wonderment, the senior Sergeant strapped on a forty-five and picked up a carbine.

"I have a vehicle outside and I suggest we use it instead of your staff car."

"Agreed."

And so I was off on my first inspection of the guard. As we left, I could hear someone calling Captain Wild.

I wasn't certain why I did what I did -- it just seemed the right thing to do at the time. I could see that I had thrown a monkey wrench into the workings of the Air Police.

"When was the last time the Commander of this base inspected the guard?" I asked as we drove away from the Air Police Center.

"Sir, as long as I have been here, I don't recall the Commander ever inspecting the guard."

"Day or night?"

"Neither."

"I would guess then that this visit to the perimeter, and that is where I want you to take me, will come as a surprise to the guards on duty?"

"Yes sir. And that worries me," the Sergeant said.

"Why?"

"Well, when you surprise men in a situation such as this, you can't tell what will happen."

As I weighed that judgment call by my senior Air Police Sergeant, we neared the first of the perimeter guards. At that post, and the following posts, I asked the standard question about orders, did a perfunctory inspection of weapons, and examined uniforms. Most of the guards recited a reasonable direction covering scrutiny, apprehension, use of fire power, self defense, etc. All the guards inspected were highly nervous and apprehensive at finding that their Commander was inspecting them. Several of the guards asked: Sir, is something wrong -- are we about to be attacked? One guard had noticeable lipstick smeared on his face but I ignored it. I was highly impressed with the dog handlers on the perimeter -- we had some great dogs -- fierce dogs -- I would not want to have been on the business end of their teeth.

Nearing the last of the perimeter guards, a pair of headlights approached. I guessed who it was and my guess was confirmed -- it was

**Wild. His clothes indicated a hurried dress -- he had a forty-five in a shoulder holster.**

**"Sir, why didn't you tell me you wanted to inspect the guard?"**

**"Because I did not want you to know. I wanted to see how things ran if you were not there -- and I have found out. Overall, your operation is pretty good. I'm sorry you felt compelled to get out of bed at this hour of the night. But, now that you are up, let's go by the G.I. mess and see if they have some coffee brewing -- I could use a cup."**

**I thanked the senior Air Police Sergeant and got into Wild's jeep for the trip to the G.I. mess. There was hot coffee in the mess and Wild and I drew a cup and sat down at one of the mess tables. I could see that the mess personnel and the handful of other night shift men in the mess hall getting a late meal were quick to comment to each other about the unexpected appearance of their Commander at this early morning hour.**

**Wild and I talked briefly about base security. I sensed that my inspection of the perimeter guard and my presence in the G.I. mess at the early hour was going to be bantered about in the coming days and I concluded that would be good. I had to assume that most persons would view my action as something special -- as if there was a proximate threat to the base. And that could only be productive.**

**Eventually, Wild again commented on my exposing myself to assassination. "You just should not run around like that," Wild stated. "You are placing yourself in jeopardy."**

**Even though I was concerned, and who would not be, I brushed away the problem.**

**[*In South Vietnam, the same issue came up when our intelligence discovered that the Vietcong, to assert their strength, sought to assassinate some senior American officers. Again, I brushed off the advice but, one night, an attack came in on one Air Force base that got within a few hundred feet of my billet. The attacking unit was wiped out by the Air Police who had been alerted by a sensor line. To my surprise, I slept right through the entire operation and did not learn what had happened until I got up for breakfast -- at which time I discovered the Air Police outside my billet were still searching for Vietcong bodies in tall grass that surrounded the area.*]**

**Finally, I had Wild drive me back to the Air Police Command Center to pick up my staff car and then proceeded to the Waldorf**

Astoria to try to get a few hours sleep before the dawn of day number seventeen.

It is very hard to describe uncertainty, concern and confusion. More and more, I found myself uncertain as to who was in charge of what. Was there a grand plan or were things just going pell-mell in any and every direction? If I had a defined mission, what was it? Was there any sense in anything that surrounded me? I had begun to think not. Apparently, all that was to happen at Kunsan Air Base would be what I generated. And, to a bottom line, I had a half thousand men I was supposed to lead. But lead to where? And, if I had a concern respecting the issue of mission, I was certain that such a concern was present among my men. Already, I had overheard men commenting to each other along the lines of: "Why in the hell are we out here?" Men will do almost anything if they perceive a purpose for their action. But there has to be logic to the prescribed purpose. To motivate the men, I knew I had to give them a sense of purpose -- something that would overcome the frustration and aimlessness with which they had been confronted. But I knew that my job would not be an easy one.

When the mind is surrounded by turmoil, sleep does not always come and, when it came to sleep, I was not going to be very successful.

I think it was about 0400 hours that I heard distant gunfire but generally ignored it. I was becoming callused. But the firing had awakened me and, awake, I got up and opened a can of beer. Then, still in shorts, I walked outside to survey the proximate world that was mine to orchestrate and defend.

I was troubled -- deeply troubled. This was not a fun and games situation -- this was serious business. Obviously, there was a missing link in the scenario but what it was I did not know. Inwardly, I wanted to talk to some of my friends in Hawaii or at the Pentagon but I did not have a secure telephone line.

And then I looked at the moon -- round, quiet, observing from afar. Perhaps, on the other side of the world, Mary had been looking at this same moon and wondering about me. In a moment of nostalgia, I went back to my bedroom, picked up the telephone and asked the operator to get me Mary back in Virginia. Thirty minutes later the verdict was in -- a connection could not be made. The operator talked about "atmospherics."

Totally frustrated by the world around me, I crawled under the mosquito tent.

**The attack came in over the sea wall. There were a half dozen junks and dark-uniformed men were flowing out of each. The single guard had fired all his clips and was screaming for assistance. The guard dog was dead.**

**I did not know why I was at the sea wall but I kept yelling for Captain Wild and the security force. No one responded.**

**And the attacking force kept coming on -- over the top of the sea wall and directly at us.**

**The security guard and I retreated.**

**Suddenly, I found a gun in my hand and fired but the bullets seemed to have no effect on the advancing enemy.**

**I tried to run but my legs would not move.**

**Then there were some wounded Americans around me. They looked at me; pointed fingers at me; I knew that they viewed me as the source of the problem.**

**Now I was clubbing the advancing enemy with the butt of a carbine. Some men moved up behind me and the enemy began to withdraw. There was a lot of gunfire. A number of the wounded Americans were smiling.**

**And then I awoke!**

**For a minute it was hard to separate reality from unreality. My bed was soaked with sweat and my mind was in a state of confusion. I knew that I needed some rest and I tried to lay back in the bed and relax. But relaxation was not to come easily. Finally, I did doze off but I was certain that it was only a few brief seconds before light entered the room and the reality of another morning descended upon me.**

**From outside, the sounds of morning began to filter into the room -- a jet engine was being run up, there was the clash of gears of a six-by, someone had turned on a stereo. Day number seventeen was underway.**

**Slowly, I swung my legs to the side of the bed, stretched my muscles and rose to face the daily unknown and unexpected. Across the face of Kunsan Air Base, hundreds of other men would be doing as I was doing -- others, their shift over, would probably now be seeking sleep and wondering about the future -- their future.**

# DAY SEVENTEEN -- A WEDNESDAY

Probably as a result of lack of sleep, or just from the result of being overwhelmed with problems, my mind was in a clutter. As I was having breakfast, I was joined by Akers. The word about my early morning inspection of the perimeter guards had already gotten around and Akers wanted to know if there was a special problem for him to worry about. My answer was that we had so many problems to worry about that I had no special one.

The rest of the breakfast conversation was rather perfunctory. I had to go to Osan for another staff meeting at 1300 hours and Akers wanted to go with me. When I asked him who was the next senior person, he stated that it was Peterson. I did not like leaving the base to ever more junior persons but I agreed. Akers was pleased and I suspected that he had some personal thing to get done at Osan.

The morning staff meeting had now developed into a routine. Those attending were comfortable with the exercise. Sergeant Butler's weather briefing was ominous -- the weather mass in the South Pacific had now developed typhoon strength and was moving rapidly to the west. Captain Polk said that he had a second swing set up and running in the ROK area. I thanked him for the effort and asked him now to build a teeter-totter. He only smiled and suggested that he thought I would get to that and he was already fashioning one. Major Turnbull had learned of my early morning inspection of the perimeter guards and he, like Akers, wondered if something was up -- I assured him that everything was normal -- whatever that meant. Jones advised that a lawn mower had been delivered to the base and he asked what he was to do with it. I was pleased pink. "Start it up, run it from daylight to sundown, change oil every ten hours and every ten hours sharpen the blade, and let's get some grass cut like it's supposed to be cut." There were smiles around the room. No one asked who was to run the mower. The next day I would send a check to my friend in Japan. Kunsan had a lawn mower and I was one more step forward on a long road!

At the close of the meeting, I advised everyone that Akers would go with me to Osan and that, in our absence, Peterson would be Acting Commander.

The Osan staff meeting was routine. The weather report was a repeat of what Sergeant Butler had given me at my own staff meeting.

The intelligence report was a virtual repeat of that at the prior Osan staff meeting -- essentially, nothing had changed. I wanted to comment about the infiltration data that Lt. Colonel Buckner had provided me but I decided to let it ride -- I was already causing too many waves. I had planned to talk to Jack Hubbard about my nuclear concerns but he had gone to Japan. The Wing Commander had nothing to say -- most of the time he just sat there and glared at me. I thought about inviting him to have a drink with me at the Officers Club following the meeting but then tossed the idea into File 13.

While at Osan, I managed to meet with the head of Counter Intelligence, a Lt. Colonel. We had a few words as to who was running what and what I would and would not put up with. To a bottom line, he assured me that his man in my area would act properly and keep me informed of problems. Mr. Olson, he said, had a Top Secret clearance "along with some other clearances." As I suspected, Olson was a junior enlisted person -- not intelligence trained, not CIA, just someone assigned to do a job and given some financial resources (probably too much) to work with. I was reminded of some persons I knew in War Two who were dropped into France with a suitcase of money and very little instruction or supervision. I had to wonder how we won any war.

On the way back to the aircraft, I noted that Osan had a swimming pool but it was not in use. When in Operations, I asked about the pool and was informed that the Koreans had stolen the filtration and chlorinating equipment some months ago and replacement items had not been received. It was obvious that we all had slicky problems. But, operational or not, I was disturbed that Osan had a reasonable range of recreation facilities while Kunsan had virtually nothing.

Returning to Kunsan Air Base, I found that Major Turnbull was waiting for me -- he wanted to report on the Airman Smith letter.

"From all I can determine, sir, most of the Airman Smith letter is simply a bunch of fabrication designed to impress his mother. He has been trying to marry this Korean girl and, for some time, everyone has been trying to dissuade him -- and, I might add, for his own good. That and other things aside, you do have one problem. Wherein Airman Smith alleges that your Air Police have used grenades to chase men out of prostitute hootches, I discovered that the real story is that one of your senior Air Police Sergeants used a grenade against some Korean children."

I knew my knuckles turned white. I wanted to explode and I almost did.

"What the hell are your telling me?" I demanded. "A grenade against kids? And an Air Policeman did it?"

"Not a frag," Turnbull answered, "it was a tear gas grenade. But it seems that it probably tore up the kids a bit."

"Why? Why in the hell *why*? Why would someone do such a God damned thing? And to kids?"

"It's an involved story, Colonel. It seems that there arrived here at the base a group of new persons for the Air Police unit and this Sergeant took them out to the firing range to instruct them on the use of the pistol and the carbine. This was before you took command. Anyhow, when he got through with the instruction and with empty brass casings laying around, he waved the Korean kids in to pick up the casings. Apparently, the kids trade the casings for candy in the local village. Now, when the Korean kids were all scrambling around to pick up the brass, he pulled out a tear gas grenade and threw it into the middle of them. When it went off, there was a lot of screaming and yelling and the kids ran away."

"How bad were the kids hurt?"

"We don't know."

"And why did the Sergeant do it?"

"This is a tough one, Colonel. But I have over a dozen sworn statements that verify it."

"Go on."

"Well, after the firing was done and the men were ordered on the truck to come back from the firing range, with the Korean kids picking up the brass, this Sergeant tossed in the grenade with the words that this would teach the new recruits who was running the base. The words used by the Sergeant were: *If you think that S.O.B. Colonel we got is running this base, think again. We run this base!* Again, this was before you arrived so the assertion may have been aimed at your predecessor and may have no current application."

Regardless of whether the assertion was aimed at my predecessor or still inclusive of myself, I was stunned!

"Are you absolutely certain about what you tell me?"

"Absolutely."

I thought a minute. There had just been a bad PR event in Japan where a female metal scavenger had been killed on a firing range. The scavenger had penetrated the range while bombs were still being dropped. But the American press had gotten all over the Air Force for the death -- according to the press the Air Force was fully to blame. My God -- what would they do with this Korean "kids" thing if they got wind of it? I called in Akers and Pastiak, briefed them on the situation and ordered an immediate summary court. As I expected, the summary court reduced the person to Private. That action underway, I called General Joyce, explained to him what had happened and what I was doing about it and then told him that, when I hung up, it would be as if I had never called him -- meaning that, if the press got wind of the event, he could deny everything and let the load rest on my shoulders.

I then called Wild, explained the situation to him and asked him to bring a tear gas grenade to the firing range along with some heavy canvas -- I had to see for myself. At the range, we exploded the tear gas grenade under the canvas -- the plastic case tore about a hundred holes in the canvas -- some were significant. I wondered how many Korean kids had been torn up. I was mad as hell but it had happened and there was no denying it. But what was this about the Air Police running Kunsan Air Base and, by extension, I was not? There was something deeper to this whole thing and I had to find out what it was. In a few days I would.

The culprit in this scenario was scheduled out of the base on the next day's flight. I was a firm believer in swift justice being good justice. Still, overall, I had, once again, to reflect on what Korea was doing to persons. This man, a five stripe Sergeant with a good history prior to being assigned to Korea, was now a Private and heading for disgrace. Where would it end? What had happened? Looking to the future, could I do anything about it? Could I prevent something such as this from happening on my watch? What was the root evil?

I talked to Wild and we both speculated about how deep the problem possibly ran -- were there others of the mind of this airman? Wild wanted to tear into his men but I suggested that we play a low key game and see what developed. Word of the summary court martial would get around quickly and that could be the end of it -- only time would tell.

Events such as this grenade incident do not readily slip from one's mind and for the rest of the day I kept visualizing the Korean kids, on their knees, scrambling to pick up the brass shell casings and then the grenade going off. I could not help but think of my own children and what I would do if they were subjected to such unthinkable action. To me, simple reduction in military grade was an expeditious but inadequate punishment for the crime committed.

# SURPRISE IN KUNSAN CITY

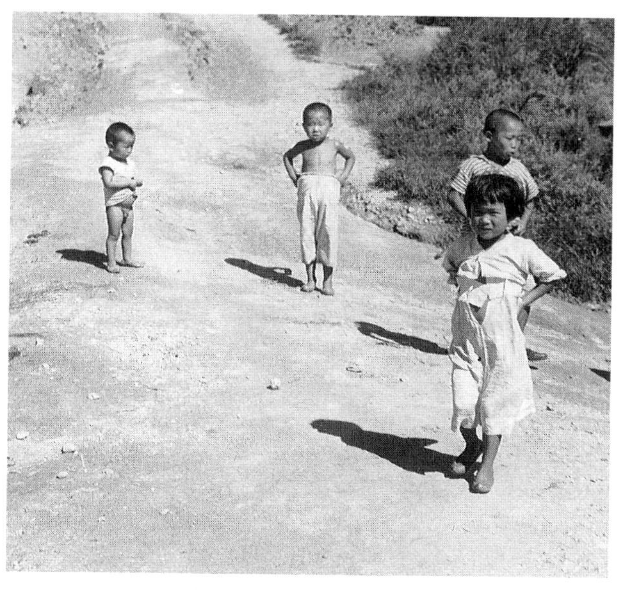

*The idea of an American serviceman harming innocent Korean children such as above was unthinkable. Note the little fellow on the left with no pants. They were great, friendly, happy kids surviving at the lowest level of the ladder.*

I was in a foul mood at dinner. The idea of an American serviceman harming any children was unthinkable -- yet, it had happened -- and on my base even though it was before my time.

That aside, I knew I had to do something about the Airman Smith marriage situation but that could wait. More important was that which might underlie the statement that my Air Police ran Kunsan Air Base?

Finished with dinner, I went to the bar and ordered a Scotch and soda. Wild joined me. I think we both wanted to talk about the idea of some of his men holding the view that they were running the base but, at the same time, neither of us wanted to discuss the matter in detail -- or openly. Unfortunately, Turnbull and those serving on the summary court would be aware of the assertion -- more might know of it. What were the thoughts, concerns and doubts of such persons? Would they come to wonder about my capability to command -- to control my own Air Police? Or would they simply relate this event to the past Commander? Inwardly, I wondered how widespread the problem might be -- was it a matter of one or two persons or a number of persons? And what would be the next steps that might be taken to enforce the views of such persons -- persons who, in the main, held virtually all the guns on the base? Was I looking at a mutiny? And, if so, how did one combat a mutiny?

Eventually, Wild and I talked about the josan problem on the base and how my policy was working. Both of us concluded that the activity had slowed considerably. And then we discussed the On-Limits entertainment in Kunsan City. And then I had a totally crazy idea.

"Wild, do you have your vehicle outside?"

"Yes."

"And what is it -- a jeep or a weapons carrier?"

"A weapons carrier."

"Covered?"

"Yes. But why do you ask?"

"Never mind the *why* of the question. Can you go through the gate without the guards looking into the rear of the weapons carrier."

"Certainly. They are my men -- at least, until recently, I thought they were my men."

"O.K. You and I are going to stroll out of the Officers Club and, when we are outside, I am going to get into the rear of your weapons carrier and you are going to drive me to Kunsan City undetected -- right through the outside gate. When we get to Kunsan City, I want you to proceed to one of those On-Limits recreation operations we saw when we visited. I want to see what is going on at night."

"But why, sir? You are a Colonel. Why would you want to do this?"

"Frankly, I don't know but right now I am starting to stroll out of this facility and I trust you are strolling out with me."

True to Wild's statement, we went through the gate without a guard looking into the rear of the weapons carrier. Some miles outside the gate, I crawled into the front of the vehicle.

"Road is rough, isn't it?"

"Sure is," Wild responded, "and at night it's hard to miss all the holes and ruts."

En route, we were waved through a ROK army checkpoint and shortly we entered Kunsan City. The city was very drearily dark -- only here and there did a light burn and much of the lights that did burn were oil lamps. There was virtually no traffic on the road. In some places, people were sleeping on the roadside. Eventually, Wild stated that we were about to pull up in front of the largest of the On-Limit entertainment establishments. It was a two-story building. Music could be heard coming from inside. As Wild's vehicle slowed in front, a person who seemed to be acting as an exterior guard came forward. And then I was spotted! Suddenly, there was much shouting in Korean. Almost immediately, there poured out of the building's front door, its windows, even from second story windows, a stream of leaping, running, jumping G.I.s, josans and male Koreans -- every person seemingly dragging another -- some persons just tumbled over other persons in their haste to vacate the premises -- a few tripped and fell into the sewage ditch in front of the establishment. The flow of persons was so terrific that no one could have possibly passed through it in an opposite direction. The scene was akin to a Laurel and Hardy comedy. And then, as suddenly as it began, it was over. The many American and Korean persons who had come out of the structure had melted into the black of the night. Now, there was a well-dressed Korean standing at the front entrance, smiling and bowing toward us.

"Colonel, you come in. See club, please," he said.

The whole scene was so ridiculous that I felt like laughing. But it was serious -- it had to be serious.

With Wild at my side, I entered the On-Limits establishment. Wild had his gun flap open.

Inside, there was a series of rough wooden tables and benches along each side wall. To the rear of the room there was a small orchestra. Except for the orchestra and a few waiters who stood stiffly and then bowed as we approached, there was no one remaining in the club. On the tables, I saw some paper cups. There was an open center area in the club which I presumed was a dance floor. The floors were made of rough wood planks -- and dirty. Some dim incadescent lights burned.

"Colonel like club? Yes?"

I did not answer. Instead I walked out of the club and climbed into the weapons carrier.

"Let's go back to the base," I suggested. I was thoroughly disgusted at what I had observed.

Driving toward the base, I looked at my watch. It was close to midnight.

"How many of our G.I.s do you think were at that club?" I asked.

"My guess is somewhere between fifty and seventy-five," Wild answered.

"And how do they get from the base to that club -- and home again?"

"It has to be the Korean buses."

"And when, tonight, is the last Korean bus to the base?"

"Not until morning."

"So, with two On-Limits clubs in the city, we may have as many as one hundred or more of our men in Kunsan City over night."

"Appears so."

"Are these men on passes?"

"Sir, we don't issue passes. The only criteria is that the men be present for duty time. After that, they are on their own."

"So, if we had a base alert, we would be a hundred or more men short?"

"I guess so."

"Does any of this strike you as being wrong?"

"It's the way it has been working. It's the system I inherited. Perhaps it is wrong but no one has questioned it. I was not aware that the number of men we saw were going into Kunsan City. It may be the effects of your josan policy."

"Well, I'm concerned as all hell about what we observed -- and tomorrow or the next day I want to review this whole thing. First it was a josan problem and now this!"

It was well past midnight when we returned to the base. My staff car had been driven to my quarters. My guess was that Jones had done me the courtesy -- I knew he had a key to the car. And my further guess was that there were those who, not knowing what had happened, thought I had found a josan and drifted off somewhere.

I needed some rest but I knew that this would be another sleepless night. Was it really that my josan policy was now driving men off the base for all night stints in Kunsan City? There is an old rule that when you take something away from a person, unless you give something back, you can have trouble on your hands. I had taken away the standing josan "perk" but had given virtually nothing in return. I knew that some of the answer rested in improvements to the base recreational facilities. But there was nothing I could do about that in the few weeks I had left to serve as Commander. Perhaps something could be done later -- but not now.

Before falling asleep, the issue of VD assumed major proportions in my thinking. Apparently, my josan policy had, indeed, driven men to the filth of Kunsan City -- and I could see the VD rate skyrocketing. But, I could not back down on the josan policy. What could I do? I hoped the Chaplains were praying for miracles -- and for me. In the vernacular, "I had arrived at a position beside myself."

# DAY EIGHTEEN -- A THURSDAY

By the time the 0600 alarm sounded, I was certain that I had not slept more than a total of a half hour. There was just too much piling in on me. Dressing for the day, I resolved that I would try to approach life at a slower pace. Perhaps, partly because I knew my time at Kunsan Air Base was limited, I was just attempting to do too much in too short a time -- perhaps I just had some Korea adjusting to do -- perhaps it would do me and the men good if I just relaxed and leaned forward in the foxhole for a while. And, with that thought in mind, I decided that I was long overdue in visiting my subordinate command at Taegu -- whatever that was. Accordingly, at the morning staff meeting, I asked Akers about using the L-20 for the trip over.

"If you're up to a bit of unusual navigation, I'll fly with you," he offered. "Peterson can handle things while we're gone."

"What do you mean -- *unusual navigation*?

There was a mild chuckle in the room.

"Well, with the ceiling down as it is, to get to Taegu, we fly the railroad track until it goes into a mountain. Then we climb on instruments and time ourselves over the mountain. When we believe we are clear of the peak, we let down on the other side, pick up the railroad track, and follow it into Taegu."

Once more I was stunned. This was "bush flying" -- not military flying.

"Don't they have a radio range at Taegu? I saw one on the charts."

"Yes, but it is unreliable -- the railroad track is better."

Well, if that was the way it was done, then I was going to do it. We took off at about 1000 hours.

True to forecast, flying down the railroad track I saw it enter a tunnel in the side of the mountain. And then we climbed straight ahead until well clear of the peak elevation. Some minutes later, Akers pointed down and I made an instrument descent. At about 600 feet we broke out of the clouds and there, again, was the railroad track. Akers grinned -- I knew he was enjoying the event. Soon, we were at Taegu.

In that we had not wired ahead that we were coming, there was no one at the field to meet us but Akers soon had a call placed to the

**local Air Force commander. About twenty minutes later, a jeep pulled up and Major Charles Newcomb saluted and introduced himself.**

**"Wish you had let me know you were coming, sir. I would have met you and we could have laid on a reception."**

**"No need for that," I answered. "This is an informal visit. I have been at Kunsan for about two weeks and felt it was time to get over here. Just run me to where it is that you work, or live, and we can take it from there."**

**"I'll take you to my quarters. My wife is already making a fresh pot of coffee," he answered.**

**Wife? I was taken back until I realized that Newcomb was a part of the Military Assistance Program and was on a two-year accompanied tour.**

**Newcomb's quarters were a small Korean house built along the Japanese style with sliding wood and paper doors, virtually no furniture, one sat on the floor to eat. The bedroom had a mattress on the floor. There was a girl servant who brought in some sweets.**

**"We get used to it," Newcomb replied to my obvious question.**

**The command arrangement at Taegu was very confused. It appeared that Newcomb was supervised by Colonel Jenkins in Seoul except that, for some things, especially support, he looked to me. Newcomb did not have an aircraft of his own -- he flew ROKAF aircraft and served as an advisor to the ROKAF fighter unit. There was a ROKAF radar at Taegu and the USAF men servicing that unit apparently were on my manning document but they reported to Newcomb -- for the control and administration of those persons, Newcomb reported to me. Taegu was also a transport terminal and the men operating that facility also were on my manning document. Quarters for all Americans were in buildings that Newcomb said were in parallel to the one he occupied. "All native, nothing fancy," were his words. Did he like his job? The answer was that "it was a picnic."**

**After coffee, Newcomb drove us around the base but there was not much to see. From Newcomb I learned that some of the men serving at Teagu had been there for more than one year. Did they have Korean wives? Newcomb shrugged and implied that some might have either a Korean wife or a regular live-in josan. "I really don't worry about it," he said. "So long as they do their job, I don't care what they do on their off duty time."**

**By 1500 hours, Akers and I were in the L-20 and flying the railroad track back to Kunsan.**

The trip to Taegu was like a vacation for me. I was concerned about Newcomb's lackadaisical approach to life but, as I reflected on it, he might have a better answer than the one I had.

For several hours, Kunsan had not existed. Now it appeared dead ahead from under the low-lying cloud deck.

One circle of the field and I set the L-20 on the runway and ran it into the ramp area in front of Operations. Jones was there to greet us.

"Problems?" I asked.

"No sir. The lawn mower is running great and we have much of the officers area already cut. The officers are having a ball with it. They insisted on using it first. RHIP has its points. The Koreans are awed by it. I guess that they have never seen one."

"Just make sure that they keep it in oil," I admonished. "We only have one of them."

"Everyone understands. Don't worry."

Akers and Jones joined me in the staff car. I wanted to talk about passes and the situation in Kunsan City but decided to wait. Instead, I raised the Airman Smith problem.

"Are your aware of the Airman Smith letter and his wanting to marry some Korean girl?" I asked Jones.

"Yes sir."

"And what do you think we should do?"

"Frankly, I think you ought to just ship him out. He's more trouble than he's worth. I understand that he's now bragging to his friends that his letter to his mother has got you jumping through hoops."

"Really?"

"Yes sir.

"Well, let's put the Airman Smith subject on tomorrow's staff meeting agenda -- something to follow the staff meeting. Alert the Chaplain, Captain Pastiak, Captain Wild and Airman Smith's boss -- I guess that is Major Peterson."

"Yes sir."

The headquarters building now loomed ahead.

"I'll have retreat playing tonight," Jones stated. "I've got the turn table fixed."

The thought made me feel good.

Jones had my administrative work laid out for me -- stacks on my desk. When that work was finished, my thoughts turned to home and the fact I had not written to Mary in some days. And that led me to think about my needed tape recorder. I asked Jones about the closing time for the PX and learned that it was still open so I went by it on the way to the Officers Club. On entering the PX, I was greeted by the Korean manager who was all smiles. Disappearing into a back room, he emerged with a tape recorder -- not a fancy one but it would do.

"Colonel work much late," the manager stated. "Colonel now can talk into machine instead of write letters. Save much time for to do good Kunsan job. I like."

The PX manager's statement startled me. How was it that he had knowledge of my working hours? And was he talking about the late inspection of the perimeter guards or the visit to Kunsan City? I did not respond.

"Also got bathroom paper for Colonel. Save big package for Colonel. One dozen rolls."

"Thank you," I said as I paid for the recorder and the toilet paper.

I left the PX troubled. Something bothered me but I could not put a finger on it.

Exiting the PX, I noticed a small, adjacent building that carried a multitude of signs: Tailor Shop, Photo Shop, Watch and Camera Repair Shop. It was one of the better base buildings. Needing some repairs to my uniforms, I entered. Inside, I found a couple all-purpose Koreans who asserted a capability to do anything for a price. I told them I would be back.

*The Tailor Shop, Photo Shop, Watch and Camera Repair Shop.*

# DAYS NINETEEN, TWENTY & TWENTY-ONE FRIDAY, SATURDAY & SUNDAY

At the Friday morning staff meeting, the item of greatest concern was Sergeant Butler's weather report. The typhoon in the South Pacific had strengthened and was speeding up. And it was definitely on the same track as the one that had hit Korea two weeks prior.

Following the staff meeting, I met with Chaplain Johnson, Peterson, Pastiak and Wild to discuss the Airman Smith situation -- Chaplain Johnson as Smith was Protestant. After over an hour of review of the history of the case, much of it on the seamy side, and considerable in the way of heated debate, I made a terrible decision. I told those present to stop fighting the situation and facilitate Airman Smith's marriage but that, once married, he had to be reassigned immediately to the States. I think, in exasperation, I stated that both Airman Smith and his mother deserved the young lady. Years later, I would hate myself for that decision. With his marriage to the Korean prostitute approved, Airman Smith would proceed to brag to his friends about how he had "twisted my tail" on the subject but the outfall was that he got married and, shortly, was reassigned to the Zone of Interior and I was rid of him. I was led to understand that, in Korean currency, he paid well over the equivalent of one thousand dollars to purchase the girl's record from the ROK police to facilitate her entry into the United States. I hoped he made a good deal but I doubted it.

Probably the most significant event in these three days was the Saturday base clean up contest. The teams did a great job and a mountain of junk was collected. I had to wonder why the Koreans had not availed themselves of all this metal just laying around and then I came to realize that things became more valuable when a fence was placed around them. In the succeeding days, the mound of fenced scrap metal seemed to vaporize more and more with each succeeding day.

During these three days I sought to get my thoughts together, particularly on the subject of base defense but also on my own rate of activity -- it was not easy.

Over the weekend, we did have some perimeter concertina stolen and we had none in stock to replace it -- so the affected border area was minus a barricade. And this added to my defense worries.

There were the other usual slicky problems but nothing major. Operations in the alert area went smoothly except for one officer who refused to eat the meal served to him in the Officers Club. Eventually, I was called and learned that, in succession, three chickens had been fried for him and he refused them all with excuses varying from too greasy, to over-cooked, to something else. And he had become almost violent on the subject. My own officers were totally fed up with his demands and they came to me for assistance. Hearing the story, I had the officer brought to my office. By then it was about 2300 hours, and I attempted to reason with him but it was impossible. In high-sounding, assertive terms, he demanded better food, claimed I was an idiot commander who could not feed his own men, and stated all sort of other claims some of which touched on the josan issue. To a bottom line, my patience with the officer wore thin and I restricted him from the Officers Club. I told him that, henceforth, he could eat in the G.I. mess. He retorted that no one had a right to restrict him from an Officers Club as he was a member in good standing in Japan -- at which time I told him he not only could go back to Japan but I ordered it. He seemed delighted at the outcome. I expected to hear from his commander about the event but nothing ever materialized. I concluded that this officer had wanted out of Korea and, by antagonizing me, he found a way to get out. I let the matter drop. I had enough worries without adding this officer to the equation. In my view, the situation would catch up with him.

Late Saturday night, the stillness was broken with considerable machine gun fire to the east. As in the prior event, we received no elaborating information from the Korean community. I called the event in to the Osan Command Center but it seemed to bother no one. I could not understand why such events were only of a concern to me.

Being awake at the late Saturday night hour, I tried calling Mary and finally got through the maze of telephone and radio systems to the Pentagon and then was connected to Mary. In spite of shouting, we could hardly hear each other and, to make matters worse, we were dealing with an "over and out" high frequency radio circuit. The call

**was unsettling to both of us. But I did learn that Mary and our children were well.**

**On Sunday, I went to the Catholic service. Father Collins seemed pleased that I was there and he made a point of it in his comments to the attending persons. I was worried, however, that he was seeking to influence me rather than talk to God.**

**After church, I went to watch a baseball game. The field had been freshly mowed -- obviously by the rotary I had brought in.**

**At the game, I did the usual rooting and cheering but was still deeply worried about the number of men working double shifts so that a few could play baseball. I decided that, come Monday, I was going to talk to the senior person on the team and seek to explain my problem. I sensed that this would not be a good conversation but I found it difficult to see men playing baseball while others dealt with such enormous mental and physical problems as perimeter defense and double shifts. Somehow, the balance of effort and focus was not proper. Had I had more personnel, the problem would not be a matter of concern -- but I was skinny, bone dry when it came to bodies. Perhaps there was an answer to the situation, a way to turn "baseball" into a "plus" rather than a "negative?"**

**When it came to Sunday night, I found the blare of the many stereo sets running at full blast to the very early hours of the next day to be out of reason and I decided that, at the Monday morning staff meeting, it would be a subject to address. Mentally, I decided that a curfew of 0100 hours on loud stereos was not unreasonable.**

**[*Loud noise is seldom heard by the person producing it but it can be an intolerable annoyance to those required to suffer through it. I was reminded of the Hickam AFB officer who had flown something on the order of a sixteen hour reconnaissance mission and had finally turned into his billet for some needed sleep. But the hour was about noon and, outside his billet window, a person was flying a tethered model airplane with the usual racking noise of the motor. Exasperated, the person trying to sleep loaded his shotgun and, as the model airplane zoomed by his bedroom window, he shot it out of the sky. Yes, he was reprimanded -- but who was there who could not sympathize with him?*]**

**I think it must have been about 0300 or 0400 hours that something else awakened me. Peering out from inside the mosquito tent, I realized that there was a figure silhouetted outside the window and I could see the shadow of a gun barrel pointed upward. I doubted**

**that the individual standing outside could see me as I was shielded not only by darkness but by the covering mosquito net. Slowly, trying not to reflect a movement, I pulled my thirty-eight from under the pillow and aimed it at the figure. And then I waited and waited for what seemed an eternity. Suddenly, almost in the blink of an eye, the figure disappeared. "What the hell," I thought, "was this the forecast assassination attempt?"**

**One does not readily go to sleep after such an experience and, now wide awake, my mind turned and turned until it settled on the matter of Efficiency Ratings -- soon I would want to write such reports on the officers and enlisted men who reported directly to me. Fortunately, Lt. Colonel Davidson was no longer one of my problems.**

**Regarding the others, I was becoming more comfortable with Akers, Peterson, Polk and many more. Most had short-comings when it came to experience but they still hung in there and sought to do a good job. I had decided that the Enlisted Club situation I encountered with Wild was to be dismissed -- he was doing a good job -- much more than one could expect from someone who had no prior experience in the work. Pastiak was still tops on my list -- a great guy -- I thought he would make a good politician and we needed that in Washington. Jones warranted the earliest possible promotion and I would make certain that his Efficiency Rating said that. Sergeant Young seemed O.K. but I sensed he needed a bit of push to get the jobs done. And so I went through person after person. Those outside the military structure do not understand the significance of Efficiency Ratings -- ERs they are called. Such ratings determine the future of an individual and they need to be treated most seriously. I intended to do that but it was not an easy chore to contemplate.**

**Eventually, I got to sleep but it seemed like only minutes when the 0600 alarm went off. I was beat. And I knew that my growing tiredness was beginning to show in my decisions. My tolerance level was getting very low. Hopefully, the Kunsan Air Base machinery would soon start to run more smoothly. Momentarily, I thought about retrieving my shotgun from the Air Police Command Center and flying to Cheju-Do for some pheasant hunting.**

# DAY TWENTY-TWO -- A MONDAY

Joe Pastiak joined me at breakfast and we began our conversation by discussing the stereo problem. He recognized my feelings but held out for a loose policy. "The men here are up tight and they need some outlet," he stated. "Stereo is one outlet and, while it makes for one hell of a racket, it really hurts no one. You've clamped down on the josan problem and the men have accepted it. To hit them on the stereos will be a bit too much. To be quite frank, you are coming across as too negative and it is hurting you."

I liked Joe -- he was willing to give me a straight shot even if it hurt. By the end of the discussion, I leaned toward easing up on my thoughts and mentally decided that, at the coming morning staff meeting, I would urge a "be kind to others" voluntary 0200 hours volume turn down.

I then discussed with Joe my concern about the number of men off base at any one time and the pass situation. We both laughed when I recounted my experience at the Kunsan night spot when Wild had secretly taken me off base and I suddenly appeared in front of one of the establishments. I told Joe that I would have given anything to have had a movie of the event. The story was so humorous that I had tears in my eyes telling it.

Eventually, we got back to the pass situation.

"As far as I know, we've never had a pass requirement here," Joe stated. "The men are accounted for at the duty times and, if they are present for duty, they are present for the daily morning report. I think a good number of men go off base every night -- probably spend the night off base. Whether we have more going off base now than in the past -- I have no idea."

"And, if we have an emergency during a person's off duty time, he may well not be on base -- a whole lot of men may not be on base."

"That's correct, sir."

"Suppose I set a requirement that not more than ten percent of the men can be off base at any one time?"

"Colonel, I just don't know what the reaction would be. You're back again doing negative things. If you could justify to the men the need, they would probably take it in stride. But, without justifying the need, there could be hell to pay. After all, they are used to the existing system. If something was O.K. yesterday, why is it not O.K. today? People can accept change, but they have need to understand the purpose. Arbitrary change is never good."

"Your argument sounds great until I get to our food situation. Because this base has had poor food in the past is an effort to get better food to be considered a negative change? Let's approach the pass problem from a different angle. Suppose I set forth a requirement that any enlisted person going off base for other than official purposes must have a pass signed by his commander. Is that not the norm in most situations?"

"I don't see that as presenting a problem other than the administrative time it takes to fill out the pass forms. But how many men can a commander authorize to be on pass?"

"And that takes us back to where we just have been," I answered.

I wanted to discuss with Joe the matter of those men living in hootches with Korean "wives" but the time had arrived for us to go to the headquarters for the morning staff meeting.

Sergeant Butler's weather briefing was ominous. Typhoon Number Two was strong and it definitely was heading our way. The best prognosis was that it would hit Korea about the coming Wednesday -- two days hence. With satisfaction that we now had a good supply of sand bags, I told Akers to get the typhoon plan rolling.

Peterson advised that a train containing about a dozen cars had arrived from Pusan and that it was on our siding. The train contained general purpose bombs and two sealed cars that were supposed to contain PX supplies. To start my day on the wrong foot, Peterson stated that the sealed cars had been entered from below and they were empty.

"Don't they put guards on the trains?" I asked.

"They do but just at the front and rear. They are Army guards -- not Air Force. For a train of any length, this theft thing can happen," Peterson answered. "I looked at the cars and the slicky guys who did it cut about twenty-four inch holes in the bottoms of the cars."

"And the guards saw or heard nothing?"

"I've talked to the guards and the only thing they say is that it must have happened during the night when they were on a siding."

"And they were probably asleep or a part of the operation. Crap!" What else could I say? Our PX was already slim and now the supply would be even less. Could I do what General Eisenhower had done when he found Jerry cans missing on arriving gasoline resupply trucks?

"Did we lose any of the bombs?" I asked.

"No sir."

"Did we order the bombs?"

"No sir. Fifth Air Force just decided to send them."

"And what are they?"

"Five hundred and one thousand pounders -- plus some practice bombs."

"The real bombs are probably too heavy to make stealing them easy and the practice bombs probably have no use in the Korean economy." I knew my comment had a bitter tone to it.

"That situation aside," Jones cut in, "we received a message that a Division inspector will arrive on today's commuter flight."

"Who is he and how long will he stay?" I asked.

"His name is William Pepperman and he is a civilian. The message we received said that he would stay overnight."

"What's his civilian grade?"

"I don't know, sir. But we usually give the inspector access to the Officers Club."

"O.K. Give him access but find him a bed in the enlisted billets."

"That will probably make him one unhappy inspector, Colonel, and he may retaliate with a bad report."

"And, in the process, he might write up the enlisted billets and we might get Fifth Air Force to improve the situation by way of a little new construction. Let's give it a try. When this Mister Pepperman arrives, bring him straight to my office. I want to talk to him."

"Yes sir."

"And the first thing after staff meeting, I want to meet with the senior person in our baseball team. Who is he?"

"That's Staff Sergeant Wilcox, sir -- Stanley Wilcox," Jones answered.

Sergeant Wilcox turned out to be a well built, personable individual. I had him join me at the office couch for a cup of Miss Lee's coffee. I asked him to brief me on the baseball situation.

"It was on-going when I arrived here, sir. I played ball in college and, when I arrived, they appointed me to head the team. I was told that Fifth Air Force demanded we have a team to compete with other unit and base teams in the Fifth Air Force area."

"How many teams have you played with and how good did you do?" I asked.

"Actually, in the six months I've been here, we only played other teams twice -- once in Korea at Osan and once in Japan at Tachikawa. We lost both times. Our problem is that, being on a small base, we don't have the talent to choose from. With the help of Lieutenant Jones, I look at in-coming personnel and try to pick out some talent but it isn't easy."

"And the rest of the time what do you do? Two games in six months is hardly a good games schedule."

"Every day we can, every day except Saturday or Sunday, we practice. On Saturday or Sunday, depending on the weather, we have a local game. If we are short persons for two teams we ask for volunteers."

This introductory conversation having moved forward with ease, I decided to approach my larger concern.

"Sergeant, I want to be frank with you. I have a problem facing me. As I think you know, we are short-handed and we have no manpower spaces allocated for baseball -- the men who play ball come out of the unit manpower. And that means for each man on the team someone in the units, probably more than one person, has to do additional duty. I am particularly concerned about my Air Police where, often, the men have to double shift to cover the essential needs. And you may know that we recently had a man in the hospital, a good man, who came apart doing double shifts day after day. How can I explain to such persons the workload they carry when there are others, such as yourself, who spend the day playing ball?"

"Colonel, I don't know. As an enlisted man, I don't set the priorities. When I arrived the team was on-going. I was just told to run it. My training was in communications and I was surprised at the detail. But I did it. If you're suggesting that we disband the team, I don't know what the impact would be. It would be up to you to handle the Fifth Air Force aspect. Locally, the base has been so accustomed to the team playing during the good months of the year that I think there would be some unhappy folks."

"Suppose we made baseball participation an extra duty assignment?"

"I don't think we'd have a team -- the men would be too tired."

"Suppose the team members only worked a half day and played a half day?"

**Sergeant Wilcox was frowning. I sensed that he saw the end of baseball on the horizon and struggled to find a way not to lose the team. I thought it best to alter the subject area.**

**"Does the ROKAF play baseball?"**

**"Not that I know, sir. We really don't mix with the ROKAF unit. They live in their area and we live in ours."**

**"I saw some ROKAF watching you fellows play yesterday. Did you ever think of inviting them to try out?"**

**"It's the language, sir. Very few of the ROKAF speak English and none of our guys speak Korean."**

**"It's a thought and do give it some thought. And, if you think about it, we are on the same team here in Korea. If something happens, the better we know one another the better we can fight together. And that brings me around to base defense and security. And that causes me to ask you a question. Your team obviously can function as a team and each person pretty well knows the other persons on the team. Am I correct?"**

**"You're correct, sir. We have a pretty good team relationship."**

**"Well, how bad would it be if the team gave up one day a week for some special team duty?"**

**"I don't understand, sir. What kind of duty?"**

**"Can your team members handle a gun? Do they know how to shoot and hit anything. They can throw a ball but when was the last time they shot a pistol, a carbine or a rifle -- or threw a grenade?"**

**"Frankly, I don't know. I haven't fired a gun since I came to Korea -- haven't thrown a grenade since basic training."**

**"Well, let me give you a proposition to think over. We are short as blazes in the area of security. Suppose I gave your baseball team a special security job -- call it a reinforcing security team -- something organized and trained to reinforce the Air Police if we had a penetration of this base -- a team that knew each other and understood the problem and the need for teamwork. And suppose that one day a week was devoted to this type of military training and, now and then, the team did some real soldier duty. Could you do it?"**

**"I think we could, sir. And, if it is only one day a week, we could get by. Actually, it might do the team some good. If they had other duty to perform it might make them inclined to work a little harder at baseball just to make sure that they didn't get some other job on a full-time basis."**

**"O.K. If you can get your team on board with that idea -- and I don't mean reluctantly on board -- I mean really enthusiastic about the**

plan -- I'll see if we can't get you a game lined up in Japan. I would think your team would like to get away for a day or two."

Sergeant Wilcox left smiling. We both had won! My satisfaction at achieving something without giving an order, however, was to be short lived. Akers was standing at the door and I could detect that the news he carried was not good.

"Sir, we have a problem."

"And what now?"

"Sir, when I passed out the word to fill the sandbags to get things ready for the typhoon I learned that we didn't have any shovels."

"What! A military base with no shovels?" I was flabbergasted.

"No sir. The explanation I get is that they have all been stolen by the Koreans."

"And the typhoon -- any change in movement?"

"No sir. It still looks like it will hit us early Wednesday morning. We may get some rain from the lead elements sometime tomorrow."

First no sand bags and now no shovels! What would it be next? And there was no time to get shovels from a supply point in time to do any good. Why hadn't someone thought about shovels? Why hadn't I thought about shovels? Why hadn't I suspected a lack of shovels when I noticed that all the drainage ditches had been silted shut?

"O.K. Let's hope that Typhoon Number Two is as kind to us as was Typhoon Number one. In the meantime, tell Major Peterson or Captain Polk, whoever is in charge of shovels, to do some emergency shovel requisitioning. And tell them that I don't want to get bogged down with Equipment Allowances and all such nonsense. In terms of numbers, tell them that I want one shovel for each man on this base and that, when we get them, I want them closely controlled -- the same as if they were a gun."

Akers saluted and left.

When -- when was it going to stop?

I picked up the telephone and called Mike at Osan. I had to learn something about the in-coming inspector -- the Mister William Pepperman. What I would learn was not good. Apparently, my complaint about the inadequacy of past inspections had triggered a "we're going to fry his ass" attitude in the Osan IG office and I was in for a bad time. The Wing Commander was in on the plan and that spelled real trouble for me. My problem was how to turn the coming "bad time" into an advantage.

# THE IG INSPECTION

Lieutenant Jones brought Mister William Pepperman, the Osan inspector, to my office just before lunch time and I thought it best to begin my interface with Pepperman by eating lunch with him at the enlisted mess. On the way to that mess, I learned that Pepperman had done one of the prior inspections of the Kunsan Air Base and I could sense that he might have been chewed out for not doing a good job -- there was hostility in his almost every word and facial expression. As we entered the G.I. mess, Pepperman noted that he normally ate at the Officers Club when he visited Kunsan. I told him that the experience of eating at the G.I. mess would do him good. I could detect that he did not like the answer.

The menu at the G.I. mess was especially bad and I found myself pleased. Pepperman commented about how awful the food was and I suggested that he might place that in his report. But I suggested that he note where the source of the problem rested and it was not at Kunsan Air Base -- it was at the supply points. I could see that Pepperman was hesitant to so place the responsibility as he suggested that the food problem was really the problem of the Commander. I countered that such could be the case only if the Commander owned the supply system. I could detect that we were off to a bad start.

Before leaving the G.I. mess, I insisted that Pepperman accompany me for a walk through of the kitchen and remainder of the facility. I think what he saw turned his stomach. I wished we had happened to have a cadaver in one of the reefers but I was not that lucky.

As we drove back to the headquarters, I suggested that Pepperman sit through a base briefing. Noting that the message covering his arrival did not include a security clearance, I asked him about it. He assured me that he held a Top Secret clearance and I let the matter drop.

Jones did a bang up briefing job and, at the close, Pepperman commented that he had never been given a like briefing in Korea. I think we made a point. And then we got down to the nitty gritty of the inspection.

"What is your inspection plan?" I asked. "Do you have an agenda to work, some specific things to look at and report on, or are you just generally going to wander through the base?"

"Actually, Colonel, I am going to begin work with the past inspection reports -- I need to determine if the prior problems have been corrected. And, as I do that work, I want to determine if there are other problems to be covered."

"So, except for reviewing action on the old reports, you have no set plan of action -- no check list?"

"No sir."

I could see that I had placed Pepperman on the defensive and I concluded that now was the time to help him out. From Mike I knew that he had a job to do and probably did not know how to do it. Thus, I could lead him through the exercise and, probably, get in the report what I wanted in the report.

"Why don't I spend some time with you?" I suggested. "There's no need for you to have to reinvent the wheel. While I have only been here for a couple weeks, I pretty well know what the problems are. We can look at them together and examine opportunities for improvement and correction. Is that agreeable?"

"It's unusual, but I can't find anything wrong with the concept. Actually, your help might assist me in my work."

"Fine. Let's you and I take a trip around this base. And, since this is a very important visit, I would like Lieutenant Jones to accompany us and, perhaps, shoot a photo or two of you at work. You probably could use a little PR. Is that all right?"

It was obvious that Pepperman liked the idea of some PR and I could sense that he was thinking of a promotion coming out of this exercise. I was certain that this was going to be one hell of an inspection report.

For the next four hours, Pepperman, Jones and I toured the base and there was not a known problem to which the inspector was not exposed. Throughout, Pepperman kept trying to place the resolution of problems on me but I carefully placed them where they belonged. I knew that the inspector did not like the outcome and especially he did not like the times when I made the point that the resolution of the problems depended on the Wing at Osan. I knew that, if he accepted my judgment on these issues and placed same in his report, the result would be that, instead of heaping a load on me, he would have heaped a load on the Wing Commander at Osan. And, according to Mike, that was not the game plan of the IG. There were,

**of course, a mass of problems that could only be addressed by Fifth Air Force or other responsibility areas in the system. The inspector, I soon learned, did not comprehend the total picture -- but what could I expect?**

**When the base tour was complete and I drove up to an enlisted billet and told Pepperman that we had found a bed for him in that facility, his face paled.**

**"But I have officer status," he complained. "Haven't you a place for transient officers? I've never billeted with enlisted men before."**

**"And that's another thing to include in your report," I added. "We just don't have that kind of facility here. I think we should but it is up to Fifth Air Force to get us that facility as all our construction is controlled by Fifth. If I had any say in it, an officer's transient facility would be going up right now. But I have no input to such things. I have talked to Osan about this and I understand that neither the Wing nor the Division has any real input on this subject. We get what we get and we have to live with it. But I still think it's a deficiency that you should cover in your report. And, by the way, I would like to give you wheels but we just don't have any I can assign to you -- shortage in vehicles is another problem you should cover in your report. We were able to get you a bed right close to the G.I. mess hall so you won't have to do much walking.**

**"After you have dinner, I will come by with Captain Wild, he is the head of our Air Police, and take you to Kunsan City to one of our On-Limits night spots. I think you might enjoy the experience."**

**Pepperman's eyes lighted up.**

**"I don't know, Colonel. I can't accept any favors in this job."**

**"No favors intended. It will be a good experience. And we all need some of those." I winked at Pepperman and he bit.**

**Jones escorted Pepperman into the billet and then returned.**

**"He's terribly pissed at the quarters, Colonel -- but he is looking forward to tonight."**

**"I expected he would be. Now we will have to see what a pissed off inspector does. We gave him enough fodder to chew on to write a book. He took some notes but how much he will remember, I have no idea. He wasn't here to help us and it may be that his anger will turn against the Osan and Fifth Air Force environments. We will just have to wait to see what develops. But, just to cover our butts, I want you to write a summary of the inspection -- set down all the problems we covered and the solutions we examined -- try to insert as many**

Pepperman quotes as you can. Then put it into a CYA file -- we may need it."

"What about tonight?" Jones asked.

"Would you like to make it a foursome? Moench, Wild, Jones and Pepperman?"

Jones could not suppress a grin. I could tell that he was enjoying his work. "I'm game," he answered.

At 1900 hours, we picked up Pepperman and headed for Kunsan City. I had made certain that both Wild and Jones were armed with forty-fives. I could tell that the ride to the city was unnerving for Pepperman. In addition to being bounced all over the ball park, he was concerned that Wild also had a carbine in the rack at the front of the weapons carrier. I told him that it was just a normal precaution -- that things in our area were rough and we had to be ready for eventualities. Wild and Jones picked up on my account of infiltration and machine gun fire to the east and did some story expansion. I could detect that the idea of anything involving shooting was terribly upsetting to the inspector. When we encountered the ROK checkpoint, I thought our guest would pass out. Clearing the checkpoint, he did relax but I noticed that, for some minutes, his hands shook uncontrollably.

On the way to Kunsan City, Wild, Jones and I played up the josan problem and I could tell that Pepperman concluded that he was in for one hell of a girlie night. And then we arrived at that two-story club that I had recently visited. Pepperman did not know how to act or what to do. When the establishment had cleared, we took him through and then headed back to the base. On the way back, I explained how short Kunsan Air Base was when it came to recreational facilities and I urged him to write up the problem -- along with some solutions. I could detect that Pepperman felt trapped -- especially in that Jones had taken some photos of him while touring the Kunsan City "club" -- fortunately, there were some scantily-clad, provocative dancers in the background.

When we deposited Pepperman at his billet at the enlisted quarters, I could see that he didn't know which way to turn. Before we said "goodnight," I told Pepperman that, in the morning, I would like to review with him his findings and recommendations. He agreed but I could see that it was with some reluctance.

On the way back from depositing Pepperman at his billet, Wild suggested that I had some built in S.O.B. characteristics. I told him that the good news was that I was their S.O.B.

# DAY TWENTY-THREE -- A TUESDAY

When I arrived at the headquarters there was a sports car parked next to my slot. I knew who it was -- Mr. Olson -- the pimply-faced Counter Intelligence man.

Olson stated that he needed to talk with me but I told him that it would have to wait until the morning staff meeting was over. I invited him to join the meeting. He rebelled at the idea indicating that it would remove his cover but I laughed and told him to get his butt in my office and suggested that he might learn something. Reluctantly, he agreed.

As soon as my staff was in place, I introduced Mr. Olson, noted that he had some super secret assignments to handle in the southern part of Korea and that he would, from time to time, visit our base. "But," I added, "if any of you here catch him using this base for a girlie operation, I want to know about it." Olson turned beet red but said nothing. I knew I was nipping his girlie operation in the bud and there was nothing he could do about it. Probably, I had made an enemy.

The focus of the staff meeting was the in-coming typhoon -- Typhoon Number Two. Already, a light rain was falling outside. Sergeant Butler stated that the recorded peak winds in the typhoon were no greater than those in the prior typhoon but that the amount of rain we could expect might be much higher.

For the benefit of the staff, I reviewed the sand bag problem and now the shovel problem. On the surface it was serious but the men could not help but laugh.

Then, giving praise to Olson's "dangerous" work, I raised the issue of North Korean infiltration in the Kunsan area. Fortified with the information Lt. Colonel Buckner had given me, it was soon obvious that I knew more about the subject than did Olson and he undertook a "one-step, two-step, side-step, shuffle" in his responses. The discussion added nothing to my knowledge but it did give some new perspective to my staff.

With the meeting over, I closed the door and sat down with Olson.

"So what have you got for me?" I asked.

"Well, sir, you sent a message asking for some intelligence information and my superiors have authorized me to pass on some data

**to you. These data are covered by special security clearances but I have been given permission to release it to you without clearance formalities."**

**Damn, there was the clearance thing again. What the hell was going on that I would now learn? I tried not to show my anger at the system. Olson continued.**

**"Colonel, this may be hard to take and I have to caution you not to act abruptly on what I shall tell you."**

**"Go ahead," I answered. "I am a big boy."**

**"Well, Colonel, you have a North Korean spy ring on your base."**

**"A what?" I almost shouted as my fists and muscles tightened.**

**"Yes sir. But it's not a big one."**

**"How in hell *big* does a spy ring have to be to be a *big one*?" I demanded.**

**"As far as we know, it's five persons."**

**"American or Korean?"**

**"Korean."**

**"And are you going to tell me who they are?"**

**"Yes. But I have to caution you that you can't do anything about it. We have these persons under surveillance and we have been ordered not to touch them at the present time. Our bosses want to see if we can catch the big guys -- the ones in charge -- the drops, the channels of information and stuff like that."**

**"And you've got these five agents under surveillance -- may I ask by whom? Do you have counter agents, U.S. or Korean, working on my base -- obviously without my knowledge? Do you hold intercept traffic that will tell me what they are transmitting to North Korea? Can you tell me how they communicate to North Korea?"**

**"I can't answer any of that, sir."**

**"So I'm sitting on a nuclear base; I've got a North Korean agent ring on the base; and I can't do anything about it -- is that it?"**

**"Yes sir."**

**"And by some means you have these persons under surveillance, possibly by U.S. or Korean persons on this base who report to you or your compatriots, but I am to know nothing about this -- is that what you are saying?"**

**"Yes sir."**

**"Well, if I can't do anything about the situation, why are you telling me this?"**

"You asked for it, sir. We could have kept it all quiet but you asked for it and my boss felt it best to give you the information."

"Why? So I would do something irrational and get my tit in a wringer? Is that what this is all about?" I was getting angry but I knew that would solve nothing and I did my best to cool down.

"Did the past Commander of Kunsan know about this spy ring."

"No sir. He was never cleared for that." Again, the clearance situation hit me square in the face.

"You said that you were going to tell me who these persons were?"

"Yes sir. The head of the operation is your Korean PX manager. They have one man in your engineering office -- a draftsman. The Korean who runs your ice plant is one of them. One man is a general labor type in the engineering establishment. And there is one person who works in the Officers Club but we don't have the name -- only a code -- we don't know if it is a man or a woman. Here are the four names that we do know."

Olson handed me a slip of paper.

"Do keep this information to yourself, Colonel. It's very sensitive."

I walked to the window and looked out. The situation just about floored me. I had to think but there was no point in keeping Olson around. I turned and thanked him for the information, assured him that I would hold it close, and he was gone. And that would be the last time I would see Mr. Olson.

I wanted to talk to someone -- wanted to discuss the situation and the options -- if I had any. But I was forbidden to talk to anyone. I was again all alone. The feeling that overcame me on my first day at Kunsan returned.

I heard a jeep pull up outside and Jones came in to advise me that the Commanding General from the local ROK District Command whose headquarters was located east of us, along with some of his staff officers, was outside my office and wanted to meet me.

"Show them in and have Miss Lee bring us some coffee."

Sun suddenly poked through the dark cloud that Olson had placed over my head. Here was a chance to talk to the Commanding General of the ROK forces that formed my exterior defense line.

The ROK General, a portly type, presented me with one of those black with pearl inlay desk letter boxes. I was embarrassed that I had no protocol items to give in return and slipped Jones a note asking

**him to get me a bottle of brandy to give each of the visiting officers as they departed.**

**It turned out that the General was not visiting me on defense matters but was seeking to have me establish an employment policy that would favor Korean military veterans. He gave me a strong pitch on the need for veteran support, the reliability of veterans and more. His arguments were logical but I suspected that there was a little payola in what he suggested -- that he or his unit would profit in some way by pay back from anyone the base hired as a result of his recommendations. Nonetheless, having just been faced with the North Korean agent problem, it seemed that I might achieve more reliability if future employment was oriented to the ROK military veteran.**

**Finally, I agreed to give the plan consideration.* But, before the General left, I asked him how long it would take him to reinforce Kunsan Air Base if we had a security problem develop. I briefed him on what I knew about infiltration but I suspected that he knew more than I did. The General indicated that he would do anything he could to help in an emergency but that he could not move his men without orders from Seoul. "And to get such orders could take some time," he added. Further, even in the best of circumstance, it could take hours, maybe days, for him to put together an effective combat unit and reach Kunsan. His primary units, he reminded me, were in a reserve status and that meant he had only a handful of active duty persons available at any one time. "The rest of my men are scattered around the country-side and have to be recalled before we really have a force at hand and ready to operate."**

**So it was that I learned that a ROK defense outside the perimeter of Kunsan Air Base was, for all intent, fictional. But I knew that there was little utility in raising it as an issue for, even if it got to the USFK/UNC level, the response would probably be keyed to a mobility statement, e.g. "if the need arises, we will deploy to Kunsan a unit from the DMZ." That such a unit might never arrive in time would be in the category of "acceptable risk."**

**By the time the ROK General had left, I learned that Pepperman had also departed -- catching the out-going commuter flight.**

**Then the rains came and communications went dead!**

---

* I did decide to bend employment rules to favor the Korean veteran but not to make that policy public. Apparently my actions became known for, some time later, I received a Letter of Appreciation from the Major General commanding the First Military District Command.

# DAYS TWENTY-FOUR & TWENTY-FIVE
# A WEDNESDAY & A THURSDAY

**Rain, rain and still more rain. It seemed as if it would never end. By noon Wednesday it was obvious that the drainage system was overloaded -- water was beginning to back up. Most of the men were hunkered down in their billets -- proceeding outside only to obtain drinking water or something to eat. Water was beginning to cover the floors in the lower situated billets.**

**By evening, I knew I had a serious water problem but it was not until morning light on Thursday that I knew how bad it was. Water was piling up on the airfield, some roads were under water but, worst of all, some critical buildings were beginning to get seriously flooded -- among them was the communications center where water was beginning to reach up to the base of the teletype machines. We were in a sea of water and it was not moving -- only getting higher.**

**The good news was that the wind did not develop as forecast. Again, we were spared from a disaster inflicted by that spectrum of nature.**

**Sloshing through the flooded areas and totally frustrated by the rising water, I talked to one of Captain Polk's older Sergeants.**

**"Do you have a blade in the engineering pool that works?" I asked.**

**"I have one, sir."**

**"Well," I said as I pointed in a direction away from the communications and operations complex and toward the sea, "it looks to me as if water would move in that direction if we had a ditch to carry it off."**

**"I think you may be right, Colonel, but we don't have a ditch that runs in that direction."**

**"Then let's cut one right now. How about getting your blade down here and cutting a ditch straight from here in the direction of the sea -- in the direction I point?"**

**"But there are roads and other stuff in the way."**

**"Set your sights on a straight line and cut right through anything in the way."**

"But, sir, that would be destroying government property."

"And, Sergeant, what in the hell do you think this water is doing?"

"You mean I can put the blade in the ground and just tear out anything, absolutely anything, in the way?"

"That's what I said and I think I'm the Commander of this base. You get that blade and let's see something happen -- kick some butt! One thing however, the direction I pointed will by-pass the runway and the taxiways -- don't cut them. We still may have to fight a war. Anything else is fair game. GO!"

The Sergeant did a quick salute as if saying "Yes Sir," and, grinning from ear to ear, ran for the engineering yard. Within minutes, his blade was down, from a wide open throttle the exhaust was belching black smoke and he was moving dirt -- plowing straight ahead, tearing out everything in the way to the sea. One could almost hear him scream with joy at his authority -- alone, he was rescuing Kunsan Air Base! And the flood waters began to recede.

Some time later, I had Jones take a photo of myself standing about knee deep in flood waters in front of the Kunsan Operations building -- by then the water was down by about a foot but it still was a good photo. There was a sign in front of the Operations building that read: WELCOME TO KUNSAN AIR BASE, K-8 KOREA. When the photo was developed and printed, I crossed out the word "air" and wrote in the word "naval" -- then I sent it to General Tate who had transferred from the Air War College to Fifth Air Force. I received no reply but I learned that the photo caused a stir in the Fifth Air Force staff. I sensed that General Tate would view the photo as a friendly bit of theatrics but I doubted that few on his staff would thereafter remain unaware of Kunsan Air Base or who was Commanding -- nor that my problems could be ignored. But I knew that "friends" was not what I had made by this . On the other hand, I knew that my job was not that of winning a popularity contest. I had a job to do and "come hell or high water" I was going to do it to the best of all my abilities and "the devil take the hindmost."

[*I never asked General Tate for special favors. My relationship with him began in USAFE Headquarters with events that would, by themselves, make a story. He was at our wedding in Wiesbaden, Germany. At the Air War College, when he was Commandant, Mrs. Tate called on me for some very special support and, in spite of considerable other priority tasks, I performed. After my assignment to Kunsan Air*

*Base, when I had a Masters Degree conferred on me by Ambassador MacArthur in Japan, General Tate was there. Junior-to-senior relationships develop into special two-way trusts and I felt that General Tate respected and trusted my judgment. I don't think I was wrong in my assessment.*]

**No one ever criticized me for the property damage done to get the water moving off Kunsan Air Base.* For my part, I was determined that, once we got in a supply of shovels, there was going to be some serious clean out of the drainage system.**

***With a channel cut toward the Yellow Sea, the water at Kunsan Air Base began to recede. Finally, with the water level down by about a foot, there was time for Lieutenant Jones to take a photo of myself in front of Base Operations. The bottom line on the sign reads: The Riviera of Korea.***

---

* Years later, I would visit Kunsan Air Base and there, across roads that had been torn out in the process of ditching to the sea, were the patch marks where repairs had been made. By then, culverts had been installed. Frankly, I was proud of the road and other damage I had caused to be done in order that more serious damage would not be done. Few would understand.

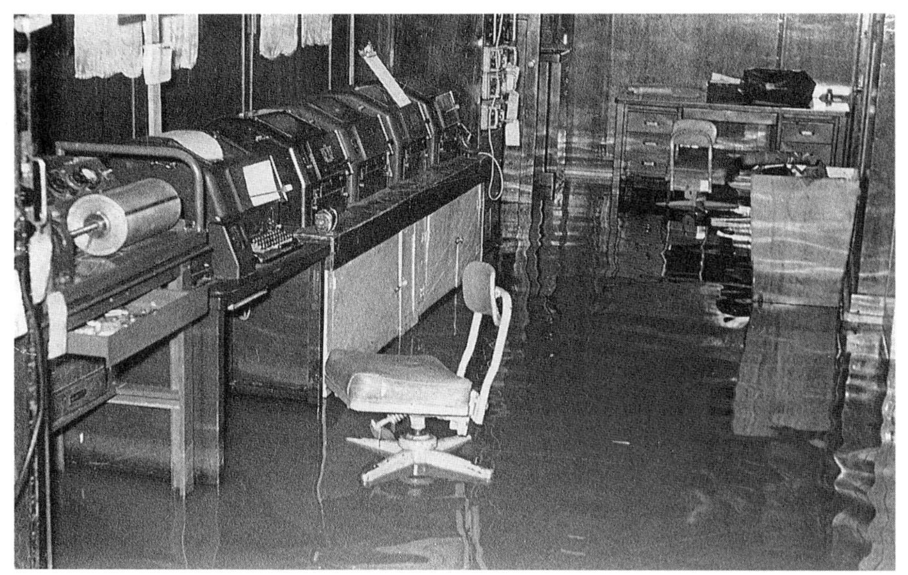

*The communications center at Kunsan Air Base. This is the lifeline of a base. Here it is seen after the water had been drawn down. (USAF)*

*Osan Air Base also had its flooding problem. Here are shown enlisted billets deep in water. Hill One-Eighty is in the background. (USAF)*

# DAY TWENTY-SIX -- A FRIDAY

At some point in the early morning hours, once more I awakened with that shadowy figure silhouetted outside my window. There had been no sound. The figure was motionless.

Again, I could make out the gun barrel. And again, for what seemed an eternity but what might have been only twenty or so minutes, I lay under the mosquito tent with my thirty-eight pointed at the figure wondering when it would shoot or disappear. And then, suddenly, it was gone. I was beginning to wonder if I had imagined the whole thing.

The perceived time between the presence of the figure outside the window and the jolt of the 0600 alarm was minuscule -- the next work day was beginning.

As I shaved and dressed for the coming day, my mind kept turning over the matter of the figure that appeared outside my bedroom window. The idea of dashing out in the night, pistol in hand, to confront the person involved seemed like an exercise in stupidity. Perhaps the person outside my bedroom window did not even speak English and would not understand a "freeze" order? But I had to do something. The question was what?

And what about Mr. Kim and the Korean guards? "A lot of good they are," I thought. "Who knows, perhaps one of the Korean guards is my appointed assassin?"

I could not, however, dwell on the subject. There was work to be done -- a lot of work -- and my time at Kunsan was running out.

The rain was over and the wind never did get to a speed that would have torn us apart. A few metal roof sheets and side panels had been blown off -- nothing more. Once again, nature had spared us.

The morning staff meeting was rather anti-climatic. Except for water, which had now receded, we had, by the grace of God, survived a second typhoon. I wondered how long fate would be on our side.

Sergeant Butler's weather briefing aside, we went on to other business. Most of that business was routine. Then Major Peterson turned on the trauma switch.

"Sir, I hate to tell you this, but one of my men, driving from the base to Kunsan city yesterday in all the rain that was falling, killed a Korean boy."

**Suddenly, it seemed that the world had fallen in on me. Had I not had enough in the way of problems?**

**"How did it happen?" My skin crawled and I wanted to scream but held my emotions inside.**

**"He was driving to Kunsan when this boy, without looking, simply ran in front of the six-by. The boy died instantly -- the wheels went right over him. I have talked to everyone who was there and the story is consistent -- the boy, without looking, just ran in front of the truck and the driver had no chance to stop. It was in an area where the houses are right next to the road. The driver was not speeding -- actually, he was proceeding slowly and cautiously. I have the driver confined to quarters right now but I have to conclude that it was not his fault."**

**"And what do we do in a case such as this?" Unfortunately, among my family were personal injury attorneys and I knew what would transpire had this been in the United States.**

**"I'm not certain," Peterson stated. "We usually let things such as this be managed by Captain Pastiak but he is off base today."**

**I looked at the Chaplain but his shrug told me that he had no answer.**

**Fuming at the course of affairs, I decided I had no option other than to call the JAG at Osan. Fortunately, he had developed into a friend -- one who stood aside from the shenanigans of the Wing Commander.**

**"Hello Ray, this is John Moench down at Kunsan. I've got a problem and need some advice."**

**Lt. Colonel Raymond Shingleton, a JAG for all of twenty years, was a quiet, even-tempered attorney -- a truly laid back individual. All he wanted to know was what the problem was and I explained it. And then he offered advice that was totally new to me.**

**"Tell me again about this solatium thing?" I asked.**

**----------**

**"You mean that I am supposed to go to the parents of the boy and give them some money, talk about the great person the boy would have been, tell them about the grief of the man who drove the six-by and how he will now be deported from Korea as punishment, and that will be it?"**

**----------**

**"O.K. I'll try to get the ROKAF Commander here to go with me and translate."**

**----------**

**"You say that the equivalent of $250.00 U.S. would be adequate and all I have to do is voucher for the money?"**

**----------**

**"And that's it?"**

**I was shocked. How different the system in Korea from that I knew in the U.S.**

**I asked Jones to invite the ROKAF Commander to have lunch with me at the Officers Club. In the meantime, I tried to compose myself -- this was not an ordinary event -- a young boy had been killed by one of my vehicles. I found it difficult to orchestrate my presentation to his mother, father and family. But I knew I would have to do it.**

**At lunch, I apologized to Colonel Lee for my failure to not have previously invited him to lunch with me. As we ate, I tried to tell him a few of my problems but he simply waived them aside with the observation that we all had many problems.**

**But then I went on to explain to Lee my most current problem. Apparently, he had already learned of the death of the boy. He seemed unconcerned. "It will all work out," he said. "You Americans get too excited about a death. Death is normal. It is only a matter of time as to when it comes to pass."**

**His Oriental logic did not serve to comfort me. But he did agree to accompany me and serve as translator. For that I was grateful.**

**Donning a full dress, white uniform with medals and all and with U.S. $250.00 converted to Korean currency in my pocket, I set out with Colonel Lee to visit the family of the deceased. "It is bad protocol not to do this," Lee assured me.**

**Wild did the driving of my staff car and we were followed by several jeeps in which were Major Peterson and others from my staff and some of Colonel Lee's staff. An Air Police jeep led the convoy.**

**About five miles outside the gate, we came to the house of the deceased boy. There were many Koreans milling about outside but they quickly stepped aside at our approach.**

**Stepping out of the staff car, it was immediately obvious who the mother and father of the deceased boy were. I struggled as to what to say. I had learned that the family name was Kim -- a rather common Korean name.**

**"Mr. and Mrs. Kim, I am Colonel John Moench, Commander of Kunsan Air Base and I come to express to you my sincere condolences regarding the unfortunate loss of your son."**

**As Colonel Lee translated, Mr. and Mrs. Kim bowed repeatedly. And then I saw the need to continue.**

**"Mr. and Mrs. Kim, I truly believe your son would have grown to become a great leader in Korea -- possibly to be a great military officer -- even to be President. That a life so important to all of us should be lost is beyond anything I can explain."**

**Again, Lee translated with more bowing by the Kim family. Frankly, the experience was beginning to tear me apart. I thought of my own children and wondered if I could be so emotionally placid in such an event as were the Kim parents.**

**Once more, the translation was over and I could see that the eyes of the assembled Koreans were upon me.**

**"Mr. and Mrs. Kim, as an expression of the deep feeling and remorse I and my government feel with respect to the loss of your great son, may I give you this small token."**

**I put forth the Korean money in my right hand and Mr. Kim, deeply bowing, accepted it. There were no tears in the eyes of either Mr. or Mrs. Kim. Those in attendance were utterly quiet. Somehow, I felt that something more was needed and I unpinned my pilot's wings and handed them to Mrs. Kim.**

**"I ask you to pin on the clothing of your son my pilot's wings and may he wear them when he and I meet in the great beyond."**

**To my surprise, when Lee had completed the translation, those who were watching the interchange applauded. I did not know what then to do but the next episode totally floored me. Colonel Lee translated the words of Mr. Kim.**

**"I am the father of the boy who has now left us. We regret that our son carelessly stepped in front of the American vehicle and has now caused such great pain to the American Colonel and to the driver of the vehicle. And we ask that the American Colonel take this small gift from us as a token of deep sorrow and regret for all that has taken place and that he forgive our son for the damage he has caused."**

**With more bowing and now with some tears, to include my own, I accepted the package offered and we returned to Kunsan Air Base.**

**Korea, I now knew, was something different. On the way back to the base, I asked Lee if he and his wife would join me for dinner at the Officers Club. The invitation was accepted.**

# DINNER WITH ROKAF COLONEL AND MRS. LEE

For balance, I asked Akers to join us at dinner. In the meantime, I had Jones arrange a special table at the Officers Club and, by personal selection, to insure that there were some reasonable steaks for all. Captain Wild suggested that I have both Scotch and sake at the table. To add to the protocol, I had Captain Wild station two armed Air Police at the Club entrance to greet Colonel and Mrs. Lee.

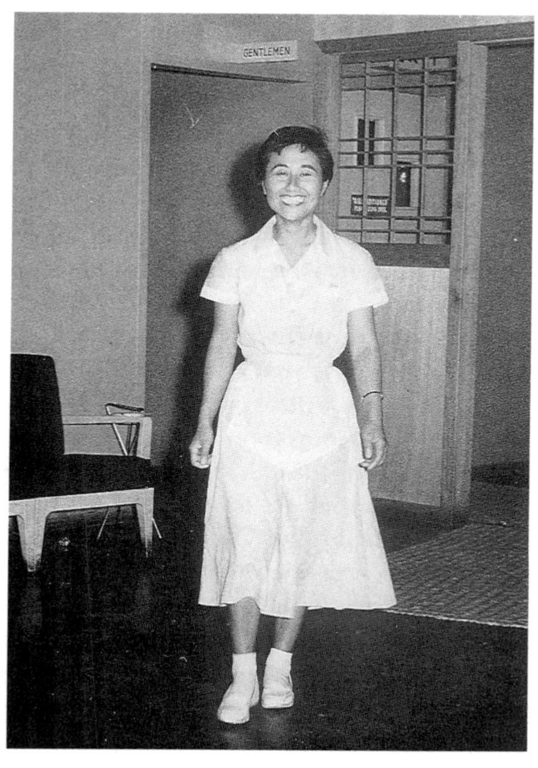


*Annie -- our Number One waitress in the Officers Club. Eventually, I would have to consider whether she was a North Korean agent.*

The Lees arrived by jeep. Mrs. Lee wore the traditional Korean dress. She spoke a little English -- very little. By prior agreement, the men, Colonel Lee, Akers and I, wore civilian attire -- sport shirts.

Annie did the serving and she did an outstanding job. Others in the Club knew that something special was happening and the atmosphere was quiet and, fortunately, not too much smoking took place with the result that the air conditioners did a reasonable job.

For all of the first hour, the conversation at the table centered on family, schooling, differences between Korean and American life. I

**learned that Lee had attended the Squadron Officer School at Maxwell Air Force Base but he was not accompanied by Mrs. Lee during his time in the United States. The Lees had one son and a daughter -- they hoped their son would become a military officer. Their plan was to enter him in the newly structured Military Academy in Korea and, if possible, have him attend West Point in the United States. As a junior officer, Lee had flown P-51 aircraft during the Korean War and he would have liked that his son became a pilot but the son's eyes were not good enough for him to qualify for flight training. As so typical in a family surrounding, we soon were displaying photos of our children.**

**By then, I realized that Lee held a complete dossier on me -- he knew I had not served in Korea during the Korean War; he knew that Mary and the children were currently living in Virginia; he knew of my World War II service and more -- he even commented on my taste for Scotch which taste, he confessed, he had adopted during his tour at Maxwell Air Force Base. "Mrs. Lee," he stated, "preferred sake."**

**Why was it that I had been provided no similar dossier on Lee? In all prior jobs where I had to interface with foreign persons, the Air Force intelligence system had given me dossiers on all key persons -- often right down to such details as their sex life. But here I had none -- and I was at a distinct disadvantage. I knew that I was going to bring this up at one of the Osan staff meetings -- and probably make no friends in the process.**

**After we had finished the main course, Lee lifted his glass and toasted me as the new Commander of Kunsan Air Base.**

**"We are pleased that the American Government has sent us such a fine officer to be the Commander of Kunsan Air Base. We already note that the American flag flies at his headquarters. Soon, we hope to see the Korean flag and that of the United Nations flying alongside the fine American flag."**

**My God! I had missed the obvious. I should have had three flag poles --not one. I raised my glass and drank.**

**"Indeed, we are well on the way," I answered. "We have two more flagpoles being made and soon all three flags will be flying. Could it be that, perhaps, you have a Korean flag you could give us for that purpose? It seems our American supply system is not what it should be."**

**"You will have such a flag on Monday," Lee answered.**

**Somehow, that little event broke the ice and we were now friends. And, before the evening was finished, I had been invited to be on the reviewing stand at the next formation of the ROKAF troops and**

Lee had agreed to sit with me and talk about a coordinated base defense plan and more. Jones had managed to get the cooks to make a cake decorated with an American and a Korean flag and, during dessert, we talked about hunting and we vowed, if possible, to go on a joint hunt. Lee assured me that he knew of "some good places." I wanted to talk about black market and some other subjects but I thought it best not to push my luck.

As the evening closed, Lee complimented me on the Officer Club facility and asked if it was not possible that he and a few of his officers might be allowed to become members. I told him that we would review that at our next meeting. He seemed satisfied at the response.

Before leaving, Mrs. Lee gave me a small package "for the Colonel's wife." I was embarrassed not to have thought of something for her and I made a mental note to make up for that error in the near future. The item in the package was a silver spoon with the ROKAF insignia carved into the handle.

As I readied for bed, I felt relaxed. In a tape to Mary, I told her about the dinner with Colonel and Mrs. Lee and about the "gift." I asked Mary to figure out something for Mrs. Lee and mail it to me as soon as possible.

The day, I thought, had turned out satisfactorily. But, shortly, that shadowy figure was again outside my window! I resolved that, whatever was on-going, it absolutely had to end. Tomorrow, I would talk to Wild about the situation.

★★★★★★★★★★★★★★★★

Well into the morning hours, my sleep having been disturbed by the figure at my window, I got up, had a cold beer and paced the floor.

Finally, I sat down and penned an intelligence summary covering Colonel Lee. "The system." I concluded, "has to start somewhere and it might as well start with me." I wondered what the intelligence officer at Osan would do with it when it was received.

From somewhere in the distance, I heard faint gunfire. I was beginning to understand how one could hear it so often that it could be dismissed as amounting to nothing.

Realizing that I was wide awake and the hour back in Virginia, I called the MARS station and asked if they could connect me with Mary.

"We've got a solid connection tonight, Colonel. The reception is fantastic. Just give me the number and stand by. I think we can make a hook up in a couple minutes. Remember, no classified discussion as we are on high freq."

And he was correct. Within a few minutes, Mary and I were talking -- and without shouting. Mary still had a problem with the "over and out" routine of high frequency communications but it all worked out.

The family, Mary and the children, were well. Life had settled into a routine in Virginia. Our respective families were doing O.K. Mary was gathering some clothes to send to me for the Korean children. Some family photos had been taken and they were en route to me. It was a great conversation and, when it was over, I relaxed under the mosquito tent and quickly fell into a deep sleep.

Until I had been assigned to Korea, I had never used the MARS communication system. Following World War II, when I was serving in the Air Materiel Command at Wright-Patterson AFB, I had been the funnel point for the movement of literally carloads of excess communications equipment to military locations setting up a MARS capability. Now, decades later, I was experiencing the results of the program and I was pleased. Technically, the MARS capability served as a back-up to military communications. With my Kunsan communications frequently failing, I wondered if, some day, I would have to fall back on the MARS capability as the only remaining link with the outside world. Once before, during Typhoon Number One, all the Kunsan communications other than MARS went out of service and, in that situation, due to atmospherics, MARS did not work. During Typhoon Number Two, while atmospherics degraded the system, we did maintain that communication link when the land lines went out. Would MARS work in the next emergency? More significant, did our enemies know when Kunsan Air Base was cut off from communication with the outside world? Unfortunately, I had to assume that their intelligence was equal to our own and that such a fact would be known. But how would our enemies exploit this information?

While I was asleep, I kept thinking and thinking -- turning over in my mind situation after situation. Intuitively, I kept weighing enemy capabilities and intentions against my own vulnerabilities. Why had not North Korea already made a sapper or other raid on Kunsan Air Base? I could find no answer that pleased me. But I could envisage the great turmoil that would be generated by such an event. And I could see myself becoming the scapegoat should such an event materialize.

# DAY TWENTY-SEVEN
# THE SATURDAY MORNING

It was Saturday and there was no morning staff meeting but I was at the headquarters by 0700 hours. I had skipped breakfast and, instead, had made a cup of instant coffee using some shave water from the hot plate. Sergeant Young was already at the headquarters when I arrived.

"Sir, we have a problem."

"What now," I asked. "Are we at war with the Soviet Union -- or what?" The idea of constant problems was beginning to strike me as preposterously amusing.

"Nothing like that, sir. We have a Sunday church problem."

"And what, pray tell, is our Sunday church problem?"

"It is that the Protestant Chaplain, Captain Johnson, has taken leave and there is no replacement to conduct the Sunday service."

"I don't recall authorizing his leave -- did I?"

"No sir. Chaplain Collins did -- he's the senior Chaplain."

"And with no replacement?"

"That's correct, sir."

"Have Chaplain Collins come to my office."

"Yes sir."

Frankly, I had enough on my mind without worrying about the operations of the religious community but I guessed that the subject was now on my plate. Shortly, Chaplain Collins arrived.

"Father, I understand that you authorized leave for Chaplain Johnson without there being a Protestant Chaplain on hand to conduct tomorrow's service. Is that correct?"

"Yes sir. Chaplain Johnson was overdue for some leave but Osan said they could not furnish a substitute to cover. I thought we could just go without Protestant service this Sunday."

"Well, you thought wrongly. I want a Protestant service so it is up to you to conduct it."

"Sir, I can't."

"What do you mean -- you can't? It's not all that different from the Catholic service. You ought to be able to work your way through a reasonable Protestant service."

"Sir, I can't."

"And why in hell can't you?"

"Sir, it's against my instructions from the Pope."

"My God," I thought, "I assumed I knew all those who were my enemies and now I find that an additional one is the Pope."

"Cut the garbage," I answered. "You're the senior base Chaplain and go do it. You won't go to hell for servicing the spiritual needs of some Protestants."

"Sir, I can't." The tone of his statement gave it the appearance of being carved in granite.

For a moment I just stared at Father Collins. Then I ordered him out of my office. I had never had a Christian Chaplain refuse to administer to those of another Christian faith -- to me, religious cross-service in an emergency was an unwritten military code -- but now I faced it. Obviously, I needed another Catholic Chaplain -- one with whom I could work. But, more important, I needed a solution for the coming Protestant service and I guessed that I was it.

Calling in Sergeant Young, I told him that I would conduct the Protestant service on Sunday and, to get my thoughts in line, I asked him to obtain a Protestant service book for me to study.

"No need for you to conduct the service," Sergeant Young stated, "I am an ordained minister and I would be happy to fill in for Chaplain Johnson."

Incredible! For once, it seemed that I had lucked out and I was quick to agree.

With the Sunday Protestant service off my mind, I realized that Sergeant Wilcox was standing outside waiting to see me.

"Come in Sergeant."

Wilcox saluted and I suggested that we sit down at the coffee table. Miss Lee was not there but, from the aroma, I knew that Sergeant Young had made some coffee and I asked him to bring in a couple cups.

"Colonel," Wilcox began, "I've talked to the team and they understand your problem and they want to cooperate."

Right then, I could have hugged a Sergeant.

"But what the men want to know is what you have in mind -- what's the game plan?"

Frankly, I had been so busy that I didn't really have a game plan in mind but I knew that this was no time to be without one.

"Well, let's talk a little about ground operations and let's assume that the baseball team can function as an infantry platoon with you as the platoon leader."

"You mean with rifles, grenades and all that stuff?"

"Approximately."

"And what would we be doing?"

"That depends on the situation. If I knew who was going to hit this base from where, with how many men and at what time, we wouldn't have a problem. But I don't know those things. So we have to be able to move in every possible direction to counter all sort of situations. Right now, we have a half dozen men sitting in the Air Police Command Center as a quick reaction force. But six men just can't hack it. They know that, I know that, and I would expect that you know that. Now let's take the some twenty men involved in baseball."

"Nineteen at present, sir."

"O.K. Nineteen. That's three times what we have available right now. With the six we have and nineteen more, that is twenty-five for reinforcement. And, if those twenty-five are well organized and trained, that's a good handful for any in-coming party to deal with. Are you and your men game?"

"They are."

"All right. I'm going to call Captain Wild and have him set up a training program for your team members so that they can get up to speed on firearms, grenades and whatever. And then we will go from there. However, as a starter, to get everyone used to the problem, I would like them to double up with the perimeter guards Monday night."

"You mean with the guards with the dogs?"

"Yes. The dogs won't hurt you all. They know friends and enemies more than we do. And your team better get used to dogs as they are one hell of an asset. Pass the word on to your team. If anyone wants to bug out, so be it. But I need your help and I'll start work to get that game in Japan set up."

By the time I had finished with Sergeant Wilcox, Jones showed up.

"Tommy, I've got an urgent request."

"Yes sir."

"We need two more flagpoles outside headquarters."

"Two more?"

"Yes. One for the ROK and one for the United Nations flag. And we need them quick. Will you get in touch with Captain Polk. If possible, I'd like to have the poles up by Monday. Colonel Lee is going to give us a Korean flag but we need a UNC flag. Call UNC. If you

**have a problem getting a flag, get back to me as I think I know someone who would help us out."**

**"Yes sir."**

**"And one other thing."**

**"Yes sir."**

**"The man who was driving the truck that killed the Korean boy . . ."**

**"Yes sir."**

**". . . get him orders sending him back to the States. It's all part of the equation. No hard feelings and no bad Efficiency Rating involved. Understand?"**

**"Yes sir."**

**I leaned back in my desk chair. Could it be that things were beginning to run correctly? Could it be that I was getting ahead of problems instead of always being behind the power curve?**

**It was in an upbeat mood that I turned my attention to the stack of papers that Jones had piled in my IN basket.**

**Two hours later, the paper stack had moved to my OUT basket and I was ready for lunch. But there was a sour note for, when I called in Tommy to clean off my desk and close up the office, I could tell that he had a problem.**

**"What's up Tommy? Have all the cows gotten sick?"**

**"No sir, it's the G.I. camera I finally got from Osan. It's already broken. I think they gave us a clunker. I tried to get our Korean camera shop to fix it but they don't have the parts. So I called Osan and all we can do is return it for repairs -- and they don't have a replacement camera for us."***

**"O.K. So I've got a 35MM Leica. You can use it until we get a solution. It's got a flash attachment but it uses flash bulbs and I've only got about a dozen that came in with my footlockers. You may have to get flash bulbs from Japan."**

**"I'll get some flash bulbs some way," Tommy answered.**

**"What a shoestring operation," I thought as I left for lunch.****

---

* According to HRA files, a replacement camera was not obtained until some time after I left Kunsan Air Base and then only when base welfare funds were used to purchase a simple camera with a strobe light attachment. This was hardly a way to run a major military facility but, in the circumstances, it was the best that could be done.

** In spite of my every attempt to raise the "standard of living" at Kunsan Air Base, according to HRA files, after I left, the support element of the 6175th Air Base Group still faced personnel shortages that "plagued every operational section, and office personnel were working on desks and tables made from packing crates. The [offices] gave the appearance of a *dirty, dingy warehouse waiting for the demolition team to arrive.*"

# DAY TWENTY-SEVEN
# THE SATURDAY AFTERNOON

Entering the dining room of the Officers Club for lunch, I saw that Wild was seated with a Second Lieutenant whose face was new to me. I wanted to talk to Wild but was concerned regarding the new face. It turned out that the Second Lieutenant was one John Wade who had just arrived from the States and was assigned as Wild's deputy. Wild was all smiles. "Now I'm going to get a day off," he asserted.

Wade was newly commissioned but he had been to an Air Police school before being sent to Korea. He came across as a likable person but he was all "spit and polish" new and I had to wonder how he would meld into the situation at Kunsan Air Base.

By the time we reached Annie's third cup of coffee, I decided to raise the subject of the nightly figure at my window. Wade was riveted by the conversation. Wild said he would check on what might be happening.

I then told Wild about the conversation with Sergeant Wilcox and the agreement that the baseball team would be organized as a defense reaction team. Wild liked the idea and we reached the conclusion that training would start with weapons indoctrination and a qualification shoot-in on the firing range. Lieutenant Wade was assigned the job. I also asked Wade to organize a weapons qualification program for all officers and enlisted men with the object of at least one qualification firing every six months.

When the subject got around to grenades, I learned that, in the main, only the Air Police were qualified. We joked about the throwing capability of the baseball team and I suggested that we might work up a throwing competition with the ROKAF using spaced, open-end 55 gallon oil drums as the targets and baseballs to simulate the grenades. Lieutenant Wade now had another job.

Discussing further the baseball defense team, I suggested that they be given instruction on the fifty caliber machine gun and become something in the nature of a mobile machine gun crew. Wild thought this might be a workable idea and then proceeded with a thought of his own.

"In addition to this Monday night thing, why don't we periodically place the baseball team members on duty with our perimeter and some of the other guards -- literally, double the guard?"

"Wild, that strikes me as a good idea. Let's talk to Sergeant Wilcox about it. Better yet, let Wade here do the talking."

With that subject aside, I asked Wild about the water situation.

"We're pretty dry and I understand the communications are back on line. But the Korean rice paddies are really flooded. The drainage system from the rice paddies is running full but it will take a few days to get the water down. I would think the high water would have a terrible impact on the rice crop but I'm no farmer.

"I'm going to check out the road all the way to Kunsan this morning. I don't want our people driving it unless it is passable. I know that recent accident in which the Korean boy was killed was not our fault but we don't need one that is our fault."

"What do you plan to drive to check out the road?" I asked.

"A six-by -- one with a winch in case we get stuck."

"Whose going with you?"

"Only a driver."

"Fine. I'll go along. You can sit three in the cab without much trouble."

"Want to bring your shotgun?" Wild asked. "The high water will have driven the birds out of the paddies and you might manage a shot or two. There are some pheasants around here -- not too many but enough. Few Koreans have guns so the bird population is growing pretty fast. When fall comes and the rice fields are dry, it's a ball."

"Does one need a hunting license for such things?" I asked.

"Colonel, this is Korea. We don't need hunting licenses for anything."

"O.K. I'm going back to the Waldorf Astoria to put on some combat boots. Pick me up there in about a half hour."

"Yes sir." Wild was smiling. I could see that his world was running more smoothly than it had been.

When I boarded the six-by, I noted that both Wild and the driver were carrying forty-fives. Wild also had a carbine in the cab. Leaning against the seat was my Browning 12 gauge that had been stored with the Air Police for safe keeping. There was a box of G.I. shells on the seat.

Almost immediately on leaving the gate we were slipping and sliding. The road to Kunsan was a mess. Here and there, groups of Koreans -- mostly women and children -- were working to drain water away and fill wash outs. Once we nearly slid sideways into a roadside drainage ditch. Most of the rice was under water. Having grown up on a farm, I could sympathize with the Korean farmers. My youthful problem, however, had not been too much water -- it was too little water in the great drought of the 1930s.

Making our way to Kunsan City, I could see that the sections of our tactical pipeline were often buried in mud. I knew that, at the next pumping we were going to have to flush the line for some time to get the mud out of the system -- if we could. I wondered how good our fuel filter system was -- I had not inspected it. Fuel contamination was not a problem I needed to add to all the other things that concerned me.

Nearing Kunsan City, the condition of the road improved. Still, there were periodic washouts that were being repaired by women and children breaking and placing stones in the traditional Korea road building system -- big stones on the bottom and then layers of ever smaller stones with a final layer mixed with tar. Although primitive, the system worked. Men set the larger stones and then, step by step, scattered ever smaller stones over the surface while the women and children sat at roadside piles of stones breaking large items into smaller items -- one stone at a time. It was a slow process consuming hours upon hours of work to make small gains. Prisoners in the U.S. would rebel at the idea of breaking stones by hand but here, in Korea, it was an accepted element of work.

Arriving in Kunsan City, I directed that we inspect the fuel storage area. Walking among the tanks, everything seemed to have weathered the storm, the dikes had held and . . . and then both Wild and I saw it. Water had washed away some of a dike and revealed a hidden pipe. Tracing the pipe, we realized that it ran from one of the USAF tanks to a Korean tank. We were being robbed!

"O.K. Who do you think did this?" I asked. "Americans or Koreans?"

"I'd say that both are involved," Wild answered.

"So what do you recommend?"

"For the moment, I suggest that we keep this to ourselves. Let me get with Peterson and quietly investigate this thing. I'll drive him out here so he can see for himself but my guess is that, by the time I can get back with Peterson, this pipe will have been recovered. Anyhow, I think Peterson needs to see this first hand. As soon as we can figure out who did what, I'll brief you. It shouldn't take too long. We know who runs the Korean tanks and I think I can get some straight answers pretty quick."

"No rough stuff!"

"No sir. No rough stuff. I've got other ways to deal with Koreans."

I felt it best not to ask what those "other ways" were.

On the way back to the base, we saw a few pheasants but they were out of range -- most scattered as we approached -- flew away to land on distant paddy dikes. Passing the house where the Korean boy had been killed, the mother and father were outside. They waved to us and I waved back. Somehow, I could not get used to the friendly attitude -- in reverse circumstances I would have been so angry at the world I could not have been civil.

Entering the main gate to the base, I noted the absence of ROKAF guards.

"Don't we use the ROKAF on our gate?" I asked.

"No sir. We consider this an Air Force base."

"But don't the ROKAF have a perimeter guard?"

"Only for their area. We man the outer perimeter."

"And how do we coordinate our respective guards?"

"Hardly at all."

"Do you stop or clear the ROKAF going in and out of the base?"

"Mostly, we just wave them through."

"And they could be carrying stolen items or black market stuff."

"True. But there is the language problem. If something is visible we act -- if nothing is visible, our guards just wave them through."

"I think I want to talk to Colonel Lee about this. I think we need a ROKAF guard at our gate and I think that the ROKAF movements should be handled the same as that of Americans."

"It may cause problems, Colonel."

"We'll see." I detected a worried look on Wild's face.

By the time we got back to the main section of Kunsan Air Base, the ball game was in its final inning. The field was on the wet side but the game had gone on. There were not many spectators. The six-by dropped me off at the Waldorf Astoria. I changed uniform. From my combat boots on up, I was spattered with mud. My unseen mama-san was going to have a hard time getting things cleaned.

# DAY TWENTY-EIGHT
# A MEMORABLE SUNDAY

Entering the church for the Protestant service, it seemed that there were more persons present than had been there on prior Sundays. As usual, I took a seat in a front pew. Soon Sergeant Young appeared, acknowledged my presence and opened the service. And then I got the surprise of my life.

When Sergeant Young told me he was an "ordained minister," it did not occur to me to ask him "ordained in what religious denomination." Sergeant Young, I quickly learned, was my equivalent of a "holy roller."

I sat there transfixed. For a minute, I gave thought to taking over the service myself. And then I realized that Sergeant Young had a responsive audience. Turning to look at the full church pews, I realized that they were heavily populated with my black troops. And the "Amens" and "Hallelujahs" that were rolling forth showed a religious enthusiasm that I had not witnessed before. Apparently, the word had gotten around that we were going to have the service that I was watching and it had attracted persons to the church who did not normally show up.

I was uncomfortable -- very uncomfortable. Yet, I realized how inadequate the Protestant formalities were for some of my troops and I resolved that, on the return from leave of Chaplain Johnson, we were going to have a discussion on the format of the Protestant service. I could see that, if he loosened up the routine, we would have much greater church participation and I could only see good coming from that. But I knew that interjecting myself into religious matters would be like stepping into a tub of hot tar.

At the close of the service, I thanked Sergeant Young for his assistance. But I resolved that this was not going to happen again -- never! I had learned my lesson.

After church, I went to the ball field. The sun was brilliant, the temperature was already high and the air was humid as all hell. I could see that we were in for a scorcher.

At the ball field, I found Lieutenant Wade -- it turned out that he had played some professional ball and he was already a part of the team. When he saw me, he gave a "thumbs up." Apparently, he had quickly made points with the team and I guessed that we were going to have a double guard mount the next day and many days thereafter. And I did not have to "order" it.

Watching the game, Wild joined me.

"I know who your window man is," Wild announced -- there was an amused smile on his face.

"Who?"

"Mister Kim. By way of the Korean grapevine, he learned that some Korean political outfit was out to get you and he wanted to make certain that you were O.K. -- it was a matter of honor with him that nothing should happen to you. So long as he heard you snoring, he concluded that everything was fine. But, when he didn't hear you snoring, he got worried. I told him to hang back from your windows as you were actually a light sleeper and his presence awakened you. He said he would."

And so my window shadow problem was solved. Thank God I had not blown Mr. Kim away. I wondered what others would have done in the same circumstances.

I was tempted to tell Wild about the North Korean agent situation but felt it best to keep it to myself. I needed a plan and right then all I had was a problem. Soon, I hoped, I could work out a plan. In the meantime, I just had to live with the problem and keep it to myself.

After the game, I went to the enlisted mess for dinner. The menu was hot dogs. Talking to the mess Sergeant about the menu, he stated that they were loaded with hot dogs and had to get rid of them some way. That evening, I inspected the reefers at the Officers Club and found that, there too, there was a generous supply of hot dogs.

Akers had taken over the Officers Club manager job from Peterson and I decided to sit with him for a while. I wanted to discuss the hot dog situation -- an idea had come to mind.

"Do we have any barbecue facilities?" I asked Akers.

"Sort of," was his answer. "What we do is cut down a 55 gallon drum as a fire pit and then place a grill made up of rebar over the top. It's crude but it works. You will see what we have when we go to the picnic this coming Friday. We are going to have it at the base of the dam from which we get our water supply. There are some trees out there -- it's a pretty nice spot."

"And what do you plan to grill?"

"Hamburger patties and hot dogs. The kitchen will make up a bunch of buns for us. And we have a tremendous supply of catsup, mustard and relish. I wish we had some good Kosher dills but we aren't that lucky. We'll serve cold soft drinks at the picnic -- free. It will be strictly a hands-on affair -- no plates or utensils -- they get lost too easily. We've taken some heavy rebar and shaped it into horse shoes and we'll set up a couple stakes for that. We're thinking about an officer/EM softball or volleyball game. We'll run some weapons carriers and six-bys from the base to the picnic area."

"Security?"

"No guns allowed. We figure to just take our chances. Wild is aware of the plan. He'll have some coverage dispersed well out."

"Why don't we serve hot dogs at the Sunday baseball game? It seems that we have a good supply and hot dogs seem to go with baseball."

"You mean to run a free hot dog stand or to charge for them?"

"How about a nominal charge in occupation or Korean currency -- something that would generate a little money for the recreation and welfare funds. We could use some new supplies but we need money to purchase them in Japan."

"How nominal -- and do you mean to let the Koreans buy them?"

"Why not? So long as we recover the unit cost, what does it matter? In the clubs, Americans can purchase food for Korean guests so why not let the Koreans do a little direct purchasing if they come to the game and want a hot dog?"

"There's probably a thousand regulations that says its illegal."

"But who is going to make a big deal of it?"

"Colonel, there's probably no end of guys out there who would like to fry your ass by sending a letter to a Congressman."

"I'll accept that risk. We have hot dogs coming out of our ears. If we can move them in a manner that appeals to the men instead of forcing it on them at dinner time, haven't we taken a step forward?"

"Can we get Captain Pastiak in on this?"

"Certainly. You and Pastiak talk and report back to me."

That night, I taped a long message to Mary. I was expansive in describing the Sunday Protestant service. Finally, the tape sealed for mailing, I sat thinking.

One role of a Commander was the welfare of his troops and I was moving in that direction. But another very important role of any Commander was the right and necessity to defend his troops and installation. And here I was out in almost "no man's land" on the Yellow Sea, the Chicoms were to the west, the Ruskies were at Port

**Arthur, the North Koreans were about 30 minutes flying time away, the area was being infiltrated by the North Koreans and I had a North Korean spy ring on the base. And, certainly, there was more to worry about that I did not know -- most probably there were the Japanese.**

**As I added up my capabilities, they amounted to an under-manned Air Police unit, no radios and little in the way of fences or other protection, a ROKAF that seemed to be there but still doing their own thing, a ROK Army unit in the general area but of little help, some ROK anti-aircraft around the field but I concluded that it was of little value, and no intelligence system of consequence. Somehow, I had to do better.**

**As I pondered the situation and thought about my worries as to whether the nuclear weapons were real weapons or only Silver Bullets, I realized that I had three possible scenarios facing me:**

**1. The nuclear weapons were real and the situation at Kunsan Air Base was just one big screw up. But, in that case, I still had a real nuclear base to defend.**

**2. The nuclear weapons were not real and the base had been set up as an artificial threat. In which case, the better the defense the more realistic was the decoy.**

**3. The nuclear weapons were not real and the base had been set up as a seemingly lucrative target to invite attack. In which case, I still had every right to defend my troops and my installation to the best of my ability although an improved defense capability could be counter to the underlying plan.**

**Finally, I concluded that the most logical thing for me to do was, while enhancing real defense to the extent I could, to create the aura of a growing and serious defense capability -- the phantom army concept. And one of the best ways to do that was via the North Korean agents on the base.**

**But I knew that, if the real or perceived base defense situation was materially modified, the North Koreans, or others, might find ways to test that defense capability and I had to be alert to that possibility. Then there was the matter of higher command. I knew I was completely out-of-bounds -- far exceeding normal local commander initiative -- in what I was thinking. But where were the higher commands -- the national strategy? All that was far over the fence and, apparently, the higher echelons were unconcerned. I was alone.**

**Struggling to deal with the increasing complex and volatile scenario that was being formulated in my mind, I fell asleep and dreamed a lot of horrible dreams.**

# DAY TWENTY-NINE
# A RELAXED MONDAY

The bad news at the morning staff meeting was the weather -- Sergeant Butler assured us that we were in for a tremendous heat spell from a high pressure area moving in from China. At 0900 hours in the morning, everyone in the room was already dripping with sweat. There was no question but that we were in for some terribly high temperatures and, in Korea, when it is hot it is really hot -- just as is the opposite -- the cold of the Korean winters.

The staff meeting was barely over when a call came in from Lt. Colonel Paul Buckner in Seoul. My conversation with my Marine friend had paid off. As the plan unfolded, he was going to have a ROKAF C-46 call in for an emergency landing at Kunsan the following morning just before noon. There would be no flight plan on record. To give a semblance of realism to the event, on board the ROKAF C-46 would be a U.S. Army advisor of Oriental descent along with some ROK infantry troops carrying normal combat weapons. Paul said that the ROK troops would have to be fed and I assured him that I would arrange that. Also aboard the C-46 would be two fifty caliber machine guns with tripod mounts and some combat boxes of ammo that would be left behind when they departed. The ammo, Paul said, would be written off the books. But I had to receipt for the fifties as a loan. "Who knows," he said, "the record on this might get lost."

The basic plan was to test what would happen on my base. Would the aircraft simply be cleared in and the men taken to the mess hall? How would my Air Police react? I felt that I was setting Wild up for this one but the concept was good. I hoped the telephone call was not monitored by my men -- or the enemy.

As a next step, I thought it was an opportune time to invite Colonel Lee for a discussion. He was available and he promised to be at my office within the hour. Outside, Polk was already raising two additional flag poles. But there was some bad news. Jones announced that the G.I. record player had broken down again and that there would be no reveille or retreat played for a day or two. "But," he said, "that will make some men happy. When we played it yesterday, we had one G.I. call in and complain about the noise."

I was furious -- since when is reveille and retreat on a military base to be considered *noise*? But there were other things to think about. Outside the office door, I could see a new officer. Jones advised me that the person was my new Deputy -- a Lt. Colonel Robert Knight. He had just arrived on the commuter plane from Osan that was en route to Japan. "His record looks pretty good," Jones advised as he handed me a 201 file.

"Send him in."

Knight saluted and we shook hands.

"I've been anxiously awaiting your arrival," I said. "But I don't want to burden you with work today. Get yourself a billet -- Lieutenant Jones will handle that. Then get yourself unpacked and stroll around the base to get familiarized. Tonight, let's have dinner together at the Officers Club. You will soon learn that its called *The Bottom of the Mark* and it looks like it. But don't despair, we have a lot going for us and, with you here, I think we are going to be able to get some real things accomplished. I'll see you at dinner tonight."

After Knight had left, I scanned his 201 file -- it was as Jones had said -- good -- very good!

Lt. Colonel Knight was hardly out of the office when Colonel Lee arrived. I invited Lee to have a cup of coffee and we sat down at the coffee table. I opened the conversation with a question that subordinated myself.

"Lee, I've got a problem and I hope you can help me with it."

Lee seemed more than willing to help. And, with that observation, I laid out the base defense problem. Soon, I called for Jones to bring in a map of the base and, within minutes, Lee and I were mapping out possible defense positions and how to counteract various intrusions on the base -- we were performing commander duties.

With another cup of coffee, I suggested to Lee that we had several mutual problems to consider.

"First, I think we have the day-to-day problems which get us into the basics of military life: josans, black market and more. I think it is in both our interests to have some control of this situation. I think you might already know that I have instituted policies that are cutting down on the base josan problem."

"I've heard about that," Lee responded.

"But we have a second problem and that is thievery and black market -- and I think they go hand in hand."

"Are you suggesting that my men are involved?" Lee asked -- he was perturbed.

"I am not suggesting that either your men or my men are involved -- they both might be involved. More significant may be what takes place as a result of outside individuals. What we cannot afford is to have this continue. Suppose that there are landing lights stolen and one of your men crash as a result? Is that to be accepted as something normal? I hope not."

"So what do you suggest?"

"I suggest that we join together to curtail the slicky operation, the black market and everything else that destroys the integrity of our base." I used the word *our* to make it a joint effort even though everything I had experienced to date was along the line that the base was "ours" in the U.S. sense and on which the ROKAF was a tenant. I still fretted at not having in hand a Status of Forces agreement covering the Kunsan Air Base operation.

"You have an idea?" Lee asked.

"Yes I do. First, I think it would be proper that you have a ROKAF Air Policeman serving at the front gate to the base. Certainly, one of your men could do a better job talking to and handling the Koreans who come to this base."

"Possibly, but we would have to agree on the interface between your men and mine."

"That is understood. But there is more. Second, I think it is necessary that we agree, in the event of an emergency, who does what where. We have already looked at the map and various defense ideas. Still, we have to go beyond that -- we need to assign areas of concern and we need to determine how we coordinate with each other. For openers, I think my Air Police need one of your men, one who can speak some English, always stationed in our Air Police Command Center. To make this a team effort, I will authorize this man to eat in our mess along with my men. And we need to establish a means of communication from your man to your organization. This can be a simple land line and a crank telephone -- but we need something if we are to work together in an emergency. And we need the same telephone link to those anti-aircraft batteries of the ROK Army that are stationed around the field. Don't you agree."

"Agreed." I could detect that Lee was on board and enthusiastic.

"Now, let's assume that something happens in your area, would you not want us to know about it and be ready to assist?"

Lee nodded agreement.

"And, if we are in trouble, would you not want to assist us?"

**Again, Lee nodded.**

**"Then let's figure out a command and control arrangement -- something both your men and my men will understand and respect. Perhaps, in an emergency, we should meet at a common place and, jointly, decide what has to be done and how to do it?"**

**I could sense that the status of Lee had moved up several notches. To this date, he had only been a *tenant* on Kunsan Air Base and I was proposing that he be a *partner*. I knew that there were risks in this but what else was there that would make sense?**

**"Can I think about all that which we have discussed?" Lee suggested. I sensed that he felt a need to talk to his superiors on the issues presented.**

**"Absolutely. But let me privately tell you that tomorrow there will be a test of this base to determine if we know our business. And I can forecast that the answer will be that we do not. Tomorrow, an aircraft will land at this field totally unannounced and with armed men on board and I can almost assure you that my men will not react sufficiently. This is my problem but the next problem could be yours. We are both here to defend ourselves, each other and Korea and, unless we work together to achieve that end, we will not succeed."**

**I knew that I had said more than enough. Inwardly, I felt that I had started something for which I could not see an end. Lee shook my hand and went back to his area while I went back to the mound of paper on my desk -- a mound that seldom seemed to diminish.**

**The day was long and tedious. Between paperwork and other problems, I was beat by the time dinner time came around. And soon I was off to the Waldorf Astoria to freshen up before going to the Officers Club. When I arrived at my billet, Mr. Kim was standing there to greet me.**

**"I understand from Captain Wild that I upset you. I sorry. I apologize. I know about those who might like to do harm to you and neither I nor my men want that to happen. We like our Colonel Boss. So sorry that Colonel Boss upset. We try to do better."**

**Mr. Kim saluted. I was struck by the sincerity of his words and stuck out my hand. Mr. Kim grasped it and bowed. I knew I had a friend and protector but I did not know how to repay the debt. Perhaps tomorrow or the next day, or the next, I might have an idea.**

**That night, I taped a long message to Mary. Things seemed to be moving in the right direction and it made talking to her a lot easier. For a change, I had a remarkable night's sleep.**

# DAY THIRTY -- A TUESDAY

**Even before the morning staff meeting was convened, the air was insufferably hot. Lt. Colonel Robert Knight was present and he was introduced all around. He made a good impression on everyone present. I concluded that the personnel system had sent me a very good man. The prior evening, he and I had a long discussion over dinner and it seemed that our thoughts coincided on most subjects. I was comfortable.**

**At the morning staff meeting, Sergeant Butler conveyed to the group the news that we had not yet seen the peak temperatures. There was a moan among those present. Peterson, Polk and others suggested that we were going to have to order the curtailment of air conditioners as our electrical generators could not handle an increased load. I immediately volunteered to turn off the air conditioner in the Waldorf Astoria and depend on open windows for survival.**

**Captain Wild and Lieutenant Wade reported that the baseball team had joined up with the existing Air Police guards during the night and the double guard set up was such a success that there was no report of josan or slicky infiltration.***

**In other matters:**

**Captain Polk reported that the two additional flag poles had been set in concrete and the bases were firm enough to raise the Korean and UNC flags.**

**Major Akers reported on the coming Friday picnic and reminded me that I was to be a guest at an affair on the Saturday thereafter hosted by the Mayor of Kunsan. Colonel Lee and a few of his staff were to be there -- Akers wanted to know who I wanted from my staff to join in -- I selected Akers, Peterson and Wild. Lt. Colonel Knight was to remain on base in accordance with our agreement of the prior evening that there would always be one of us on base.**

**Major Peterson advised that 600 shovels had been placed on emergency requisition.**

---

* Following my departure from Kunsan Air Base, the Air Police and the interior guard of Korean nationals (Mr. Kim's organization) were integrated into one flight and, working with Kunsan City, there "was a lessening of the *slicky boy* activity and a virtual elimination of local prostitution." (Source: HRA files.)

There were some other minor items of interest but, that over, I summed things up and told the staff that I would take the L-20 the next day for a staff meeting at Osan. For the day, I wanted Akers to check out Knight in the Gooney Bird.

The staff meeting over, I looked at my watch -- 1000 hours. In about an hour the C-46 with the ROK troops would be landing. I felt apprehensive about the coming event but was soon absorbed by paper work. And then Jones came in.

"Sir, we have a ROK C-46 that just landed with some mechanical problems. They have some ROK Army troops on board and they asked permission to feed them at our mess. There is an American advisor with the unit. They have called for transportation. Is it O.K. to feed the ROK Army troops?"

"If you think so," I answered. "And, by the way, where is Captain Wild?"

"He may be down at the Air Police Command Center. I'll get him if you want."

"Yes, by all means. Do have him come to my office."

I felt awful. I had set up Wild but I wanted to make a point.

In a few minutes, Wild arrived.

"You wanted me, sir?"

"Yes. Jones tells me that we have a ROK C-46 on the field that came in with some troops on board and they needed feeding -- they are probably already at our G.I. mess. Are you aware of it?"

"No sir. I had no call from the tower. Is there something that we need to do -- do they need guards at the aircraft?"

"Not exactly. Let's say that C-46 is an enemy aircraft and right now you have a unit of armed men on the base intent on causing major damage. And no one is doing one damn thing about it. What would you think about that?"

Wild turned pale and then red.

"You're kidding me. I hope you're kidding me. Are you?"

"I am not kidding. I set up this intrusion just to see what would happen. I think we have been all too lax on a lot of things and I wanted this to demonstrate the point. And I guess it has been demonstrated. Let's go out and meet our guests."

As we drove to the G.I. mess, I asked Wild about aircraft landing at Kunsan Air Base without clearances.

"We have it relatively often -- frequently," Wild answered. "Mostly, it's Army liaison aircraft or helicopters. Since I've been here, we did have some landings by transport aircraft -- landings that I believe took place when the weather at Osan or Kimpo was down. These were unmarked aircraft but flown by Americans -- they wore flight suits and they might have been civilian pilots. What bothered me was that they had passengers on board but did not allow them to deplane. At the time, I thought they might be prisoners."

"And how did you know this?"

"Well, while they were parked waiting for the weather up north to clear, they asked us to deliver food -- box lunches -- to the aircraft."

"Did you place a guard on any of those aircraft?"

"No. The pilots asked us not to do that."

"How many meals did you deliver to these aircraft?"

"Something like a dozen or so -- I don't recall exactly as the delivery was made by our mess personnel. However, I seem to recall that one of our mess Sergeants spotted one of the passengers and he swore that the chap was Chinese."

Holy Moses! I recalled Mike's comment about Mickey Mouse operations and had to conclude that Wild was talking about CIA movement of Chinese, most likely Chinese Nationalists, to intelligence listening posts in Korea -- probably in the area of the DMZ or even on aircraft flown out of Osan Air Base or other locations -- or they might be infiltration teams intended for operations in Communist China. As we arrived at the G.I. mess, I found myself cursing my lack of knowledge.

The visiting ROK Army troops were already seated -- rifles leaning next to each of them. I introduced myself to the American advisor and thanked him for his cooperation. I pointed out that he had taught us a good lesson and I was certain that, in the future, my staff was going to pay a lot more attention to unknown aircraft landing at the base. He laughed at how easy it would have been to turn the base upside down with the troops he had. The good thing, he said, was that his Korean contingent was going to have a better meal than they did in their home unit.

"O.K. Wild. We have the classic situation of an unknown aircraft, one without a filed flight plan, landing at our base. What should have happened?"

Wild was embarrassed.

"Well, sir, the first thing that should have happened was my unit being informed that we had such an aircraft inbound -- or landing without instructions, if that had been the case. Then my reaction team, should have moved into position to surround the aircraft and let no one debark until the occupants and their purpose were known. If in doubt,

**we should have contacted you or, in your absence, our new Deputy Commander, Lt. Colonel Knight."**

**"That's about it and I want you to set up the instructions. In the meantime I have a surprise waiting for you on that aircraft as soon as these men are through eating. I suggest you get a six-by and a few of your men out to the aircraft. I'll be out there after I finish talking to the American advisor."**

**[*At the time and in relation to base defense, I was deeply concerned that the Chinese Communists -- even the North Koreans or the Japanese -- might attempt a nuclear "snatch" at Kunsan Air Base. In my projected scenario, the approach to the base would be from the Yellow Sea in one or more U.S. built transports (such as C-47s or C-46s) with either ROK or USAF markings. After landing, well-armed troops would disrupt the base and effect the nuclear "snatch."***

***Some years later while serving on the Joint Staff of the JCS, I drew up a full blown, minute-by-minute scenario on how this could be done with, at the conclusion, the U.S. authorities left in doubt as to what country was involved. Assisting me in the development of this scenario was an outstanding Army Colonel -- later, he became a Major General. Eventually, we briefed this scenario to senior officers in the Joint Staff and were told to forget that we had ever conceived the operation -- "Bury it!" was the order. There was no practical defense.***

***Later, I would learn that, without my knowledge (the clearance problem), Kunsan Air Base had been designated as a recovery base for Chinese Nationalist and other overflight of Communist China. This meant that the base, possibly with radar warning, could have been approached from the west by an unidentified aircraft seeking landing rights and occupied by neither U.S. or ROK personnel. The ingredients for a terrible tragedy were obvious.***

***Reflecting on this later knowledge, I had to wonder if that was not a consideration that led to there being no ROK Army anti-aircraft guns located to protect the seaward approach to Kunsan Air Base -- literally to create an open door. But "open doors" could be used by anyone -- friend or enemy!*]**

**The two fifty caliber machine guns with the tripod mounts and the boxes of ammo were like gold to the Air Police troops that assisted in unloading them. I checked the serial numbers on the guns and signed for them. Then, as soon as the ROK Army men were on board, the C-46 took off.**

"All right, Wild. These guns are not here because we did good. They are here so that you and this base can do better. And one of the first things I want you to do is to work with Lieutenant Wade and the baseball team and make them into an elite, quick reaction machine gun reinforcement unit. Teach them how to fire and maintain these guns. And, when they know what they are doing, I want you to figure out how to have a second team. In the meantime, I want to trigger a mock exercise for the baseball unit -- possibly something on the sea wall perimeter. If the sea is clear of boats, we may let them set up and fire a few rounds for excitement -- a little PR effect for those who have ears."

"Colonel, I think I understand and you'll get your wish." Wild was one happy soul even though he realized that the system had not worked to my pleasure.

With the sound of the C-46 disappearing into the distance, I became aware of the pop of firing from the gun range.

"Has the qualification program gotten underway?" I asked.

"Yes. We're firing in some of the officers today. Tomorrow we will start on a schedule for the enlisted men."

"And what are you using for targets?"

"The regular bull's eye cards pinned to a plywood backboard."

"Find yourself someone who can draw and get him to make some North Korean and Chicom silhouettes -- enemy officer and enlisted men. Let's make this exercise more focused. And while you're at it, develop some hand outs that depict the rank and unit insignia of the North Koreans and the Chicoms. Title it as a *know-your-enemy* paper and plaster it on bulletin boards."

Wild looked puzzled.

"You have a problem with that?" I asked.

"Well, no sir. It's just that I don't know what their uniforms and insignia look like."

"Well, then you better find out."

With a "Yes sir," Wild saluted and left.

I was exasperated but I smiled. Things were working out and I was now going to go to the PX and play my next card. If I was going to have a North Korean spy ring on my base, I was going to give them something "to write home about."

My Korean PX manager bowed as I entered. He was the first to speak.

"Sorry we no have much here today. Loss of railroad cars of PX stuff very bad. Much hurt. Maybe soon we get more. I hope so."

"And if you don't get more, maybe you won't have a job," I suggested.

The manager paled a bit at my words.

"I try," he said.

"You better more than try. You better find a way to get these shelves filled or I am going to have to get someone in here who knows how to do it."

"I try hard," the manager said as he forced a smile. "I try hard like Colonel does. Colonel should get some rest. No work so hard."

"And what makes you think I work too hard."

"I hear much boom, boom. No hear boom, boom before. Something big maybe happen?"

"Something big will happen if your cousins from up North decide to come down here or if their Chinese friends from across the Yellow Sea try to do something. What you hear is just practice for what would happen to them."

If my North Korean manager was indeed a North Korean spy, I could almost read the report that would be sent to his superiors:

| INDICATION IS THAT NEW KUNSAN BASE COMMANDER IS INCREASING DEFENSE CAPABILITY IN ANTICIPATION OF OPERATION FROM NORTH KOREA OR FROM CHINA. |
|---|

And I could almost read the instructions that would follow:

| PROVIDE DETAILS ON INCREASED KUNSAN DEFENSE AS SOON AS POSSIBLE. |
|---|

Two could play at this espionage game. And I had to wonder what my pimply-faced Olson friend would have to say about all this? I laughed. For the moment, I was having fun. But I knew that it was dangerous fun.

After visiting with the PX manager, I returned to the office and called in Captain Polk. I asked for the names of the Koreans in his various offices. When he showed me the names in the drafting room, I queried him about how much drafting work they really had to do. As I suspected, it wasn't much but they kept the Koreans on the payroll as it was something "outside budget." I then discussed with Polk the utility of cross-training personnel and suggested that he switch around some persons so as to raise their skill level. We went through several possibilities and before we were through I had maneuvered the named North Korean spy into an innocuous position -- but without having him singled out or fired. And now I could read the next message passed out by my illustrious spy ring:

> AGENT XYZ HAS BEEN MOVED AS A PART OF A GENERAL REORGANIZATION OF THE KUNSAN ENGINEERING OFFICE. NO OTHER SOURCE IN THAT OFFICE AREA CURRENTLY AVAILABLE. ALL OTHER KUNSAN SOURCES REMAIN. ADVISE.

Now the problem was my next step.

Undoubtedly, the PX manager would seek collaboration of what was developing from the other agents. There was, of course, the normal visual observations that anyone could make. Surely, the landing of the C-46 with ROK Army troops on board would raise the specter of a reinforcement exercise as it was something new -- and new developments were a focus of all enemy agents. But more was needed. Even if I did not have a good base defense, I believed that I could create in the enemy mind that one was present.

Examining possible opportunities, I had to conclude that the agent working in the ice plant was not a good avenue of approach -- his job, at best, might be, at some point, to contaminate the ice -- even to poison the ice. To counter that threat, I had to find a way to talk to Doctor Baker about the possibilities without revealing what I knew.

The agent with access to the bomb dump -- that was really a non-thing. The real information was the delivery systems that would carry the bombs and that had even eluded me.

The best agent to work was the unknown person in the Officers Club. I concluded that that person would hardly be a back room worker or cook -- the best positioning of an agent in that facility would be where conversation could be overheard. And that meant a waitress or a bartender. Thinking about that, my mind alternated between Annie and the bartender named "Joe." I decided to hedge my bets and work both of them in the days ahead.

I was about to leave the office for the day when Jones advised me that a call had come from the tower advising that a "hot" aircraft had landed and was parked at the end of the runway.

"Captain Wild's reaction team has surrounded and secured it."

"The lesson has been learned," I thought but I might as well go out and see how things were working. Undoubtedly, the pilot would be surprised by the development -- particularly if he had landed at Kunsan before with no reaction taking place.

The "hot" aircraft was a C-54 based in Okinawa. The alleged purpose of the visit was to trade out a nuclear weapon on a one-for-one basis. Turnbull was at the aircraft when I arrived. He had a team arriving with a fork lift. According to established procedure, my foam truck was standing by.

"First time I've seen your men move to surround an aircraft like this," Turnbull stated. "And so fast."

"And you ain't seen nothing yet."

I felt good. Already, I could envisage still another agent report:

| SECURITY FORCE AT KUNSAN NOW REACTING TO LANDINGS OF CERTAIN AIRCRAFT. BASE MAY HAVE BEEN ALERTED TO PREPARE FOR POSSIBLE AIR SUPPORTED INCURSION. |
|---|

And now, if my scheme worked, I would expect a test of some sort -- possibly a test of resolve rather than of force. If it came, I wondered if I would recognize it?

I could also imagine that Mr. Olson and his friends in the Mickey Mouse arena were going to have some new intercepts of enemy traffic to analyze. And I wondered what their reaction would be? Would Olson or his boss in Osan contact me?

Suddenly, life was becoming especially interesting as well as challenging. I had to wonder how my staff would respond if they knew what was going on -- the game I was beginning to play?

But then a new and troubling thought snapped my mind to attention. Suppose the mission of the alleged spy ring was not that of espionage and sabotage? Suppose the mission of the spy ring was to make Kunsan Air Base appear to the U.S. military system as sufficiently troublesome, vulnerable and costly to cause its use as a forward strike base to be curtailed or canceled? If that was the case, many of the problems at Kunsan Air Base, even the poor PX situation, might be traced to the initiatives of this ring and their scattered friends in South Korea. Perhaps the theft of the two railroad cars of supplies was not the work of slickies -- perhaps it was the work of North Korean

**agents who might have been activated by my own Korean PX manager -- a person who knew of in-coming shipments and their content?***

**And then I recalled Wild's statement that a deployed Matador unit had been penetrated at one time but no damage was inflicted on the weapon. Was this a way by which North Korean agents might seek to undermine the Matador deployment -- to cause a pull back on the basis that it would be too costly to provide adequate defense to the dispersed and isolated facilities?**

**The above thoughts aside, regardless of the mission of the North Korean spy ring, I had to proceed on the basis that the Korean PX manager was a key player. If the focus of the ring was to discourage use of the base by the Air Force, an indication of enhanced use might trigger actions aimed at further degrading the environment. If, on the other hand, the focus of the ring was primarily that of reporting deployments, developments and readiness to North Korea, then I could expect some test of the perceived enhanced situation as a form of intelligence confirmation. Such a test would be in line with the repeated tests each side made of the other in the area of the DMZ. However, there was an aside to all this. If the superiors overseeing the PX manager concluded that he was failing in his job, it could lead to his withdrawal -- possible a "termination" by those superiors. That conclusion, however, was a two-edged sword for, while it might remove the PX manager from the spy scene, I probably would not know who the replacement senior agent would be.**

**The game was beginning to develop more facets than a cut diamond. And I had only another thirty days to pull the strings of the game puppets. I had to cool my mind by talking to someone and decided that the best bet would be Doctor Baker -- I called for him to come to the office. When he arrived, I asked him to close the door.**

**"Doctor, as a part of the defense planning for the base, have you given much thought to the chemical and biological questions?"**

**"I hope you're kidding?"**

**"I'm not kidding. I already observed that we have no gas masks on this base and I wonder just how unprepared we are in the whole chemical and biological field?"**

**"Colonel, I think the answer is simple -- we aren't prepared at all. My hope is that we will never have to face that problem. Beyond**

---

* Eventually, during the 1966-1968 confrontation in Korea, as a result of increased vigilance by the ROK military and other elements, to include the organization of the Homeland Defense Reserve Force, some 2,500 North Korean agents and informants would be uncovered.

**hope, I have no ready solution. I hardly have enough capability to handle routine physical problems -- accidents, typical diseases and the like. I have no protective clothing, no decontamination equipment, nothing. If we got hit with chemicals or biologicals with a widespread contamination, I think we would be helpless."**

**I knew what the answer would be but it was an opener for the ice plant situation.**

**"What if we had something less than the situation you describe. Suppose, as example, one of our Korean employees was instructed to sabotage our base by way of the ice we make. What might be the properties employed and how could we counter the situation?"**

**Baker thought for a while and then replied.**

**"The easiest answer is not to use the ice -- if we could quickly determine that it was the source of the problem. For me to make such a determination is near unto impossible. Right now, the only check I make of the water is the residual chlorine level and a periodic scan of culture slides. I don't have the equipment to make a detailed chemical analysis. But let me review for you what might be passed to the men through the ice we use in drinks."**

**And, following, I got an education that I really did not want. When Baker finished reviewing all the possibilities he could think of, there was only one option left and that was "hope" -- hope that none of the possibilities described became realities.**

**The game being played was a dangerous one. My command was vulnerable, if not threatened, and, as I had already concluded, I was virtually alone in orchestrating the counter attack.**

**Reflecting on the situation, I concluded that the North Koreans, if they had not already done so, would be assembling a dossier on me -- apparently the ROK already had such a dossier on me. What that dossier showed was important to the defense situation. If that record showed weakness, the North Koreans might be enticed to do unwanted things. If that record showed strength, the North Koreans might seek to think twice. I wanted that record to show strength.**

# DAY THIRTY-ONE -- A WEDNESDAY

As planned, I took the L-20 to Osan. I had begun to like the little bird even though it sort of mushed through the air. Leaving Kunsan early in the morning, the air was still smooth but I knew that, in a few hours, the heat of the day would be causing thermals and the return trip to Kunsan would hit considerable turbulence.

General Joyce seemed in a good mood at the staff meeting and, when I briefed about my "sandbags with no shovels" problem, there was a guffaw around the room. It made me angry that so serious a situation should be treated so lightly, but I let it pass.

Probably the most significant presentation at the staff meeting was the intelligence report that indicated a growing disenchantment with President Rhee and there was indication of his overthrow sometime in the near future. The general advice to everyone was to stay out of the picture and let happen what was going to happen.

I wanted to talk about base defense but the opening did not arrive so I let the subject ride.

After the staff meeting was over, General Joyce called me into his office and reminded me that I had only a month to go before my replacement was in and I would be moving to Osan. Then he asked me if I could find the time to fly to Kangnung and give him my view of that operation. At Kangnung, on the eastern shore of Korea and just south of the DMZ, was a radar installation in which a couple dozen Americans served. And then he told me to visit Kimpo Air Base as the U.S. Ambassador had told him to expedite a property transfer to support President Rhee's desire to have that base made into an international terminal. I did not like the idea of time being taken from my work at Kunsan Air Base but General Joyce was the boss.

Again, I managed to have lunch with Mike and she imparted to me all the local gossip. General Joyce, she stated, was becoming more relaxed in the job -- it seemed that all the officers, enlisted men and civilians liked him. But the Wing Commander was on a discipline and regulations kick that was driving everyone crazy.

We talked about her flying and it seemed that her next objective was a trip to Hong Kong where she seemed to have many friends in various businesses -- furs, clothing and more. I asked her

**about the price of mink stoles and she assured me that, if I wanted one for Mary, she could get a bargain. I put it on my "will do later list."**

**Before leaving Osan, I had a session with the senior Chaplain. I reviewed my meeting with Father Collins and stated that I needed a Catholic Chaplain at Kunsan who was more understanding and flexible. I was assured that I would get one.**

**It was evening when I arrived back at Kunsan Air Base. Parking in front of Operations, I saw that my staff car had been washed and was waiting for me -- the keys were in the ignition. Getting in, I decided to drive around the base before turning in for the night and soon found myself disturbed about something. Retracing my route, I was shocked. Where there had been a building the prior day, none was now present. Parking the staff car, I got out and looked. Sure enough, there was a concrete slab foundation there but no building. I drove to the Air Police Command Center and stormed in.**

**The duty personnel were playing cards to pass the time. At the sight of me, they "popped to."**

**"Who in the hell was on duty last night -- who was supposed to be supervising the security on this base?"**

**Captain Wild was not there and the senior Sergeant did not seem to know.**

**"Let me check the roster, sir . . . . It was Staff Sergeant Berkowitz, sir."**

**"And where is Sergeant Berkowitz?" I asked.**

**"He's probably in his hootch."**

**"Get him," I demanded. "And I will wait."**

**It took all of twenty-five minutes for Sergeant Berkowitz to arrive. I could see that he had dressed hastily.**

**"What took you so long to get here?" I asked.**

**"Sir, I was in my hootch."**

**"So?"**

**"Well, it took the men some time to locate me -- my hootch is at the edge of the base."**

**So here was one of my shacked up men. I was about to say something and then let it ride. The missing building was more of a current problem.**

**"Were you aware that there was a building stolen last night?"**

**"A whole building? No sir."**

**"And how often did you inspect the guard last night?"**

**"Sir, things were quiet last night. I didn't inspect the guard."**

"And so, in the quiet of the night, you had a building dismantled and stolen right from under your nose? Come with me and tell me how this could happen. And then, if you can, tell me how and why this is not going to happen again."

Undoubtedly, I should have called Wild and turned the matter over to him but I was mad as hell -- an entire building stolen and, apparently, no one was aware of the event -- even the next day! This was preposterous.

I drove Sergeant Berkowitz to the building site. It had been a Quonset storage hut and there was nothing left but the concrete slab. Fortunately, the building had been empty.

"I think this building was in Sergeant Dupont's area last night," Berkowitz suggested.

"You think?"

"Yes sir -- we were spread pretty thin last night but I think Sergeant Dupont's area included this building."

"And this whole building is taken apart and carried right through the perimeter without you or anyone knowing about it? And you don't have time to inspect the guard and pay attention to what is going on?"

"Sir, I think I goofed."

"And you probably did. How long have you been stationed here?"

"Three years, sir."

"Three years? Why?"

"Well, I sort of like it here."

"And where is this hootch of yours -- take me there."

I could see that Sergeant Berkowitz did not want to do this but he knew I meant business. The "hootch" turned out to be a grass covered shack, some corrugated metal was used for the walls but most were mud. There was a Korean woman there and I did not have to ask more.

"Sergeant, I want you back in the barracks tonight and every night you are based here at Kunsan. Is that clear?"

"Yes sir, but . . ."

"No *but* about it. And this hootch of yours is on this base -- I want it removed."

"But . . ."

"Did I not make myself clear. I want you back in the barracks and this hootch off base property. And I want it done by tomorrow night. If an entire building can be stolen while you are supervising the

**security of this base, you can find the means to move this hootch. And the farther from this base the better."**

**With that, I got back in the staff car and drove Berkowitz to the Air Police Command Center. Obviously Wild had been called -- he was driving up as I arrived. I asked him to join me at the Officers Club.**

**At the termination of my conversation with Wild, I had ordered him to insure that every one of his men was sleeping in the barracks and not in hootches on the perimeter and, further, I wanted all perimeter hootches moved outside the base proper. "And, if the hootches are not moved, I want them burned down. Tell your men, and any others, who are shacked up in those things that it's their choice -- move the hootches or get them burned down. And as to Sergeant Berkowitz, I want him reassigned immediately to Taegu. For the longer range, I want a plan developed wherein there is a person sleeping in every building every night. We aren't going to have any more buildings stolen from under our noses."**

**Reflecting on the situation, I realized that the Koreans were adept at thievery. Mike had already told me about the "little old lady" who was caught at Osan carrying out a jeep engine on an A-frame -- the engine concealed by grass. And then there was the story of the stolen anchor chain so heavy that it was estimated to have taken 200 men to carry it. But a whole building? I thought about reporting the event but decided that the best route was to let the matter die. Certainly, I was not going to put myself on report to the Wing Commander.**

**Of greater concern, I anticipated some backlash from my order to bring the men back into the barracks and get rid of the perimeter hootches. Apparently, the men living in those hootches viewed them as "home." And, kicking a person out of his home, I had to expect a reaction. Fortunately, I was not looking at a large number of men but they were senior noncoms and, over the years, their influence might have grown to be more than I would normally expect. For the moment, I would have to watch and wait -- play my cards close -- and be ready for everything and anything.**

**When we departed for the night, I asked Wild if he thought we could recover the stolen building.**

**"I don't think so," he answered. "By now, it's probably scattered to a hundred or more locations and the pieces will look like all the other pieces of metal that have been scrounged in the past."**

**What a hell of a situation. I was still mad when I doused the light in the Waldorf Astoria to try to get some sleep.**

# DAY THIRTY-TWO -- A THURSDAY

Well before the men gathered for the morning staff meeting, the temperature again was unbearable. To conserve power, all air conditioners around the base had been turned off. And I could see that, as a result of the oppressive heat, everyone was irritable.

I had Wild brief the staff members on the stolen building of the prior day. Sergeant Berkowitz, he assured me, would be moved to Taegu by nightfall. "And from there," I added, "I want him sent home. He has been in Korea too long. Something tells me that persons who extend in Korea have motives that I cannot share and I want to look into all such men with the idea of moving them out."

"That's going to really hurt the Air Police section," Wild answered. None of the other officers had a comment.

"Talk to me later about the effect and how we handle it." I already knew from the report Jones provided to me that a good number of senior Air Police personnel were among those on extended status and I was beginning to suspect that there might be a link between such persons and the black market and slicky operations on the base -- and it might extend to prostitution. Perhaps I was becoming overly suspicious -- perhaps Korea was wearing on me?

[*Thievery was not exclusively a Korean problem -- all too much of it was tied to the American community in Korea. Unfortunately, opportunities abounded -- particularly in respect to the black market outlets.*

*One especially interesting theft took place at Osan Air Base where there was a large construction project on-going. As a part of the contract for this construction, the contractor was allowed to draw fuel from the Air Force supply system. Accounting of fuel drawn was accomplished by way of some simple issue slip paperwork.*

*Observing the loose system, an enterprising Airman drove a forty foot flat bed loaded with 55 gallon drums to the fuel dump where they were filled. He signed an issue slip for the fuel indicating that it was intended for the construction project. Then he drove off the base and sold the full load to a black market buyer.*

*In all probability, the theft would not have been discovered had not the sudden flow of fuel into the black market caused a dramatic*

***lowering of the price of such fuel. This price change was so severe that its cause was investigated and the theft revealed.***]

**At the close of the staff meeting I asked Knight to stay.**

**"Bob, one thing I would like you to take on as a special project is the food situation. In the short time I have been here, I've tried to upgrade the food but I doubt that I have scratched the surface -- mostly because I've got a bundle of other priority things to handle. Do me the favor of being my director of food services for all the mess and club facilities. As far as I can determine, food is the biggest gripe subject on this base and, if we can improve that area of concern, some of our other problems may go away.**

**"Secondly, there is the matter of security and base defense. This subject has bugged me from the first day I was on Kunsan. We obviously have limited resources but I think the problem runs much deeper. And I think that, between the two of us, we ought to do some nighttime inspection of the guard. I have done it a couple times and I believe it paid off. Captain Wild is, in my view, doing a good job -- really busting his butt to do the right thing -- but I think a continuing, direct interest and participation on our part will help. This stealing a whole building with no one seeing it happen really bugs me. I know that the Koreans are good but we have to have some sleeping guards for such a thing to happen. Or else some other things are happening on the guard posts." I told Knight about the lipstick I had observed on a guard on my first night inspection. We agreed, for the next month, to conduct at least one random inspection a week and observe what effect it had.**

**Knight was about to leave the office when Wild entered.**

**"Sir, this is hard to believe but we have a protest demonstration at the main gate."**

**"A protest about what?" I asked.**

**"It's the prostitutes from around the base and from Kunsan City. As far as I can make out, the josan policy you directed has cut down on their activity and income so much that they decided to march toward the base. They are congregated outside the main gate and screaming and yelling like banshees. I sent the reaction team to reinforce the guards on the gate."**

**"I never heard a banshee yelling but is our water pumper working?"**

**"It is," Wild replied.**

"Well, roll it out to the front gate and, if they try to force their way in, give the banshees a good bath. And, Bob, you go out and watch what happens. If Wild or the guards need any special instruction or if the situation gets out of hand, figure out something."

A prostitute protest march! This was one for the books! What in the hell would be the next thing? And was this really a prostitute protest march or was I being tested in some other way? Could the protest march be a diversion for some other event on-going or that was about to happen? I wanted to reveal to Bob some of my worries but I could not. Finally, I decided to drive around the base and determine if I could observe anything unusual taking place.

By now it was past noon with the heat bearing down unmercifully out of a clear sky. Driving through the base, I could see that the uniforms of the men were soaked with sweat. Ahead, the roadways shimmered with the rising heat giving the appearance of lakes of water. Then, passing Operations, Akers waved me down.

"Sir, we have a runway problem. The pilot of an aircraft that just landed reported that the runway has buckled."

"Hop in and let's take a look."

In minutes we were at the end of the runway and, flicking our headlights to be recognized, a green light from the tower cleared us onto it. About halfway down the runway, we could see it. The expansion of the heat had caused abutting slabs of concrete to tilt upward at the joint. There was at least a ten inch rise at the slab joint and it extended half way across the runway. On the other half of the runway, it was apparent that the pressure was about to cause a similar upheaval. The cause was obvious -- there had been no expansion joint maintenance on the runway.

"What do you think?" I asked Akers.

"I think that, if an aircraft took off and hit this, it could get airborne prematurely and then hit a stall -- a landing aircraft might be bounced pretty bad -- we might lose an undercarriage."

"And that suggests we close the field until the situation can be fixed. Call in Major Kitchens, the new senior officer in the alert area, and brief him on the problem. There will be hell to pay when we issue a NOTAM to close the field as the nuclear chaps will have to reschedule. Keep a watch on the slabs and, as soon as they settle back into position, probably as soon as the sun sets, open the field again. Tomorrow, do a check of the slabs every thirty minutes. I'll call Osan and maybe we can get a maintenance team in here to clean out and repair the expansion joints on this runway."

I was tempted to call Jack Hubbard, the Division Director of Operations, as I felt he would get me some fast action on a runway repair team but then decided to give the Wing Commander the problem. The reception I got was cool but he finally agreed to call Fifth Air Force for assistance as there was no runway repair capability in Korea. The next thing I knew, I had a call from the Engineer at Fifth Air Force.

"You can't close the field," the Engineer was almost shouting at me.

"But I just did close the field," I answered.

"Damn it, I passed through your base this spring and that runway looked good. You don't know what you're talking about."

"If you think I don't know what I'm talking about, fly over here and take a look for yourself but don't try to fly in when the sun is out or you might get killed. I've inspected the bulge in the runway and I deem it unsafe. And, if I deem it unsafe, it's unsafe. I happen to be the Commander of this base."

"But I tell you you're crazy. That runway couldn't bulge that much. You're making a mountain out of a mole hill just to get a repair team out there."

"This is not a mountain nor a mole hill; it's some expansion joints that no longer do the job. You can expect that the runway will be closed until past sundown when things cool off. But you can also expect that, so long as we have this type of weather, about noon of every following day the runway will buckle again and I'll close the field once more. Just get a team over here to clean out and refill the joints. If you chaps in Engineering at Fifth had been doing your job, this runway would have been repaired before now."*

The telephone at Fifth Air Force slammed down but before it hit I detected some loud cursing aimed at "those sons-of-bitches in Korea." About an hour later, I received a call from the Wing Commander who advised me that a Fifth Air Force runway repair team would be in Kunsan on the coming Monday. In the meantime, he asked me to try to keep the field open as long as possible. I assured him

---

* As already stated, due to the conclusion that the nature of the military establishment in Korea (personnel turnover) did not allow for continuity, the construction program that would otherwise have been run by the 314th Air Division was run directly out of the DSC/Engineering office of Fifth Air Force in Japan. For any in-country management, Fifth Air Force established a two-man Korean Installation Office at Osan. This unsatisfactory operational and management arrangement would be phased out after the time of this account with in-country responsibilities assigned to the 314th Air Division. (References on this action may be found in HRA files.)

that we had set up an every-thirty-minute watch on the runway and would do just that. To my surprise, the runway slabs did not settle into position until almost two hours after sundown. In the meantime, we marked the offending slabs with flare pots and Majors Akers and Kitchens worked out a plan where, should an emergency occur, aircraft could get airborne by holding tight to the side of the runway with the least disturbance. Akers advised that the ROKAF had been notified of the runway problem and that they were taking it in stride.

Late in the afternoon, I heard the repeated tut-tut-tut-tut of a fifty caliber machine gun. The sound was reassuring and comforting.

That evening, it was difficult to determine if the prostitute protest march or the runway problem dominated the bar discussion. As the men talked, I tried to observe Joe, the bartender, to see if he was especially interested. I noticed he smiled considerably when the conversation focused on the prostitute march but he seemed uninterested in the runway problem. By time for dinner, I had no strong inclination one way or another as to Joe's possible tie to the Korean spy set up. At dinner I shared a table with Knight and Annie served. She seemed uninterested in anything we had to say unless it was to order something. Perhaps the agent in the Officers Club was neither Annie nor Joe -- if it was one of them, I had to place my bet on Joe.

Bob stated that he would do an inspection of the guard at about two or three in the morning. I signaled Wild to come over and told him of the plan but advised him not to alert his men. Wild wanted to go with Bob on the inspection and I approved. Before leaving the table, Wild stated that he had advised those of his men, and others, living outside the barracks in the perimeter paddy hootches of my directive and that he had faced some "plenty pissed off" senior Sergeants.

"Are they going to comply or not?" I asked.

"I think they will but you have got to realize that, as much of a dump as those paddy hootches are, these men have been viewing them as their homes and they have pretty well settled in."

"My suggestion is that we give them a new home at Taegu and then ship them back to the States as soon as possible. Jones can take care of the paperwork."

"And the Korean women?" Wild Asked.

"If they are married, they can follow -- if they are not married, then they'll just have to find a new sponsor. How many are married? Do you know?"

"I sense that there may be some kids involved but, as far as I can determine, none of the men is actually married."

"And, as senior Sergeants, they are some damn good role models for the rest of the men. Get them back in the barracks and then move them out of here. And I know you'll be short-handed some bodies as a result of this action but something tells me that these shacked up Sergeants have not been all that effective -- and they may have been the cause of problems that we are yet to discover."

"As to problems, sir, when I visited the men in the paddy hootches I noticed in one hootch some cases of soft drinks that may have been obtained from the base. The Sergeant stated that his josan was holding them for a friend."

"Did you buy the story?"

"No sir. But I took no action at the time. My thought was that the problem, if there was one, would now be altered."

I nodded agreement.

I continued to be concerned about this action to bring the Sergeants living in the paddy hootches into the barracks and the planned move or destruction of these paddy houses but I felt it was necessary not only as a matter of defense but as a matter of principle. Further, having these Sergeants living in paddy hootches was hardly a plus when I cracked down on the activity of other men by way of the josan policy.

Still, I knew that I was following two standards in that, according to Major Newcomb, the Taegu Commander, at least some of the men at Taegu were living in houses with Korean "wives." Undoubtedly, unless the affected men at Kunsan Air Base were moved to the States, they would soon set up housekeeping at Taegu. And I had to wonder if these homes-away-from-home were tolerated at Osan Air Base and at other Air Force locations? I already knew that this sort of arrangement was tolerated by the U.S. Army in the Seoul area.

What a hell of a situation!

[*I don't think that General Joyce or the Wing Commander was ever aware of it, but, after arriving at Osan, I soon learned that some billets maintained "live in maids." That, however, was not my problem -- I had more than enough other things to do than concern myself about such things.*]

# DAY THIRTY-THREE -- A FRIDAY

The morning staff meeting was routine:

Sergeant Butler repeated the prior day's hot weather forecast -- we were in for another sweltering day.

Lt. Colonel Knight told of the inspection of the guard at 0300 hours.

Major Akers briefed on the runway buckling problem.

Captain Wild outlined his experience with the prostitute protest -- the water pumper did not come into play -- after about an hour of screaming and shouting, the prostitutes got tired and dispersed.

Captain Pastiak commented about the plan to get the men back in the barracks and the move to destroy the hootches. He said that many of the men had approached him with a request that they be allowed four to five days to sell the hootch materials. I agreed to let them have the time to dispose of the materials but emphasized that, if the hootches were not gone by the end of five days, I would burn them down. It turned out that all but two of the hootches were occupied by Air Police.

Major Kitchens from the alert area told us that the runway closure had lead to major retargetting problems and that there had been many nasty telephone calls from his command echelon. He stated that the Deputy Commander of his Group would fly in during the morning, well before the heat of the day would again buckle the runway, and wanted to meet with me and take a look at the runway.

Captain Polk said that he had a call from Fifth Air Force confirming that a runway repair team would be arriving on Monday and that there was a need for some twenty beds for the team -- the team chief was a Master Sergeant. Jones said he would take care of the billeting arrangements. It was expected that the team would be at Kunsan Air Base for about ten days or more. The team's air compressors and other equipment would be flown in by Air Force transport based in Japan.

At the close of the staff meeting, Major Akers reminded every one that the scheduled picnic would be at the dam site starting at 1600 hours.

The meeting had barely terminated when I heard a jet circle the field. It was the Deputy Commander of the fighter Group to which

Major Kitchens belonged. I drove out to the alert area to meet the Deputy Commander.

After an inspection of the runway, the Deputy Commander asked what time I thought the runway would again buckle.

"Based on yesterday, I would guess that it might buckle around 1300 hours or a little thereafter."

"And that gives me time to take off, do a little air work and land. Would you care to fly with me?" The Deputy Commander had arrived in a two-seater F-100 and I happily agreed.

Quickly fitted with pressure suit and helmet we were airborne for Koon-Ni range where the Deputy Commander dropped a few practice bombs in simulated nuclear attack mode. I wasn't used to the G-pull and my neck almost snapped on the first run. Then he headed toward North Korea on the deck, slicing between mountains well below even our own radar coverage. When we were just short of the DMZ, the Deputy Commander lighted the after burner and headed upward. Just before crossing the DMZ, he swung the aircraft in a tight 180 degree turn and headed back to Kunsan. The maneuver was to test the speed and reaction of the North Korean air defense system and to generate some chatter for the Mickey Mouse listeners.

"Pretty dangerous," I suggested. "If you miss on navigation, you are going to get your ass shot off."

"The answer is not to screw up on navigation."

[*Some time later, an American pilot flying a ROKAF F-86 at low-level would become disoriented and, to determine where he was, he would pull up on a northerly direction. Unfortunately, he crossed the DMZ into North Korea and, immediately, the North Koreans launched and intercepted him. He would be shot up badly and, eventually, crash on approach to Kunsan Air Base. Obviously, if we tested the North Koreans in this fashion, we had to expect to be tested by them. And, for me, this was a constant worry.*]

The runway was still operational when we landed. Refueled, the Deputy Commander took off for a return flight to Japan. He was satisfied with what I was doing and he offered, if Fifth Air Force dragged its heels on runway repair, to bring pressure to bear from his Group. Before he left, I learned that his base did have a baseball team and I arranged to have our team play his team in Japan on the Saturday coming.

The early afternoon was uneventful other than at 1400 hours the runway had to again be closed due to buckling. By 1700 hours, I was at the dam site for the scheduled picnic. The retention dam rose steeply from the surrounding terrain and, unlike so much of the surrounding country-side, there was a reasonable stand of trees.

The picnic was attended by about 250 men. Korean cooks had several barbecue tables going and the mood was upbeat. I participated in a number of races to the top of the dam and the men allowed me to win one or two. The make-shift horseshoes were crude but they worked. Someone had located a volleyball and net and a vigorous game ensued between the officers and the enlisted men -- the enlisted men won.

On all sides of the picnic area there were gathered hundreds of Korean children. Now and then, some of the men offered hot dogs to the children and there was much scurrying and screaming by the kids to get one. I did not object.

With dusk drawing near, the picnic was terminated and the men returned to base. It was a good day and I left happy.

The next day would be Saturday and my scheduled evening reception with the Mayor of Kunsan. I wondered what would be in store for me at that event.

*The retention dam rose steeply from the surrounding terrain. Shown here, some of the men have arrived in a weapons carrier and, already, the Korean children are gathering.*

*The Korean cooks set up some barbecue tables in the more heavily wooded area.*

*As word of the American picnic spread, Korean kids by the hundreds gathered -- curious about what was taking place and looking for a hand out of food.*

It must have been past midnight -- I was taping a message to Mary when the lights went out. Fumbling in the dark, I located the telephone and asked for the Duty Officer.

"They are out where you are and you are on back-up power?"

- - - - -

"What about the Air Police Command Center?"

- - - - -

"Do you know what happened? Did we lose a main generator?"

- - - - -

"Well, give me a call as soon as you know something. I'll stay here at the billet."

After I hung up, I found my flashlight. Shortly after arriving at Kunsan, I had noticed a supply of candles in a drawer in the living area of the Waldorf Astoria. Now my problem was to find a match as I did not smoke. Fortunately, there were some matches in the candle drawer and I soon had flickering light in the bed room and the living area.

It was something like fifteen minutes before the telephone rang. The Duty Officer was on the other end of the line.

"And you say that there is no generator problem -- that something has happened to a main feeder line?"

- - - - -

"And Captain Polk has his men out tracing the lines now?"

- - - - -

"What about the alert area and the bomb storage?"

- - - - -

"O.K. But I'm awake. Let me know what develops."

Another twenty minutes went by and then the telephone rang again.

"A ROKAF troop? Are you certain? Was there any ID?"

- - - - -

"At least he was wearing a ROKAF uniform?"

- - - - -

"Electrocuted?"

- - - - -

"And he had a bolt cutter -- you think he was trying to steal some wire and did not know the line was hot?"

- - - - -

"Well, he might have been cutting the line and not stealing wire. Call Colonel Lee and get him into the act. In the meantime, make certain that Captain Polk gets a splice on the feeder line as soon

**as possible. If something else happens, order an increase in the guard in critical areas and call me immediately."**

**Damn! Was it never ever going to ease up?**

**The picnic had been a great event and now this! Obviously, significant elements of the base could be penetrated and sabotaged. Even if the person electrocuted was out to steal wire, the message was the same -- Kunsan Air Base was vulnerable as all hell. And there just was no good solution at hand.**

**I called Knight. He, too, had been blacked out and, like myself, he had communicated with the Duty Officer. For a few minutes we discussed the impossible security situation. Eventually, I learned that he did not keep a gun in his quarters and I suggested that he check out a forty-five and keep it around -- but locked up when he was absent the quarters. He agreed.**

**It was probably 0300 hours when I crawled under the mosquito tent. I had not finished the tape to Mary and there was no use in trying to continue.**

**For a very long time, I just lay in the bed and stared into the blackness above me. If the person involved was a ROKAF party, would Colonel Lee be willing to admit it? But, suppose the person involved was not ROKAF -- only wearing a ROKAF uniform?* What message would I derive from that? Could this be an action to test our security and base defense? Could this be an action to discourage use of Kunsan Air Base by the Air Force? And would this event be followed by something else -- a deeper, more serious action? Could it be that this was an event staged to drive a wedge between myself and the ROKAF?**

**Perhaps I went to sleep -- I was not certain. In any case, even before the morning alarm sounded, I was wide awake.**

---

* When, in January 1968, North Korea undertook the infamous "Blue House Raid," the infiltrators donned ROK Army uniforms and, in a near successful operation, blatantly marched toward their objective.

# DAYS THIRTY-FOUR & THIRTY-FIVE A SATURDAY & A SUNDAY

The headquarters Duty Officer was waiting for me when I arrived at the Officers Club for breakfast. I sensed that the news would not be "good news."

"So, can we have a cup of coffee before you tell me?" I asked.

The Duty Officer seemed more than willing.

After we were seated and with Annie doing her very best, I asked the question.

"So what happened last night?"

"Sir," the Duty Officer began, "I called Colonel Lee as you ordered. He and some of his officers arrived at the electrocution site in about twenty minutes. He was most upset and there was a lot of conversation in Korean that was beyond me.

"To work on the cable splice, we had pulled the ROKAF body out of the manhole in which the main feeder line ran through -- it was pretty well scorched.

"Colonel Lee's officers examined the body, went through the pockets again but there was nothing there, and then did a whole lot of gesturing and talking in Korean. Finally, Colonel Lee told me that the body was not that of one of his men. He went on to explain that a ROKAF uniform could be obtained by many persons and he had no idea who the person was who had cut our feeder line. He did say that he was certain that the bolt cutter used in the operation did, based on the markings, come from his organization but he could not explain that. He suggested that it had been stolen by the person who died. He offered to take care of the body and, after talking to Captains Wild and Pastiak, I let the ROKAF have it.

"He said that he wanted to meet with you this morning but he would await your call to him for a convenient time."

Holy Moses! If the person who cut the main feeder line was not a ROKAF slicky, then who was he? Or was he a ROKAF person and Lee just sought to deny it? Still, Lee's assessment might be correct and the person who wielded the bolt cutter might be neither a ROKAF individual nor a slicky -- he might have been related to the spy ring on the base -- or who knew what? Apparently, my worst fears had come true!

**Slicky activity was seldom reported up the chain of command. If I viewed this as a slicky operation, there need be no report. But, if I related this to more serious activity, I would probably be criticized for what did I have as proof? Many, I knew, would simply think I was crying "wolf" and trying to bring attention to Kunsan Air Base or myself.**

**When I met with Colonel Lee, the conversation was direct and understanding. I asked Lee if he could shed any light on who the culprit might be -- he stated that he could not. Lee further stated that he had checked with local Korean officials none of whom could identify the intruder. When I asked Lee if the body contained any hidden tattoos, he stated that they had checked all orifices and none was discovered -- obviously, Lee knew about the significance of hidden tatoos. Eventually, we mutually concluded that the event was something serious and it gave us a special reason to work closely on matters of security and base defense. With that as the outcome of the happening, I was satisfied. "One step at a time." To myself, I kept repeating the dictum.**

**At the Saturday baseball game, I found that Lieutenant Wade was serving as umpire at home plate. During an inning break, I told him about the scheduled game in Japan for the following Saturday. That news quickly spread among the players and many gave me a "thumbs up" signal. At an inning break, Wade told me that he was ready for the first dry run of the team in a real security exercise. He stated that they knew how to move and set up the fifty and were pretty good on the firing line. I told him to aim for the coming Tuesday but that I wanted first to coordinate the exercise with Knight and Wild and to inform Colonel Lee.**

**Later, about 1600 hours, a convoy of two weapons carriers was formed to take my selected staff participants and the ROKAF party to the Mayor's reception. Wild had placed two of his Air Police in each vehicle -- one to drive and one for security. The party members rode in the rear. By 1730 hours we were at Kunsan city.**

**En route to Kunsan City, we were waved through the ROK Army check point at which a line of duty persons stood at attention. Obviously, there had been advance notice of our movement and that concerned me for, if the check point was informed, our supposed assassin or others might also be informed.**

**Stopping in front of the building in which the party was to take place, I learned that it was one of the Off Limits establishments -- off limits due primarily to the unsanitary conditions prevailing. It was a**

**two story frame building and quite run down. Inside and out, the air was heavy with the smell of singed chicken feathers -- a most nauseous odor.**

**A shallow, slimy green, raw sewage ditch ran past the front of the building -- a wooden plank served to span from the road to the doorway.**

**I knew that information on where the party took place would spread to the enlisted men and others and I could already hear the complaints: If it's O.K. for the Colonel and other officers to go there, why is it off limits to us?**

**The Mayor greeted us at the door and we proceeded to the second floor. On one entry wall hung a photo of President Rhee and on another one of myself.**

**On the second floor, in an almost bare room, was a long, low table and some straw mats. Around the sides of the room were many girls in traditional Korean dress. The Mayor invited me to sit next to him. As soon as I was seated, one of the Korean girls sat next to me and one sat behind me. This was, in the local scenario, "one high class event."**

**"We are pleased to have the new American Colonel as our guest," the Mayor announced.**

**"And I am pleased to be here," I stated. Inwardly, I was not at all certain that I was pleased about anything but I knew the protocol.**

**Immediately, small cups of hot sake were poured and the Mayor lifted his cup to me. Simultaneously, the cups of all hosts and guests were raised. I knew the routine and lifted my cup of sake to the Mayor and, looking him directly in the eye, we emptied our cups and then turned them upside down to prove the point.**

**As if by lightening, the Korean ladies refilled the cups and they were exchanged. Again the procedure was repeated. And then the Mayor clapped his hands and scores of ladies appeared with dishes of things -- most of which I had never seen before.**

**The routine, I learned, was to start with raw egg mixed with something that tasted like a combination of soy sauce and Worcestershire sauce. I was told that this was to line the stomach for the evening's drinking. While there were chop sticks on the table, I soon learned that I did not pick up my own food -- the Korean lady sitting next to me picked up food for me from the serving dishes (there were no individual plates) with her fingers and fed me. I looked at the dirty finger nails and surmised that I was looking at imbedded worm eggs.**

**As to my officers, they were enjoying the hell out of the affair. Some of my men smoked and soon cigarettes were shared with the Korean ladies.**

*My officers enjoyed the hell out of the affair.*

*Some of my men smoked and soon cigarettes were shared with the Korean ladies.*

**With each of the many courses served, we went through the drinking routine again and again but it soon expanded with every host**

**person as well as the ROKAF persons drinking to me and exchanging cups. This meant that, if it kept up, I would be drinking about fifteen or more drinks to every single one consumed by others. To even the score, my men began working on the "enemies" of the evening.**

**While some of the food served was recognizable, most was not. Soon I discovered a new logic. A delicacy is something of which there is little. By extrapolation, steak is not a delicacy as there is a quantity of it on an animal. And, shortly, I became aware that most of the dishes were built around the sexual organs of fowls and animals. One delicacy turned out to be sliced, pickled penis of the bull. But it was probably a lot cleaner than the roasted chicken that was torn apart by the Korean lady serving me and fed piece by piece to me by her terribly greasy, dirty fingers.**

**The meal done, Scotch replaced sake at the table and some entertainment started. One Korean girl put on a skit depicting an American G.I. leaving his Korean girl friend to return to the States -- it was hilarious. And then the entertainment turned to individual singing beginning with the Mayor, and then the ROKAF Commander, *and then it was my turn!***

**I was thoroughly embarrassed. The voices of the Mayor and the ROKAF Commander were terrific -- me, I could not keep a tune in a bushel basket -- but there was no choice.**

**For a moment, I could not think of the words to a single song but, downing a slug of Scotch, I took center stage -- my mind racing all the while -- trying to get the words and tune to a song put together. Reaching center stage, all I could think of was a song my mother sang when I was a child. The song over, I sat down with much applause -- I had passed that test. But more was to follow.**

**The Mayor engaged me in private conversation.**

**"Korea is very hard place for Americans," he stated. "Summer -- it is much hot. Winter -- it is much cold. Americans, they far away from home. Much lonely to be far from mama-san. Your mama-san, she where?"**

**"My wife and children live in Virginia near our capital city of Washington," I replied.**

**"That far, far away and you no see for long time."**

**"For a year," I answered.**

**"Yes, for one long year you are here you no have mama-san and that can make Colonel much unhappy. We know."**

**I nodded my head in understanding of his words. But, inwardly, I sensed that something else was coming.**

"You like ladies here tonight," the Mayor smiled.

"Yes, they are very nice." Actually, in spite of the bulky Korean dress, it was obvious that all of the ladies were well proportioned and endowed.

The Mayor smiled broadly.

"We like American Colonel to be happy. Unhappy Colonel no good for Kunsan. But Colonel no can be happy when his mama-san far away. To make Colonel happy, we give to Colonel any of ladies here he like. If Colonel like more than one lady, we fix. If Colonel find he no like a lady here, we find other lady for Colonel."

Whoa! I had to get out of the box in which I found myself. I wondered what the past Commander of Kunsan Air Base did -- did he accept or reject the offer?

"I appreciate the most kind offer of the Mayor," I answered, "but my religion forbids it. Were I to accept the Mayor's offer, I would not pass to our heaven."

"Very strange religion," the Mayor stated as he shook his head in wonderment. Then, accepting my statement, he held up a glass of Scotch and we drank.

And now it appeared that the object of the party was to get me drunk. Between the sake and the Scotch, I knew I was already well on the way. Soon the Scotch was being poured in water glasses -- straight. Secretly, the Korean lady attending me would either only partially fill my glass or manage to empty the contents on the floor. I did not know if she felt sorry for me or was trying to qualify herself as my "mama-san away from home." Finally, I saw a way out. This time I personally filled both the Mayor's glass and my own -- full. And, with now unsteady hand, I drank to him and he to me. The glasses empty, in minutes, the Mayor fell forward -- passed out. *The party was over and I had won. But is was a Pyrrhic victory.*

I am not certain how I got to the vehicle for the trip back to base. Vaguely, I recall the world spinning in ever larger and faster circles. Then we were at the Waldorf Astoria and I was in bed not to wake up until well into Sunday afternoon. And, when I did wake up, there was a question as to whether life was worth living. Somehow, the pay of a Colonel was not worth the headache I had. I had a cold beer and crawled back into the bed.

Kunsan Air Base could do without its Commander this Sunday.

I hoped Knight had things in hand.

# DAY THIRTY-SIX -- A MONDAY

Annie was especially attentive at breakfast. Without my asking, she placed a large glass of tomato juice in front of me. I knew that word of the Mayor's party had spread. Knight joined me.

"Rough party?"

"Next time you can go," I answered.

For a while, we just sat in silence.

"Hate to tell you this so early in the morning," Knight finally commented, "but we have some visitors scheduled in for tomorrow -- for Tuesday -- the Vice Commander of PACAF."

"Oh boy! I hope by tomorrow my eyes are not as bloodshot as they were when I shaved this morning. What time is he due in and how long will he stay?"

"He's going to Osan first. General Joyce will be with him when he visits here. He will have some PACAF staff with him. He is scheduled to arrive here at 1400 hours and spend about two hours. He is coming in on a C-54. From here, they will go to Seoul for the night."

I signaled Annie for another cup of coffee and thought for a few minutes.

"Let's review the base briefing first thing this morning. When the Vice Chief comes, rather than Jones giving the briefing, I'll give it. That will allow me to ad lib if some subjects come up.

"After we review the briefing, I would like a session with Wild on security and . . ."

"I might as well give you the bad news," Knight cut in.

"What bad news."

"We have a problem in the Air Police unit."

"What kind of a problem?"

"Well, on Saturday, I heard some comment that the black market activity had been considerably curtailed, mostly as a result of the cut back on josan activity and the emphasis on security."

"And why is that a problem?"

"I really hate to say this, but it appears that the Air Police -- at least some members of the Air Police section -- may have been involved in this activity. A number may well have been those long timers you ordered out of the hootches and back into the barracks. Those hootches and the associated Korean females and families could have

**been black market conduits. Plus, I think at least one of the hootches was a prostitute bed down. In any event, there was an accompanying rumor that spread pretty fast. According to this rumor, someone was going to kill you when you next did a night inspection of the guard. The idea would be that you would be challenged and, by prior agreement, the guard would not hear you and fire. It all was framed to make it look like an accident. I heard words such as: *The next time that old S.O.B. inspects the guard he's going to end up dead. He may think he's running this base but he isn't.*"**

**Damn! Those were the same words that were associated with the Air Police Sergeant who had tossed a grenade into the Korean kids -- the idea that the Air Police ran the base and the Commander did not!**

**"Are you certain of all this? This is something serious -- not just a *so what* thing."**

**"As certain as I can be without a direct interrogation of persons."**

**"And did you discuss it with Wild."**

**"I did and he is furious. He blames himself for not recognizing the problem. I think, if we let him loose, he'd kick some butts so hard he'd kill one or more of his men. But he did not want to take any action without talking to you."**

**"Did he have any sort of plan?"**

**"I think he was too mad to have a rational plan."**

**I signaled Annie for still another round of coffee. This news was akin to mutiny -- perhaps mutiny is what I was looking at. Kill the Commander? Could I be hearing correctly? And, in about twenty-four hours the Vice Commander of PACAF and General Joyce were due in. "What great timing," I thought.**

**"Let's change signals a bit. As the first order of business following the morning staff meeting, I want a closed door session with you and Wild -- let's do it in my quarters."**

***Mutiny* -- it had crossed my mind following the grenade incident but I had discarded the thought. Now, suddenly, it seemed to be a real possibility. *Mutiny!* Was I to go down in history as the first Air Force Commander to face a mutiny? Would I end my Kunsan Air Base career, possibly my military career, with a comparison to the story of the *Bounty*? Surely, the men planning this escapade had to think beyond just killing me and it did not take a genius to forecast the next events -- the investigations, the inquiries, the courts-martial, the press. What a terrible situation! Was it again a case where Korea had taken over and subverted all rational thinking?**

# MUTINY!

*At the Mayor's party, a Korean hostess mimics an American G.I. leaving for the States and saying good bye to his tearful josan At the end of the skit, the josan quickly wipes away her tears and happily picks up the next arriving G.I.*

**It all seemed unreal -- the hangover I still had and the thought of mutiny. And, lurking in the recess of my brain there remained the Mayor's party and, especially, the performance of the Korean girl who ridiculed the separation of the American G.I. and his Korean josan.**

**Throughout the morning staff meeting, I only half listened. The word *mutiny* kept running through my mind. One thing I knew, I was not going to cave in to threats -- were I to do that, I might as well give up my command. But how was this new problem to be attacked?**

**Impatiently, I waited for the staff meeting to end. As soon as it did, Knight, Wild and I were in the staff car and on our way to the Waldorf Astoria.**

**When we arrived at my billet, my mama-san was there making my bed and cleaning. This was the first time I had seen her. She smiled and bowed and was a bit unhappy when I told her that we needed to be alone and she needed to go elsewhere for a while. I think she thought she was being fired.**

**"Number One Colonel unhappy with mama-san?"**

**"No. Colonel happy. Colonel just needs to be alone. Now go."**

I felt I had made an enemy of the mama-san but I could not help it. At the moment an unhappy mama-san was the least of my worries.

Inside the Waldorf Astoria, Knight, Wild and I sat down in the living room area. For a while we all just sat in silence.

"Let's begin at the beginning," I suggested. "Is this a real threat or are people just making noises?"

"Whether it's real or not," Knight suggested, "I think we have to treat it as real."

"Well, this matter of the Air Police running things here -- Wild, you've been out here for some time and it's your men -- what do you make of it?"

"In my view, I think we're talking about a few ring leaders and a bit of braggadocio. If there is a problem, and I conclude there may be one, it's got to be the long timers. I should have recognized this some time ago -- those long timers living in the hootches were an obvious route for black market stuff -- possibly even for josan activity. Tied into a local female, these persons could work both sides of the fence -- Korean and American. I consider myself pretty stupid not to have seen this and I apologize. I think I just got swallowed up by the idea of having bodies that were experienced and I fell for the assertion that these men in the perimeter hootches provided a forward line of defense. I just don't know why I didn't catch on. These guys were pretty good at what they apparently did."

"Are the long timers out of the hootches and back in the barracks?"

"As of this morning, yes."

"And the hootches?"

"Most of them have been sold and are being torn down -- the Koreans are carting off the materials."

"Most of them?"

"I think we still have two standing."

"And you are certain that the long timers are in the barracks?"

"Yes."

"Could there be ring leaders who are not long timers?"

"That's possible," Wild answered, "but my thinking is that what we are looking at was sort of a closed shop and they would not want to open the doors to a newcomer. My guess is that this all started years ago and it turned out to be a good deal. So the concept was just extended and, much like myself, others were happy to have anyone stay in Korea who wanted to stay -- no questions asked."

**"But a guard on an outpost, one that's supposed to take me out, he would not be a long timer."**

**"No, but my guess is that there could be some who would be sufficiently intimidated to carry out the order -- probably under a threat that, if the selected person didn't do it, he would end up dead."**

**"Which takes me back to the grenade-in-the-kids event. This almost sounds like Mafia." Both Knight and Wild nodded in agreement.**

**I got up and started pacing the floor. Pacing the floor was a habit I had gotten into whenever I had a really big problem with which to deal. Fleetingly, the thought crossed my mind that this rumored action by my Air Police might, in some complicated way, be tied to the assassination information that had been furnished to me by Mr. Olson. But the route from a South Korean dissident group to an American serviceman seemed too remote a prospect to consider seriously and I dismissed the thought.**

**Assuredly, there was no text book answer to the situation at hand. Historically, there had never been a mutiny in the U.S. services although the *Caine Mutiny* had been a well-publicized Hollywood scenario. And what was the proof that there was really such an event in the making at Kunsan Air Base? The situation could be serious as all hell or it could be one great big spoof designed to intimidate me or make me look ridiculous. In the circumstances a direct frontal attack did not seem wise. Perhaps I was being goaded into something foolish?**

**"Just how many long timers are we talking about?" I asked Wild.**

**"Six."**

**"And they are in the barracks -- are you certain?"**

**"One is on duty, the others are in the barracks or somewhere on base -- one or two may still be at the hootch sites."**

**"Do the men not on duty have access to firearms?"**

**"Only if they have a personal one. The regular arms are stored in the Air Police Command Center and issued when a man reports for duty -- then returned at the close of the duty period."***

---

* By regulation, only officers were allowed to possess personal arms and, normally, that related to sporting guns. Much later and long after leaving Kunsan Air Base, I would learn that many of the enlisted men had obtained illicit arms. In part, the acquisition of such arms was an outgrowth of individuals recognizing, as I did, the vulnerability of the base to incursion and the time it would take to draw issue weapons from supply points. I would have preferred a policy that required the men on base be armed at all times but that was not in the cards -- on this point, I was a maverick.

"In that these men just moved into the barracks, their stuff should be pretty well packed up at this time?"

"I would guess so," Wild answered.

"And do you think we could get all six, with baggage, assembled and on an aircraft by noon -- or shortly thereafter?"

"You obviously mean: Can I keep them from becoming violent and maybe shooting up the place?"

"Something like that."

Wild thought a while and then answered.

"I've got some men whom I trust fully -- mostly three stripers. I think I can arrange that."

"O.K. Get Akers ready to fly the C-47 to Taegu. Move the long timers and their baggage to Taegu. You ride shotgun on the flight. Take a man or two you can trust with you. The men are not to be arrested or anything like that -- only intimidated. Just get them the hell off this base. Knight, you have Jones get orders for the immediate movement of these men from Taegu to the States -- give these men the orders when they debark at Taegu -- not ahead of time. Wild, when it comes to Efficiency Ratings, not a word of this in the record -- understand?"

"Yes sir."

"Now," I added, "when you get back from Taegu, I want a dusk formation of the Air Police Section. Keep a thin line of guards out -- try to get the most Air Police you can assembled in formation. When they are in formation, I will arrive and address them. I'm not certain what I shall say but I better have the right words in mind by then."

What an ungodly mess! Had I allowed the base to run as it was when I arrived, this situation probably would not have come about. But I could not live with the josan, security system and both slicky and black market situations that I had inherited. So I did what I believed to be correct. And now I was paying the price. *Mutiny! By God, it would not be on my watch!*

For the rest of the day, I found myself scrutinizing every Air Police person I passed. Actually, I had begun to scrutinize everyone with whom I came in contact. Suspicion is a terrible disease and I knew I had to shed it if I was to do my job.

Around noon, I asked Wade if he could move up the baseball team security exercise from the Tuesday schedule to early afternoon of this day. I explained that the Vice Commander of PACAF was due in tomorrow and I would like to know if the team could perform. Whether or not I set up such a performance for the Vice Commander, I thought the exercise would be a stabilizing influence on those regularly assigned to the Air Police Section. Wade thought it could be done and, at 1400 hours, although the exercise was highly artificial, the team quickly assembled, drew individual weapons, mounted the fifty on a weapons carrier, dashed to the sea wall, dismounted the fifty and placed it on a tripod and sand-bagged the legs, then lined up the rest of the men in a protective shield. An infantry officer might have laughed at the exercise but I was not laughing. Scanning the sea, I could see nothing. "Order one burst." There was a tut-tut-tut-tut-tut and I could see some tracers arc out to sea. I knew the sound of the firing would be heard across the base.

With the exercise over, I personally congratulated each of the baseball team members participating and reminded them that we had a game coming up on Saturday. I also told them that the Vice Commander of PACAF would be visiting the next day and not to get too far from home base as we may want to show our stuff. They all smiled.

By evening, I had decided that a direct attack on the mutiny thing was the only way out. Certainly, the men in the Air Police Section would know that the old timers were no longer present. As to what had happened to them, I had to assume that rumors would fly and stories would be exaggerated.

For my meeting with the Air Police formation, I donned combat boots and strapped on my thirty-eight.

Shortly after the formation was assembled, I drove up in the staff car. Wild called attention and saluted me as I approached. I saluted back and stood silent in front of the formation for a few minutes during which time I slowly and critically moved my eyes from one person to another. Then I spoke.

"Men, I have received some disturbing rumors -- rumors that suggest some among you, or some who were among you, may have lost sight of the duty and responsibility of an Air Policemen. Undoubtedly, you have heard these stories.

"Korea is not the most pleasant of assignments and there are a lot of temptations here. Fortunately or unfortunately, one of the jobs of all Air Policemen is not only to provide security to this base but to work to minimize the wrong things that can happen. Further, all Air Policemen have to be models for others. And, in that respect, I expect each of you to do your job.

"Now, to these rumors that have been circulated, I want to make one thing clear just in case there remains someone among you who is really committed to the story that was spread.

"Tonight, and any night I decide to do it, I will visit you on the perimeter and at other guard posts. And just in case one of you is of a mind to carry out the story that has been running around this base, I ask you to think twice and, if you do decide to commit such a foolish act, shoot well for you will not have a second chance to shoot.

"I may be looked upon as an old son-of-a-bitch Colonel but one thing I can do is shoot straight and if you decide to shoot at me when I visit you on duty, and you miss, you will never get off a second shot."

There was a deathly silence, Again I waited -- my eyes moving from one face to another. I wanted my words to sink in and I wanted the line up of men standing before me to see that I was not running -- I was not "shaking in my boots."

Then I saluted Wild and returned to the staff car.

That night, at about 0300 hours, I inspected the guard. Wild accompanied me. I would not be honest if I stated that I was not apprehensive -- I was. But there was no shooting and all encounters were professional and friendly. The mutiny, if there ever was one, apparently was broken and the rumors died a quick and natural death.

I remained in command of Kunsan Air Base -- probably more in command than I had ever been.

Before I dozed off, my adrenaline running high, I reviewed some of the many things on my unfilled agenda. One of those things was the naming of Jones as my Executive Officer -- I made a mental note to do that first thing in the morning.

And then there was something else which I had all but forgotten about. Each month, the Air Force system required that a history statement be submitted for every unit in the system. Since arriving at Kunsan Air Base, I had not seen one and, if one had been submitted, I wondered what it said. What I did not want were history statements that reflected some of the things I was doing -- or thinking -- and I was beginning to lose sight of that which I had thought about and that which I actually did. I assumed that Jones must be the person who was responsible for writing the monthly unit history statements. Thus, when I told him that he was to be my Executive Officer, I would also have to brief him on the construction of the Kunsan Air Base history statements.

"Trouble, trouble, boil and bubble." Or was it a case of "What a tangled web we weave . . . ?"

# DAY THIRTY-SEVEN -- A TUESDAY

With the soon-to-be arrival of the PACAF Vice Commander, I had to set aside most of my other concerns but I did manage to talk again to Colonel Lee about the Korean person electrocuted in the course of damaging one of our main electrical feeder lines.

Once more Lee assured me that the person involved, while he was wearing a ROKAF uniform, was not a member of the ROKAF. As to who he was, Lee had no idea but he stated that ROKAF intelligence had been called in and, if he learned anything, he would advise me.

Without revealing to Lee my knowledge of a North Korean spy ring on the base, I suggested how vulnerable we were to infiltration and wondered if some of the shooting we were continuing to hear did not mean that North Korean agents could be in our midst without our recognizing it. Lee viewed it as possible and readily joined with me in the thought I had previously set forth relative to a need for a better, coordinated defense plan. He said he would immediately have one of his men work with mine at the front gate and that he did not object to his men and vehicles being scrutinized as they passed through that gate. To me, this was a big step forward and we did a firm hand shake on the arrangement.

Then, to emphasize the importance of Kunsan Air Base to Lee, I told him that, in a few hours, the Vice Commander of PACAF would be landing. Lee was highly impressed and especially pleased to see that, for this visit, all three flags were now flying in front of the headquarters. "What a picture," I thought, "if the Vice Commander had arrived some weeks before and there was no more than a crooked tree trunk in front of the headquarters with no flag flying."

I decided to have two Airmen serve as side boys for the arrival and departure of the PACAF Vice Commander's C-54 and asked Wild to arrange that one of them be Amos Anderson -- the Airman who had so impressed me on my initial visit to the Enlisted Club. Wild agreed to that, to the posting of two area guards at the aircraft and to implement the assassination watch we had established for General Joyce's previous visit. A Follow-Me jeep would lead the C-54 to a parking spot in front of Operations as I wanted to comment to the Vice Commander about the deteriorated surface of that area. The Fifth Air Force runway repair team had arrived on Monday and sufficient work had been accomplished that I was confident that the runway would remain open. The presence of that repair team would give me the opportunity to talk generally about the prior lack of maintenance of the base.

I had never met the Vice Commander, a Lieutenant General, but he turned out to be personable and seemed to be well briefed on me. He asked about Mary and the children and, to my surprise, went on to say that he had a hand in getting me assigned to Kunsan. He implied that there were some bigger plans for me. I did not know if he was talking about Osan or something else but, in another ten months, I would have the answer when orders arrived assigning me to PACAF headquarters.

The base briefing went well. During that briefing I was able to concentrate on the base as I had found it and what had been done in the approximate month since my arrival. I was careful, however, not to heap blame for any of the Kunsan ills on the Osan Wing Commander, the Division or Fifth Air Force. What conclusions the PACAF Vice Commander reached in that regard, I did not learn.

The primary focus of the Vice Commander was the nuclear alert aircraft, base defense and welfare of the men. In relation to the latter point, I make a strong pitch for increased on-base recreational facilities, pointing out how little existed and how isolated the base was from all conventional activity.

After the base briefing, we drove through the central base area and visited the nuclear alert facilities. I was pleased that men saluted as we passed and that the uniforms of everyone looked good. At the nuclear alert area, Major Kitchens gave the General a short briefing on his operation following which there was a visit with the alert air crews and an inspection of a few of the F-100s.

As we traveled, the Vice Commander took note of the still open drainage ditch that had been carved out to get rid of the water of Typhoon Number Two. I outlined the situation as it had developed and my emergency action. Then I told the Vice Commander I would send him some photos that would illustrate how serious the situation had become. I used the conversation to outline my equipment shortages and I sensed that something would be done to alleviate that problem as the Vice Commander's Executive Officer made many notes.

The Vice Commander was especially concerned about the runway and he commented about my recent closing of the field. There was no criticism in that comment. We drove the full length of the runway and, periodically, the General asked that I stop so that he could examine the expansion joints. When we arrived at where the Fifth Air

Force team was working, the General talked to the men, discussing the extent of the problem and the techniques of repair.

By pre-arrangement with Lieutenant Wade, while we were in the runway area, the baseball security team made a dash for the sea wall. When the Vice Commander asked me what was going on, I explained that he was looking at the baseball team in action. He seemed impressed but did ask about the fifty. I commented that every Commander had a responsibility to do all he could to defend his base and the question was dropped.

Returning to the C-54, the Vice Commander was very complimentary about the visit, the briefing, and our discussions. I could see that General Joyce was pleased. And then the cabin door of the C-54 closed; the runway was cleared of workers; and the Vice Commander was off to Seoul.

With the PACAF C-54 disappearing northward, I thanked all those around me for helping to make the visit of the PACAF Vice Commander run smoothly. I made a special point of complimenting the Airmen who did the side boy job and who had stood guard at the Vice Commander's aircraft. Somehow, I sensed that everyone stood a bit taller than before. Amos Anderson seemed especially pleased to have been selected for the side boy honor.

Driving back to the base headquarters, I wondered what the Vice Commander would have said if I had told him about all the things that had happened in the last month -- to include the rumored mutiny situation of the prior day. Some things need to be said but some things are best left unsaid. And, with that thought in mind, I decided to visit the PX.

At the PX, the Korean manager did the usual bowing. I smiled and mentally said: You son-of-a-bitch.

"You have much important visitors today?" the manager stated.

"Yes, we have senior American Generals come today. But I did not have them come by here as you still do not have enough PX materials for the men."

"I try," the manager stated.

"Well you better try harder. The next time we have Generals visit this base, I want to bring them here and you better have the shelves full of good stuff for the men. If you don't, the Generals will be most unhappy and both of us may have a new job. Perhaps we will be sent to Siberia."

The manager's face turned ashen.

"I try very hard," was his answer. "More stuff, I think it come tomorrow. I think maybe I then have radio for Colonel."

I doubted that the manager understood the "Siberia" comment but I could see that the threat of him losing his job had an effect. And I had to wonder if the North Korean system was so pervasive in South Korea that they might work to insure that the slicky of in-coming PX supplies would be turned off as a way of insuring that their key agent on Kunsan Air Base kept his job. If the North Koreans, rather than ordinary slicky persons, were involved in some of the PX losses, it might be that they would find it useful to supply some missing "stuff" to the Kunsan Air Base PX just to keep their man in place. It was an interesting thought.

Before the day was through, a message arrived from the PACAF Vice Commander complimenting the men on the base for the work being done and thanking everyone for their service on the front line of defense of the United States and its Allies. I thought it was a nice touch and had it copied and posted on the bulletin boards to include a posting in the entrance to the PX. One way or another, comment covering the visit of the PACAF Vice Commander would get to our enemies. I hoped Mr. Olson's organization was listening.

That night, I taped a long message to Mary -- for a change, one not interrupted with rat noise, gun fire and other worrisome happenings.

The tape to Mary sealed for posting, I found myself reflecting on the PACAF Vice Commander's visit. He had to have seen the terribly inadequate security covering the nuclear storage and alert aircraft but he had made no comment relative to the situation. So what was it that I could conclude?

If the nuclear bombs were real, the PACAF Vice Commander, any commander, should have been disturbed by the minimal security. But neither General Joyce nor the Vice Commander was disturbed -- it was as if security was not an issue.

But, if security was not an issue, that had to mean that there was nothing significant to protect -- which seemed to tell me that I was sitting on Silver Bullets and not real nuclear weapons.

Obviously, there were things I was not being told. For some reason, I did not have "a need to know" -- at least others were of the view that I did not have "a need to know."

The more I thought about the situation, the more disturbed I became. Eventually, however, I fell asleep although it was a troubled sleep.

# DAY THIRTY-EIGHT -- A WEDNESDAY

"The inspection report is in and you are not going to like it," Knight announced.

"Let me see it."

For the next half hour I read. The report was almost verbatim that which I had discussed with the inspector except that responsibility for action was not as we discussed -- allegedly, all action rested directly with me. Beyond that which was discussed with him, the inspector had nothing to report. At the tail of the report, I found that I was given thirty days to correct all deficiencies noted.

"What a bunch of crap. Thirty days to correct things that are not within our power to correct. We need this kind of inspection assistance like we need holes in our heads."

Knight agreed. Then, with a start, I heard three well-spaced shots. Something had happened and an Air Policeman was calling for assistance. I shrugged it away -- Wild could take care of it.

"What I think we can do is turn this thing around by dealing in minute detail -- give them such a voluminous report back that they will choke on it."

"And how do we do that?" Knight asked.

"Well, first we break the inspection report into each element and sub element. Then we gather everything we can in regulations and paperwork that applies to those elements. With that in hand, we do a one-two-three on the subject matter -- quote regulations or the lack of same, append requisition forms and the turn down replies, attach any and all letters on the subject, discuss the supply situation out of Inchon and other places, take a bunch of photos to back up the stories -- literally give them back an encyclopedia. If we do that, either we get help or we get someone fired and both are good prospects."

The words were hardly out of my mouth when Captain Wild excitedly rushed into the office.

"Sir, we are being invaded!"

"Whoa, wait a minute. Invaded by whom? What sector of the base? I didn't hear any shooting other than the three signal shots? What the hell are you talking about?"

"Its the Koreans, sir. They're coming across the sea wall by the hundreds -- maybe a thousand."

"Let's go," I commanded.

Running to the staff car, I grabbed a holstered forty-five from Sergeant Young. Then, yelling at Jones, I ordered him to call the Air Police Command Center and get the reaction team to the nuclear alert area. "And tell Wade to get his baseball team together for some real work."

If there was a speed limit on the base, we broke it several times over. Careening to the field area, I could see what Wild was talking about. Hundreds upon hundreds of Koreans were coming in over the sea wall and approaching the runway from the side opposite of which were the nuclear alert birds.

"What the hell can we do, Colonel?" Wild was beside himself. "We can't shoot Koreans?"

"How many dogs you got?"

"A dozen."

"Well, get them out -- space them out on the runway -- and, if this onslaught of Koreans continues, we'll let them loose. In the meantime, call up the next shift of Air Police and spread them on line down the runway. Have them bring billies."

The staff car had been followed by one of Wild's Air Policeman in a jeep and Wild ran to the jeep and left with the tires screaming.

On and on, the Koreans came -- not running -- just proceeding at a deliberate walking, threatening pace. They were spread out uniformly as if by plan. I could detect no guns.

Soon a six-by-six was careening down the runway dropping off dogs and handlers. The dogs, tugging at their leashes, were setting up an awful racket but the Koreans kept on coming. As the lead Koreans stepped onto the runway, I signaled that the dogs be released.

*The dogs went crazy!*

**The resulting scene would be hard to describe. The dogs went crazy. But the onslaught of Koreans was turned around -- literally, it faded away as if some mysterious order had been given. And I did not have to bring to bear the second shift of Air Police which had rapidly formed a protective shield on the east side of the runway.**

**When it was over, we looked at each other in wonderment.**

**"What in the hell led to that?" was all we could say. There was no good explanation and we never learned from the local community or the ROKAF what might have triggered this onslaught or what the objective was. Obviously, some of the approaching Koreans were well marked by the dogs but there was never an issue raised. I suggested to Knight and Wild that we let the matter drop. "No reports on this one," were my words.**

***[This was not an easy decision. The decision not to report this incident could be categorized as a "cover up" and could have resulted in a reprimand, even loss of command and reassignment for me. But a detailed report covering the dog attack of the Korean intruders probably would have resulted in Monday morning criticism from far away, career oriented personalities who shared none of the responsibilities for Kunsan Air Base. Further, a report up-the-chain-of-command could have triggered all sort of investigations and unfavorable Air Force press. I think, in the circumstances, I made a proper decision when I buried this event.***

***A few years later, the 6314th Wing Commander at Osan Air Base was faced with a hostile demonstration by Korean employees marching down the main street of Chicol Village toward the main gate. This was a sizable demonstration and the adults had brought children into the fray. There was doubt that the local Korean police could restrain the crowd and the Commander lined up a small force of men, less than a dozen, with fixed bayonets across the entrance to the base. Fortunately, the demonstrators did not break through the line of local police. If they had and bayonets had been used on the South Korean adults and children, the resultant bad public relations would have been of national and international consequence. Frankly, I would not have used bayonets nor would I have used such a minuscule force but every commander has to reach his own decision in such emergencies.***

***The media did not get involved in this Osan event. Had they been there, the resultant story may have paralleled the story that went out at a still later event at Kadena Air Base when there was a small march on the***

*base but the resultant American headlines read that "TEN THOUSAND STORM THE GATES OF KADENA."]*

*A hostile demonstration by Korean employees and others on the main street of Chichol Village proceeding toward the main gate at Osan Air Base. There was doubt that the Korean police could restrain the crowd. (USAF)*

*The Osan Air Base Commander lined up a handful of men with fixed bayonets to repel the advancing Koreans. (USAF)*

Back at the office, I did a lot of wondering about the day's invasion event. Were the base defenses being tested? Was this something triggered by the North Korean agents to see what would happen? Was this event aimed at discouraging our use of Kunsan Air Base? Was there something happening elsewhere in Korea that caused this event?

Reflecting on the latter, I realized that I had been away from major news sources for over a month. There was no newspaper of consequence at Kunsan Air Base and I still did not have a radio. Then I recalled the prior day's comment by the PX manager that he might have one for me in a current shipment and I headed for the PX. When I arrived, the manager was smiling. From the back room he brought out what he termed "a good Japanese radio." It was not a big thing -- but it would do. As I thanked him and paid for the radio, he asked, "Why so many Koreans they come on base today from sea?"

"I thought maybe you would know the answer to that. Are they not your friends and neighbors?"

"I do not know," the manager replied. Whether that meant he did not know if these persons were his friends and neighbors or why they came on the base, was not clear.

"Well, the next time something like this happens, we may have some dead Koreans."

The manager's eyes widened.

"You would shoot Koreans?"

"Why do you think my men have guns? Today, those who came on the base were very lucky. Today, we only used dogs. Next time we may use bullets -- lots of bullets."

"Perhaps people do not know?"

"Perhaps you could tell them?"

"I do not know. Maybe I try."

"You try."

As I left the PX with the radio under my arm, I wondered how that conversation would be reported to North Korea. And I wondered about the speed with which a "good radio" had suddenly appeared.

That evening, I noticed that Joe, the bartender, had a fresh bandage on one arm. When I asked him about it, he stated that he had cut it on a can -- it was obvious, however, that he did not want to discuss it and the location of the wound hardly fitted the "can" explanation. Suddenly, I suspected that I knew who my North Korean agent was in the Officers Club. If that was a dog bite on Joe's arm, it could indicate that he was among the approaching Koreans that came over the sea wall. And, due to his job at the Officers Club, I knew that he was not a Korean who would be searching for food on the mud flats -- he would have no business being out there.

The emerging conclusion was disturbing for it indicated that a large element of the local population could be triggered by the North Korean network. And I was reminded of the information imparted to me by Akers on my first Gooney Bird flight -- the ambush of the retreating Americans from Kunsan, allegedly by residents of the North Korean village. Still, what could I do with what I suspected? Probably nothing. One thing I did resolve, I was going to work on Joe as a potential channel to North Korea.

Having a drink at the bar and studying Joe, I realized that I was mentally and physically tired and I concluded that I needed a break - a change of scenery. And then I recalled General Joyce's request that I visit Kangnung and Kimpo. Signaling to Akers, I asked him if the C-47 was in commission and available for a flight the next day. It was. But I knew that my flying to Kangnung and Kimpo might raise questions among my staff so I concocted a quick cover story.

"Ops at Osan asked if we could make the ice cream run tomorrow. I'd like to see how some other folks live here in Korea. How about it? Can we make it -- pick up some ice cream at Kimpo and fly it out to Kangnung? We should be back by evening but pack a bag just in case."

"No sweat, Colonel. The weather for tomorrow looks good. What's the time for wheels in the well?"

"Let's get rolling at 0800 hours. Knight can take the morning briefing."

Back at the Waldrof Astoria, I placed a call to Jack Hubbard at Osan and explained the situation. He agreed to cover on any questions asked. I hoped no one was listening.

And then I had an idea. After some thought, I called my Marine friend at the UNC Compound, Lt. Colonel Buckner.

"Paul, I want to thank you for all your help. And now I have a question. I'm going to Kangnung tomorrow. How would you like to go with me? If you haven't been to Kangnung, this may be an experience."

- - - - -

"No sweat. All you have to do is be at Kimpo about 0900 hours and, if you are there and we are there, climb aboard It's a one day trip but pack a bag just in case. I'll be flying a C-47."

# DAY THIRTY-NINE -- A THURSDAY

With the Fifth Air Force runway repair team clear of the runway, we were airborne shortly after 0800 hours. There was a slight haze in the air but no clouds in the sky. I did a circle of the field before heading north to Kimpo. Looking down, the base seemed to be in a much better state than the day I arrived but it might have been my imagination -- or my desire.

Kimpo airfield was on the south side of the Han River and slightly downstream from the capital city of Seoul. Akers briefed me on the approach and the need, in case of a go-around, not to wander to the north as the North Koreans loved to take shots at aircraft that violated their territory -- and their territory was just a bit further down stream on the north bank.

After landing, a Follow-Me jeep took us to the south side of the field where we parked in front of an old, beat up hangar which I learned was used as an Air Force military transport terminal. On the opposite side of the field, a ROKAF F-86 unit was based. Due to Akers having called in my code, the base commander, Lt. Colonel George Buck, whom I had met at an Osan staff meeting, was there to greet me. While Akers arranged for the ice cream pick up, I had George drive me around the U.S. facilities -- such as they were. Mostly, in addition to the hangar where we were parked, he had some beat up housing; a club of sorts that served all grades, this near the west end of the runway; a small motor pool; and a limited aircraft servicing capability. It did not take long to see all that was there to be seen.

I asked George about President Rhee's international terminal project at Kimpo, the related land issues, etc. but he could add nothing to my knowledge.

"How about security?" I asked.

"We have a small Air Police unit but can't handle much more than protocol for transient VIP. Our land area is limited and, as you saw, with Korean houses right alongside. We have a lot of slicky problems and just sort of live with it. Fortunately, most of the slicky stuff is minor."

"What about maintenance?"

"Maintenance? What's *maintenance*? I barely have enough men to provide fuel servicing and other basics. We don't even think about maintenance of aircraft, facilities or anything -- we just live -- survive is more like it. Sometimes the food situation is so bad we go to the Eighth Army mess in Seoul. I don't know how Army does it but they seem to get some pretty good food."

"What about VIP traffic? Don't you get quite a bit?"

"We do but the passengers don't stay here at Kimpo. If they are Air Force, they are usually taken to the Seoul House. If they are Army they head for the Eighth Army compound, Camp Walker or other facilities. We see them only coming and going and all I have to provide are some men to park and service the aircraft, a ramp, some side boys, a happy face and a glad hand."

"Like your job?"

"Frankly, hell no! But I'm here just like you're down at Kunsan. I bet you didn't ask for Kunsan any more than I asked for Kimpo."

Back at the aircraft, Buckner had already arrived and he and Akers were engaged in a lively discussion. Akers told me that the ice cream was on board and that we had to move quickly or it would be melted before we landed at Kangnung. I thanked George for his time and climbed into the Gooney. Inside, were several padded containers tied down to the cargo floor.

The flight from Kimpo to Kangnung took about forty-five minutes -- Buckner took up a position between the pilot and co-pilot seats and related to us some of the history of the U.S. Marine combat action in Korea.

The land below was nothing but irregular mountains, winding streams and an almost absence of trees. Without question, it was made for the type of assault made by the Chicoms. I had to sympathize with the ground troops that had to fight through it.

Examining the roads and trails, it was obvious that east-west travel was very restricted -- even north-south movement was far from easy. And I could see how low flying pilots could easily get lost in the meaningless terrain.

The landing strip at Kangnung was built out of PSP during the Korean War. There was no evidence of maintenance to the strip having been performed since then. I had not landed on PSP since World War II but the rattle of the steel planks brought back old memories.

No USAF or ROKAF aircraft was based at Kangnung and movement to and from the base depended on infrequent supply or other flights in and out -- such as ours. During the summer months, about once a week a special ice cream flight was made to Kangnung.

Air Force communications from the base were mostly via the radar support network terminating at Osan -- the ROKAF had a special line to their headquarters. There was no Air Force Air Police at Kangnung and not much attention given to security -- such matters were left to the ROKAF.

At Kangnung, other than shooting birds when they flew north or south, there was little one could term recreational opportunity. Periodically, a movie film would arrive from special services. "What a hell of an assignment," I thought. "If Kunsan is an outpost, what in blazes would I call this?"

North of Kangnung there was virtually nothing short of the DMZ but rugged terrain. In the Operations shack a hand-lettered sign read:

| TO HELL WITH YOUR ALTIMETER<br>WATCH YOUR COMPASS |
|---|

*Eventually, Kangnumg was named "KangNung Air Patch" and, decades later, the cautionary words, now slightly altered, could be found on a sign outside the operations building. Unfortunately, in spite of the warning, some pilots wandered to the north.*

Compared to the buildings at Kangnung, most of the ramshackle buildings at Kunsan Air Base were high class. Probably the most disgusting element of the Kangnung facilities was the water

**tower. It was a rectangular wooden affair perched on top of a score or more large utility poles. It leaned about ten or more degrees and was kept from falling over by a half dozen supporting poles on two sides. Against the advice of the local commander, I insisted on climbing up in the tower where I found most of the ladders and steps rotted -- periodically, one of the steps would break under my weight. The top of the water tank was open and I did not need more evidence to realize that live and dead things were in the water.**

***Compared to the buildings at Kangnung, most of the ramshackle buildings at Kunsan Air Base were high class. Shown here is the Kangnung water filtration and pumping building. As was the case at Kunsan Air Base, grass cutting was not on the agenda.***

**Gingerly, I worked my way down the wooden ladders and steps. None of the local persons had followed me to the top of the tower. My climb was probably foolish and I would have to admit that on stepping again on solid ground I breathed a sigh of relief.**

**Water is vital to any facility and the water system at Kangnung was absolutely terrible. But I knew that there was hardly a chance in hell that I would be able to provide a fix when I got to the Osan job -- a whole new system was needed.**

**As we traveled around the Kangnung area, Buckner kept shaking his head in disbelief.**

"I wish that some of the U.S. Army types on the DMZ could see this," he stated. "They think they have a bitch of a situation but, compared to this, they are pretty well off."

Eventually, Buckner and I got to the Kangnung water pumping station and filter facility, the dispensary, the motor pool and other elements. All were junk heaps. Repeatedly, Buckner stated that "he could not believe what he was seeing." And then we went to the Kangnung mess hall that served both the officers and enlisted men. Buckner exploded.

"John, I have visited a lot of the Army elements in the DMZ and none of them look like this. Frankly, I don't know what to say. I would like to help you but I just don't know what to do -- let alone how to do it."

Returning to the Kangnung flight line, I was shocked to find an attractive American girl and two Caucasian children present. Akers explained that we had been asked to fly the children to Osan for medical treatment.

The girl, I learned, was the wife of an American missionary who was based further north -- by the DMZ. We discussed some aspects of her life and, at the close of the conversation, I was humbled by her statement that she and her husband, both of whom had lived in the Kangnung area for years, could never do a proper missionary job in Korea. "But," she added, "with our children growing up in Korea, they can take over from us and really do a proper job for Jesus." I marveled at the dedication and the willingness to accept as conditions of life what most of us assigned to Korea complained about.

With "good-bys" to the mother and with the children of the missionary family aboard the C-47 and fitted as best we could with, for them, over-size parachutes, we took off for Osan. There was no clearance form filled out, no flight plan filed -- nothing. The children, I learned, would be treated at the Osan hospital with no paper work involved -- it was simply something that was done with no questions asked. I could see how easy it was for the things I had inherited at Kunsan Air Base to have run with equal informality. Perhaps I had moved away from that status of "the new kid on the block" and was beginning to understand more of the situation that surrounded me.

Boarding the Gooney Bird, I asked Paul if he had ever been to Osan or had a briefing on Air Forces Korea. He had not.

"In that case, rather than flying you back to Kimpo, why don't we drop you off at Osan. I'll radio ahead and have billets and a briefing set up for you. If I can reach a person named Mike, I'll ask

**her to meet us at the aircraft and take over. You will like her -- a hell of a girl and she knows more about Korea than any officer. To be certain that everything is lined up for you, after we land I'll call the Division Director of Operations, Colonel Jack Hubbard -- he may get you in to see the Divison Commander, General Joyce. If that can be arranged, go for it. Joyce is a great guy. When you're ready, Mike will arrange to get you back to Seoul. Is it a deal?**

**"You can bet your ass it is," Paul replied.**

**On the flight to Osan Air Base, I had Paul fly in the co-pilot's slot. He was a good pilot.**

**En route, Paul and I did a lot of talking and comparing of experiences and observations. Apparently, the U.S. Army was living a lot better in Korea than was the Air Force. We both concluded that the Army had the lock on supplies in that they owned and managed the depots. And we both knew that that could lead to preferential treatment.**

**I told Paul how, in Europe in World War II, we had managed to break into the Army system by painting Army insignia on our vehicles and wearing Army insignia on our uniforms. We both laughed.**

**I also told Paul how we had managed to pick up a crate of parkas on Omaha Beach and ended up using them as trading material for food and supplies across Europe in the 1944 - 1945 winter campaigns. "You would be surprised what a shivering guard standing in snow and ice would do for a fur-trimmed parka," I stated. Again, we laughed.**

**About half way to Osan Air Base, I radioed ahead for an ambulance for the children and then had the tower connect me to Mike. Mike met us at the aircraft. I introduced her to Paul and gave her a rundown of what I thought should happen in the way of introductions and briefings. She already had made arrangements for Paul to stay at the VIP quarters on Hill One-Eighty and suggested that Paul come to the girls quarters that evening for a drink. As Mike continued to talk to Paul, I went into Operations and called Jack Hubbard to be certain that all was well -- it was.**

**Knowing that Paul and the children we had brought in were taken care of, I got back in the Gooney, fired up the engines and taxied out for takeoff.**

**It was dusk when we arrived at Kunsan Air Base but I still took the time to circle the field and appraise that which I commanded. It was becoming home to me.**

**Knight was standing in front of Operations when we parked. Seeing him, I was worried that I might be in for some more bad news but there was none -- the day had proceeded without incident.**

**For a change, I did not dream much during the night. Apparently, the day away from Kunsan did me some good.**

***The Kangnung wooden water tower. It was thoroughly rotted, the roof collapsed and interior tanks open to the sky. Bracing timbers on two sides kept it from falling over.***

*The Kangnung Air Base flight line and aircraft parking area. The operations office is in center behind the two-post sign. Other buildings are barracks and Officers Club. The water tower shown on the preceding page can be seen on the skyline to the right of the light-colored Quonset. The base's transportation, one jeep and an ambulance, are in the photo.*

# DAY FORTY -- A FRIDAY

As I came awake, I could hear reveille playing -- apparently Jones had the turntable fixed again. The sound was on the scratchy side but the wake up call was recognizable.

At the morning staff meeting, I briefed on the prior day's trip and the missionary girl and her two children. I then talked about the conditions at Kangnung to make the point that what we had at Kunsan Air Base, on a comparative basis, was not all that bad.

At the close of the staff meeting I stated that my long-promised inspection of some of the enlisted barracks would take place the next morning at 1000 hours. I selected by location a dozen barracks and asked Jones to notify the occupants.

Jones had a large stack of paper in my IN basket but I just did not feel up to tackling it. I knew that this was not my normal self as I was a Type A workaholic. Somehow, I could not focus my mind on the papers in front of me. I knew I was not sick and I thought I had a good night's sleep but my whole system seemed lethargic. Finding myself staring into space, I called in Jones and suggested that we do a drive around the base.

As we drove, I recalled that the baseball team was to go to Japan on the following day and I suggested to Jones that, if space was available on the Gooney Bird, he accompany the team and take a few photos. He was delighted at the opportunity.

Passing by one perimeter section of the base near the dog kennels, Jones noted that it had the only fence that was not stolen.

"I have been watching that fence for some weeks," I stated, "as I, too, became curious as to why, of all the fences that were stolen, that one section was not stolen. And, last week, I got the answer."

"What is it?" Jones asked.

"Simple. Every once in a while, apparently during the night, the Koreans who work the paddy on the other side of the fence pick it up and move it slightly forward. By morning, they have a new paddy area on the other side and we don't know the difference. They are clever thieves -- most clever."

"But you know! Are you going to do something about it?"

"Not now. Those Koreans worked so hard for such a small parcel of land -- land we can spare, I'm not about to ruin their day. I think it's fun just knowing that we know and that they think we don't."

"Colonel, I am beginning to think you are getting soft."

"Maybe I am?"

And that thought worried me.

Driving on and searching for something to talk about, I asked Jones about the personnel picture.

"Pretty good," he answered. "I had a call from Osan and it looks as if we are going to get in close to a hundred new men this coming week -- all types. Someone must have turned on the faucet for us. Did you have anything to do with it."

"I'd like to take credit for it but it may be that we are becoming noticed by the outside world. If those hundred men came with a hundred portable radios, I would really feel good. But a hundred men arriving leads me to ask what we normally do in the way of indoctrination -- anything?"

"Really nothing, sir. Each unit -- mostly the old hands in the barracks -- sort of indoctrinate the new men."

The idea of the "old hands" indoctrinating the new men worried me. Obviously, this is what had been taking place in the Air Police organization. There had to be a better answer.

"Do you suppose that you could put together a regular indoctrination program for newcomers -- something that covered Korea, the area, rules and regulations, VD, drugs, leave, Red Cross -- the works. I don't mean for you to cover it all but to organize the thing. Could you do it?"

"It could be interesting -- I'll give it a try. But, for a start, would you be willing to open the orientation briefing?"

"You schedule me and I'll do it."

Jones was pleased.

And then I recalled my plan to name Jones as my Executive Officer.

"Do you know what an Executive Officer does?"

"Not really. I saw that General Joyce had a Captain with him who had that title -- this when he visited here some weeks ago. And the Vice Commander of PACAF had an Executive Officer in his party. But, no, I'm not sure what an Executive Officer does."

"Well, the answer is just about everything. And you have been doing just about everything for me so, to clear the air, I want you to write an order naming yourself as my Executive Officer. The work will not change but the title will look good in your record."

Back at the office, I forced myself to go through the collected paperwork. Frequently, I found myself at mid-page and just staring at the words -- not reading them. Finally, the hour getting late, I placed the paperwork in my safe and went to the Officers Club.

Joe was behind the bar and I asked him to make me a Scotch and soda.

The bandage on Joe's arm was much smaller and I assumed that, whatever the wound had been, it had partially healed. I commented to him about it but he simply looked downward and did not reply.

"Joe, where do you live?" I asked.

"Outside the base."

"I gathered that but where outside the base."

When Joe described where he lived, I realized it was in the vicinity of the "moving fence" that Jones and I had discussed earlier.

"Do you live with your family?" I asked.

"My family, a lot of my family, live in that area."

"And some of your family farm rice?"

"Most of my family raises rice -- most Korean farmers here -- that's all they do is raise rice and maybe small patches of cabbage and vegetables."

"And hot peppers, and garlic," I suggested.

"That too."

"Does your family farm rice down by the dog kennels?"

Immediately, I perceived a change in Joe's attitude. I sensed that I knew the problem.

"Some," he answered.

"Well, tell your family that I think they are very clever farmers."

"What do you mean?" Joe was suddenly cautious and curious.

"I mean about the fence. I know that they move it toward the base and plant a rice paddy in back of it but it is getting a bit too close. Tell them that if they don't stop moving the fence forward I may have to move it back and they will lose the paddies they have built."

I could see that Joe did not know what to say. Actually, he dropped a glass and it shattered on the floor.

"Don't worry Joe. Not too many people know what I know. It's just that, if the fence gets much closer, I may have to do something about it. And tell them that I appreciate that they have protected that fence from those who might steal the wire."

Joe nodded. But I could understand that he did not comprehend the logic of the situation. I was certain that, in his family, there would be much discussion resulting from this conversation. I decided to change the subject.

"Are there many pheasants in the fields by your family?" I asked.

Joe nodded.

"Too many and they eat too much."

"Does your family put out poison to kill the pheasants?" I had already learned of this Korean practice and I found it revolting -- especially in that the Koreans used a persistent poison that could pass down the food chain.

"I don't think so," Joe replied.

"Well, if I walk through the area where your family farms and shoot a pheasant, do you think they would mind?"

Joe looked at me for a minute. I knew he was unused to this type of conversation and, most likely, this was the first time an American had asked permission of Joe to do anything. Finally, he answered.

"My family will not harm you."

I found the answer most interesting. Literally, Joe was giving me "safe passage." But that meant that I might not have "safe passage" in some other areas around the base. Suddenly, I was again reminded of the briefing I had received on my first indoctrination flight -- the tunnel in Kunsan city where the retreating Americans had been bottled up and executed. Supposedly, the Americans and the South Koreans were on the same team but I wondered just how much of a "team" there was. And here was Joe. Supposedly, he was a South Korean but was he a North Korean spy to boot? Or could he be related to the political organization that had me on its assassination list?

"What a hell of a way to live," I thought. "I've got to protect myself in an ever widening circle -- no rear -- all front. And nothing but suggestive or mixed signals."

"Joe, give me another Scotch and soda."

I detected that Joe's measure of Scotch was extremely generous. And, for the first time since I had observed him, he smiled broadly. I hoped I understood what the smile inferred.

# DAY FORTY-ONE -- A SATURDAY

The baseball team was to be airborne at 0700 hours. I was there to see them off. Wade and Jones accompanied the team -- Jones had my Lieca and a bag full of other stuff. Akers and Peterson had joined up to do the flying; Sergeant Phillips was going as Engineer. In a loud voice, I reminded everyone that this was not an RON and that they were due back to Kunsan by nightfall. Then I winked at Jones. He grinned and gave me a "thumbs up."

"And if you are not back on this base by midnight, I'm going to court-martial the hell out of Lieutenant Jones. And don't tell me about engine trouble or stuff like that. I've been around too long."

Everyone laughed.

As the last man got on board, I yelled. "Bring us back a victory."

There were happy waves at the window. In minutes, the C-47 was rolling down the runway and they were gone. A quiet Saturday was settling over the base.

As the C-47 disappeared from view, I wondered what the team's reaction would be when they arrived in Japan and found the team they were to play against all decked out in special baseball uniforms? All my team had to play in were fatigues. Again, I reminded myself: One thing at a time!*

Back at the Officers Club, Annie asked me if I thought we would "win game with Japanese ball team."

"They are not Japanese," I explained. "They are Americans living in Japan. As to winning, I hope we do."

"I hope also. Men work very hard to play ball and now make like ground troopers with machine gun and all that."

Annie's statement made the hair on my neck stand up. This was a broader comment than I would expect from a waitress. Was it that I was wrong and, rather than Joe, Annie was my Officers Club agent -- or did I have two North Korean agents in the Club? Or was it just that I was getting paranoid?

"They will do O.K.," I answered. "They are good men."

---

* Some time later, the baseball team would be scrubbed due to the lack of transportation -- local softball would be continued. (Source: HRA files.)

"All American man good," Annie responded, her smile revealing her white teeth. "Me like Americans."

I was still troubled by Annie's comments when I realized that Jones would not be with me for the inspection of the enlisted barracks. "Oh well, go it alone," I thought.

On schedule, I took the formality of knocking on the door of the first barracks. I could see that the men inside were confused by my knocking. There was a "please enter" invitation and a call to attention. I gave an "at ease" order.

As I went through the barracks, I shook hands with each person and asked about things such as home town, how long the person had been in Korea, etc. Periodically, I made a point of congratulating the men on the construction of clothes racks and other items. On the one hand, I could see that my inspection of the officers quarters had paid off. On the other hand, since arriving at Kunsan Air Base, I had been such a bastard on so many points that I wanted the men to see that I was a reasonable and understanding person.

In the second or third barracks there were a number of center-fold, magazine "pin ups" on the walls. When I got to the end of the inspection, I motioned the men to join me. I congratulated them on the "pin ups" and their choice of American women, "but" I suggested, "if the Osan Wing Commander visits, I urge you take them down and put them in your footlockers or under your mattresses until he leaves. I understand he has a thing about girl pin-ups."

Someone in the back of the group responded.

"Colonel, we already knows about him and don't you worry yourself no bit. We knows what to do."

At the final barracks, when I had reached the end of the line, I asked that the men gather in a rap session.

"Under the circumstances," I said, "your barracks look pretty good and I am proud of you guys. And now I want to hear from you. I've been trying to make life a little better for you but I know that some of my policies may have hit you in tender spots and one of those has been my crack down of the open-ended josan visits to the base. You're all healthy Americans and I would want you to stay that way. But I can't run a whorehouse and call it a military base and that was about what this place was when I took over. I may have pissed off some of you but I had to do something. Now I want to hear from you -- hear from you on any subject other than that of josans -- that's off limits right now."

"Are we going to win today's baseball game?" someone asked.

"Sure hope so. And what do you guys think of that team volunteering to assist the guard set-up and serve as a machine gun reinforcement team?"

"Right on," came a voice from the rear. "We're sitting ducks out here unless we get some defense rolling."

"What about tools and equipment?" one of the older men asked. "Most of our stuff is old and worn out. And there is a lot of stuff we should have that we don't have. If we had more and better supplies and equipment, we could to a better job. Right now, I spend most of my time repairing tools instead of getting the repair jobs done."

"I'm on your team on this one," I answered, "and there are problems in this area that I don't understand. One good thing on the horizon is that Ashiya Air Base in Japan is scheduled to close down and I think we will have first priority on capturing tools, equipment and supplies from that place. Secondly, I am raising enough hell about conditions here at Kunsan that I think we will soon see some construction and other money coming this way."

"How about education?" an up front G.I. asked. "We're sitting out here without a place to go except where you tell us not to go but we've got time on our hands. Why can't the Air Force set up some college instruction programs we can work on. I got half a degree and I'd like to get the rest. This is a year of sitting on my ass or getting into trouble and I'd prefer not to get into trouble but, if all I have to do is sit on my ass, I'm probably going to get into trouble."

The man's words hit home. I had attended night school for some seventeen years to make up for lost education time. And I believed that education was the answer to most things. I agreed entirely with the voiced comments but we were at the "end of the line" on such things. Even Osan had no university level educational program. I had already checked.

"I can fix a lot of things," I answered, "but I don't know if I can fix this one during our tours here in Korea. It takes time to set up such things. In my view, good instruction needs good instructors and that creates special problems. Is any one interested in mail order study? How about the mail order programs of the military schools? I know they are not accredited but, if you complete them, you might have a better chance for promotion?"

From the back of the group someone shouted.

"Colonel, you get them for us and we'll use them."

**And so I left with another task in my "to do" book. I knew that, in the few days I had remaining to serve as the Commander of Kunsan Air Base, I could accomplish nothing in the area of education but there would be opportunity after I left.**

**"Why," I wondered, "did those in charge of such things not already have a program set up for outlying bases such as this -- why was it that the best assignments always carried with them the best accouterments and the worst assignments were made even more difficult by the lack of same?"**

**[*I firmly believed then, as I believe now as I write this account, that education is the key to success. I had been promoted well ahead of my contemporaries in World War II but I knew that, unless I obtained advanced education, I was heading for a dead end road. And in 1945 I started night school -- working 10-12 hours a day and finding the time to squeeze in 3-4 more hours of night school. It was not easy. When married, my wife and I used to have dinner together one night a week. The rest of the time I was working or in school. A few months after the cited discussion, I was called to Tokyo to be in a graduation ceremony conducted by Ambassador MacArthur -- I was the only graduate student present. The seventeen years of work had paid off. And, without this education, there was little chance that I would have ever become a General officer. In all my positions, so long as educational facilities were available, I ordered my officers and men to attend school. Many resisted the order but many of those who resisted later thanked me for that which I had forced them to do.*

*While in Japan for the cited graduation ceremony, I spoke at length to Fifth Air Force personnel about the need to establish an educational program in Korea. I pointed out that Japan had such a program -- why not Korea? The main argument set forth against an educational program in Korea was the assertion that the one year tour created such instability that it would be impossible to administer. A secondary argument was that the environment in Korea was such that no worthwhile instructional persons could be hired. It would take years to reverse this thinking.*]**

# DAY FORTY-TWO -- A SUNDAY

**In the civilian world of the United States, a forty hour week was a norm and some were advocating a shorter work week. Yet, here in Korea on the shore of the Yellow Sea and subject to "God knows what" every night and day, my men and I were working seven day weeks and, usually, much more than eight hours a day. And we were doing this in the worst of conditions without even the most normal of supplies. Further, we were separated from family and living in hell hole conditions even though, out at Kangnung and some other places, conditions were even worse. No Congressman and no Washington official would live in this environment -- most did not even know it existed. But here we were and who gave a damn? As far as I could determine, no Washington official had, in recent time, been on Kunsan Air Base -- most had never been to Korea in their lifetime. I was pissed off.**

**And then I went on a rampage. I not only demanded that the Chairman of the Joint Chiefs of Staff do something about the situation but I went to the hill and visited Congressmen. And then I addressed a joint session of Congress. But, when I talked to the Congress, all the persons in the audience went about doing other things -- some glanced at me and smiled -- I recognized a few faces. I talked louder -- soon I screamed at them. And then I screamed some more.**

**And then I awoke!**

**The sweat poured off of me. The air conditioner was running but I was soaking wet. It took me a few minutes to realize where I was. And what day it was.**

**For my own amusement, I had penciled the passage of days on a FIGMO calendar that had been presented to me during my first days at Kunsan Air Base.* I had joked to Mary about the FIGMO calendars many of the men kept -- some were highly artistic creations. Now, as I looked at the "X" marks on my calendar, I saw it was Sunday and my forty-second day in Korea. I had marked day sixty as my projected**

* The FIGMO term has many translations -- probably the most vernacular is "Fuck you Joe, I got my orders." There is probably no one who has served in Korea, or in a situation where there is a poor surrounding environment and a fixed tour, who does not know of or has not kept a similar calendar. It is not different than calendars kept by prisoners who mark off their days to release.

**day of departure from Kunsan Air Base to take up my new duties at Osan. And that was only eighteen days away! I was horrified at the passage of time -- and there was so very much to do!**

**Even as I showered, I now had hot water as a result of the acquisition of a hot water heater and some plumbing from Osan, my mind kept dwelling on my dream of the preceding night. I began to worry. Why would such a dream not erase from my consciousness?**

**Fortunately, by breakfast, it was gone.**

**Annie's quick cup of coffee and smile was very comforting. I had not realized it before but Annie was there every morning -- seven days a week -- and always smiling.**

**"Baseball team -- it no come back," Annie announced in a worried tone.**

**I was not aware that the team had not returned. But I was not worried.**

**"Perhaps they won and had a big celebration party?"**

**"Maybe so. I hope so. They work hard." Was it that Annie was not a North Korean spy -- only a baseball fan?**

**When Annie came back with the breakfast plate of ersatz eggs and canned bacon along with the usual fried potatoes and onions, I asked her about baseball.**

**"You like baseball?"**

**"I watch play game. American game is much interest to me."**

**"Do any Koreans in Kunsan play baseball?"**

**"No got place to play. All rice paddies."**

**My mind went into high gear. Circumstance had given me an opportunity but I had only eighteen days to go. Could I do anything in those eighteen days? I had already talked to my own men about working in Korean baseball players but the objection was that they did not speak English. On the other hand, in Japan, some great baseball talent was surfacing -- and they did not speak English. Perhaps there was a way to bring a whole lot of things together that were now separated. It was an interesting concept.**

**"You no want me to talk?"**

**Annie's comment jolted me back to reality.**

**"Annie, my mind just went far away -- on a trip -- I have to bring it back to earth for I have much to do. Today, I must go to church and then do some other things. Do you go to church?"**

**"I no understand your God," Annie observed. "We think much different in Korea."**

"Perhaps we do not think differently," I suggested and let the matter drop.

I would have to confess that all through the church service I was thinking about baseball -- and I was no baseball fan. But, suddenly, baseball seemed to be an answer to a whole lot of things -- an opportunity. When the church service was over, I still sat in the pew -- oblivious to the fact that the service had ended.

"Are you all right," the Chaplain asked as he shook my shoulder.

Embarrassed by the situation, I suggested that I had a bad night's sleep and was on the tired side.

Leaving church, I went to lunch and then back to the Waldorf Astoria where I donned some combat boots and drove to the Air Police Combat Center to retrieve my Browning shotgun. Somehow, I thought a good walk would do my mind and body good. Captain Wild happened to be there and he asked where I was going. I explained that I wanted to try my luck at shooting pheasants. He insisted on accompanying me.

"I don't have the kind of gun you have -- all I have is a good old G.I. twelve gauge pump gun with a rather short barrel. But it will kick out a lot of bird shot. I just have to get the shot off while they are in close range."

Wild did not carry a holstered forty-five but I noticed that he slipped one into his back waist band.

"You still worried about someone assassinating me?" I asked.

"Colonel, I worry about so many things, I can't tell you."

"Well, stop worrying about me. Nothing's going to happen to me. And, if it does, so what? We only live once."

"That may be so but a lot of us would like you to live a little longer."

That statement told me a lot. Instead of trying to get rid of me there were those who wanted me around. It was a good feeling. I hoped it was true.

As we walked, two pheasants popped up in my range and I got one of them. Wild had no luck. Walking back toward the base, I elected to give the pheasant I had shot to a Korean family. There was the usual bowing and conversation I could not understand -- but it was apparent that the Korean family was appreciative. I felt stupid at not being able to understand the Korean language.

As luck would have it, the Korean family to whom I gave the pheasant was part of Joe the bartender's family and, the next day, he would thank me for it. Apparently, I had made a Brownie point with Joe. What that might later translate to, I had no idea.

On return to base, I deposited my shotgun with the Air Police and told Wild that he and the senior enlisted men could use it if they wished but to be certain that it was cleaned after use. I then examined the racked guns in the Air Police armament room -- they were all clean and appeared to be well maintained. Next, I examined the weapons issue cards to determine how many weapons were on permanent assignment. I was surprised that the number was very small.

"What is the policy on permanent gun issue?" I asked.

"We really don't have one," Wild answered. "If an officer wants an issue forty-five, we give him one, plus two clips, but he has to maintain it and that keeps the issues down. Some pistols and carbines are issued organizationally and usually signed for by the senior enlisted man in charge of the section. We do a periodic check of the guns to insure that they are not lost and that they are maintained."

"Do we lose any guns?

"Now and then and we always examine the circumstances before we write them off the books."

That evening, I had a beer with Knight and Wild.

"Any more Air Police rumors about knocking me off?" I asked.

"I haven't heard a thing," Knight answered.

"Nor I," Wild added.

"Then I think we can conclude that the long-timers had something going and we threw a monkey wrench into their operations. Ever since I got to Kunsan and learned about persons extending in Korea I was concerned about the reasons that led to such decisions. Further, I always suspected that the reasons that were stated were not the real reasons."

"After what we have just gone through," Wild responded, "I have to agree. It took a two-by-four but I've learned my lesson. And, frankly, I haven't missed the men we moved out although, at the time, I thought it would be a great loss of experience and stability. Somehow, I think the remaining men are happy that the long-timers are gone."

We shared another round of beer and called it quits for the night. Mutually, we agreed not to inspect the guard for a few days.

Turning in for the night, I was relieved that the Air Police threat against my life had disappeared but it was only one of a vast multitude of concerns. Dropping off to sleep, I found myself mentally inventorying my residual problems.

# DAY FORTY-THREE -- A MONDAY

With the alarm ringing in my ear, I awoke. Normally, I was awake before the alarm went off.

For a while I lay under the mosquito tent and tried to figure out if there was an easier way to do whatever had to be done. Had I been accomplishing anything of worth or was this all a waste of time? Was I alive or dreaming? Already, I had been in Korea for almost a month and a half and what had I achieved? I could not even recount the days that had gone before -- it was as if they had all been ground up in a meat grinder.

Rising to confront a new day, the water splashed on my face seemed to bring me to the world of reality.

I was the Commander of Kunsan Air Base and I had more problems than I could count. And it seemed that every day there were still new problems to be added to the accumulation. Had I failed in my job? Perhaps I should have relaxed and just flowed with the stream instead of trying to swim upstream?

Looking at my reflection in the mirror, a mirror that still distorted the view, I saw a person who was developing dark circles under the eyes -- eyes that were bloodshot but not from excess drinking.

I wondered what my officers and men thought of me? Did they see what I observed in the mirror?

Back in the bedroom, I realized that my mama-san had, again, placed some flowers next to my bed. "I wonder if she really likes me or is this part of a con game?"

I had not seen Mr. Kim for many nights and I wondered if he had been out there the prior night. And did Wild really check on him?

And then I recalled the pipes at the Kunsan fuel storage area. Why had I not had a report on it? Was there a cover-up in the background?

By the time I got to breakfast at the Officers Club my mood had darkened. I was beginning to feel as if all those around me were against me. I even rebelled at Annie's white-toothed smile. I tried to shake the mood that dominated my thinking but it was difficult.

Knight broke up the thoughts that consumed me.

"Colonel Lee would like you to review the ROKAF troops today. His formation is at 1100 hours."

"And what do I do when I review the ROKAF troops?" I asked.

"Frankly, sir, it beats the hell out of me."

For a moment, Knight and I just stared at each other.

"O.K. I promised him and I'll go. But I'd like to send you. Something tells me that I'm going to make an ass out of myself. Am I supposed to make a speech to a bunch of Koreans who don't understand English?"

"I don't think that is on the agenda, sir."

"O.K. I'll do my best not to embarrass the United States. Tell Colonel Lee that I will be there."

Damn. I didn't even know what the National Anthem for Korea sounded like and, yet, I was certain it would be played. How in the hell did I get into this situation?

At the morning staff meeting, Sergeant Butler had another typhoon on the chart. And, once more, it seemed to have a forecast track that would bring it in our direction. I asked Polk about the shovels and was informed that they had not come in yet -- he would follow up with Peterson when he returned and, if necessary, call Japan.

Neither Peterson, Akers, Wade or Jones was present. They should have been back no later than Sunday night -- the game had been Saturday. Something was wrong! An overnight stay in Japan was O.K. -- but this was Monday -- not Sunday! And, if there was a problem, why did we not have a message?

Wild's report on the pipes we had observed at the Kunsan city fuel dump brought me back to reality.

"There is no doubt about it, sir. There was a deal going with the Korean side of the fuel dump to siphon some fuel from our tanks to their tanks. The problem was that, when our man left, he did not disconnect the pipes and we discovered them.

"I discussed this whole thing with Captain Pastiak and we decided to bring our man back to Korea for interrogation and possible court-martial. He is due in on the commuter flight of today. Based on our reports, he has been arrested and he will arrive under escort. I'll place him in the jail unless you want something else done?"

The question angered me.

"Do you want me to have him as a house guest?" I asked. "Keep him under control -- and, if that is in jail, do it. Interrogate him, take him to the scene, do what you have to do. But, if he was stealing our fuel and you have testimony to back it up, prefer charges. If it's a general court-martial, it will have to go to Osan and, if it goes to Osan, I want it to stick."

**"There is a side laugh to this, Colonel."**

**"And what is that?"**

**"He got paid off in gold. But the gold brick he got was just that -- a *gold brick*. When he got to U.S. customs they discovered the gold brick but it turned out only to be lead or something with a heavy gold plate. They confiscated the brick but they didn't do anything to him."**

**"So we lost a bunch of fuel and he got suckered?"**

**"That's it, sir."**

**"Well, let's sucker him once more. Maybe it will serve as a lesson to others but, sometimes, I doubt that punishment of one deters the stupidity of another. Keep me informed. And, if the charge is something that requires a general court, move him to Osan as soon as possible -- I don't want to feed him here -- let Osan feed him. But a second question is what do we do about the Koreans on the other side of the fence?"**

**"I've talked to Captain Pastiak about that," Wild answered, "and it seems that we really don't have much we can do. It's the old case of denial, finger pointing to others, pay off to officials, and the language barrier. Plus, we have no legal jurisdiction off base. We are all but dead in the water."**

**I thought a while. I hated to be taken and the Korean system was taking me. Apparently, I could not do anything about it -- or so it seemed.**

**And then I had an idea -- but I did not want to disclose it in front of the entire staff. I asked that, following the staff meeting, Knight, Pastiak and Wild meet with me.**

**A quarter hour later, Knight, Pastiak, Wild and I sat and reviewed the theft of fuel from the Kunsan fuel storage area. After everyone seemed to be in agreement on the particulars, I spoke.**

**"O.K. So some unknown quantity of fuel has been siphoned from our tanks to the Korean tanks. And, the consensus is that we really can't do anything about it. Well, try this one."**

**Knight, Pastiak and Wild leaned forward in their chairs.**

**"Tomorrow, the three of you visit the Mayor of Kunsan. As background, take him to the fuel storage area and show him the piping that was used to siphon off our fuel. Tell him about the Sergeant we have being brought back to Korea for court-martial and how this Sergeant will confess to all things. Blow up the story. And then tell the Mayor that, if we don't get repaid in kind or by money for the stolen fuel, I will place the entire city of Kunsan off limits to all Americans -- period -- all Americans. Further, if that does not get his attention, tell**

**him that I am contemplating canceling all Korean employment on the base -- and this will extend to grass cutting."**

**"That's a tall order, Colonel," Pastiak suggested.**

**"There is one rule in negotiations -- start big and fall back as needed -- but never start small and try to grow."**

**"Suppose the Mayor tries some similar tactic?"**

**"Such as?"**

**"Well, suppose he does not allow our vehicles to pass through the city?"**

**"Put some Air Police escort on the vehicles."**

**"Suppose he does not allow Koreans to work on the base?"**

**"That would kill him. He can't afford to create such a restriction and stay in office."**

**"What if he cuts our telephone lines?"**

**"We might be better off without them," I answered. "Look," I continued, "the Mayor needs us more than we need him. We are stolen blind, his people work here, we have him by the small parts. Now get yourselves to Kunsan and see what happens. As negotiation room, if there is a counter offer, bring it to me."**

**"Do we tell Osan what we are doing?" Knight asked.**

**"No. Definitely NO!"**

**As Knight and the others were walking out the door, I glanced at my watch -- it was 1035 hours -- twenty-five minutes to the ROKAF review of troops. I knew I would have a hard time at the review but "for the good of old United States of America" I would go. Actually, I got along pretty well. My cue was to salute when the ROKAF officers saluted. I think I came out O.K. But I would never know for certain. What I needed was a ROKAF aide-de-camp but I knew that was impossible.**

**The ROKAF formation over, I returned to the office only to learn that our Gooney Bird with the baseball team had still not returned. I called the Osan Command Center with no result. Then I called the Fifth Air Force Command Center. After a seemingly endless wait, they acknowledged that they knew where our Gooney Bird was -- it had lost an engine after take-off in Japan and landed at a Japanese Air Force base -- a new engine had been flown to that base and it was being installed at present -- a return to Kunsan was expected tomorrow.**

**Why had we not been informed? It seemed that someone forgot to send Kunsan Air Base the message.**

**With a curse, I slammed down the telephone.**

# DAY FORTY-FOUR -- A TUESDAY

The morning staff meeting was uneventful. Peterson, Akers, Jones and Wade were still out. Typhoon Number Three was building and moving on the track of numbers One and Two but there was still some six or seven days before it would hit Korea -- if it did -- time enough for Peterson to get back and the shovel situation to be resolved.

The meeting over, I decided that the first order of business would be to inspect the on-going construction and the runway repair. And I decided that I ought to be wearing combat boots for that exercise instead of uniform shoes.

Returning to the Waldorf Astoria to change shoes, I found my mama-san doing the laundry in the bathroom. And, horrors of all horrors, she was rinsing my clothes in the john by dipping them in and out as she flushed.

"No! No! You don't do it that way!" I shouted.

"But that good way. Get real nice clean this way," she answered.

"No!"

I stumbled as to how to explain to the mama-san that the toilet, no matter how visibly clean, contained germs.

"Toilet not clean," I told her.

"But I clean good," came the response.

"Don't care. You no rinse clothes in toilet. You rinse clothes in bath tub. O.K.?"

"O.K. If Colonel like me do it that way, I do."

Shaking my head in wonderment, I left the Waldorf Astoria for my planned visit to the construction and repair sites. I had to marvel that I had not developed a skin rash or other complication from what I had just witnessed.

My first stop was the runway.

The supervisor on the runway repair job forecast completion by the next day so long as there was no rain -- and the forecast was for several days of dry, hot weather ahead. He was sufficiently confident regarding the job completion date that he had called for transport aircraft to haul out his men and equipment. I walked the length of the runway with the supervisor and the work looked good. By tomorrow, at least one more problem would be history.

**My next stop was the G.I. mess hall under construction. The Army Corps of Engineers representative for that job was at the site and we did a walk through. The building was at the dried out stage, roof finished but still no windows installed. Progress was virtually at a standstill. "Materials shortages" was given as the answer. The missing kitchen equipment was the primary problem but there was also a problem getting windows. And then I noticed the water pipes -- they were not water pipes, they were EMT -- metal electrical conduit.**

**"You have got to be kidding. These are not water pipes."**

**"It's all we've got -- they will work. We've designed seals for the joints -- they won't leak."**

**"Impossible," I thought -- but the construction was not under my control -- not until the building passed to the base did the Commander have a say in it.***

**From the mess hall, I had the Army Corps of Engineers representative accompany me to the water system improvement project and the nuclear igloos being built.**

**The water system improvement consisted of the laying of new feeder lines. Most of them were six or eight inch lines, white PVC with slip on joints. The system was new to me.**

**"When the pressure gets in the lines, what keeps the pipe from coming apart?" I asked.**

**"We pour a concrete buffer at the end of the lines and at each turn point."**

**I examined one of the "buffers." Poured in the weak sub soil, I had to wonder if, over the long haul, the system was sound. But, like the mess hall, I really had no say in the matter.**

**At the nuclear igloo construction, work was held up for lack of concrete -- cement, sand and gravel. The Army Corps of Engineers representative stated that he hoped to get in materials in a week or two. In the meantime, he had Koreans hand polishing the exterior of the concrete that had been poured. I marveled at the waste of effort.**

**"Where do you live?" I asked the representative -- I had never seen him in the Officers Club.**

**"I've got a house in Kunsan. Some time ago, I was billeted on the base but base life did not agree with me so I rented a house in Kunsan."**

---

* Months later, when the water was turned on in this building, the EMT pipes blew and the entire water system had to be redone.

The entire visit to the construction projects left me unsettled but I had already been told by the Wing Commander to keep my hands out of the operation of the Army Corps of Engineers.

Driving back to the headquarters, I saw a Gooney Bird circling the field and presumed it was ours -- and it was. By the time the C-47 was parked in front of the operations building, I was standing, waiting to talk to Akers and Peterson.

"O.K. fellas, what happened?"

Akers responded.

"Sir, we were about fifteen minutes into our return flight when the right engine began running rough and we had to shut it down. Perhaps we should have taken the bird back to the Air Force base but, with all the passengers on board, we decided to set it down at the nearest facility -- and that was a Japanese field. After we got on the ground, I contacted Fifth Air Force -- and that was one hell of a job as there was no direct line to Fifth from the base we landed at. Eventually, we got to Fifth through the Japanese communication system and they arranged to fly a new engine, maintenance stands and a work crew to our location to change out the bad engine. The Japanese military at the base we landed at were very understanding and helpful -- we got free housing and eats. While we were waiting, we even played a game with them -- they beat the hell out of us."

"Why didn't you get a message to me as to where you were and the problem?"

"We asked Fifth to do that -- didn't they?"

"They didn't. When you didn't return on schedule, I called Osan and Fifth. Eventually, I got some information from Fifth -- but no message. But let's not worry about that. The main thing is that you and the team are back and in one piece. How did the game go at the Air Force base?"

"We won," one of the debarking men yelled. Akers smiled. I had my answer.

"O.K. That's the good news. The bad news is that we may have another typhoon hit us. As soon as you and Peterson get unpacked, come to my office and let's review the situation."

About an hour later, Akers and Peterson were at my office. They already knew about the typhoon from their own check on the weather for the return flight to Kunsan.

"Shovels?" I asked. "What's the story?"

Peterson answered.

"I've been following up on our requisition. Apparently, they are not in stock in Japan. The last I heard, they were trying to locate some in Okinawa or the Philippines. If they have to go back to the States, we won't see the shovels for a couple months. And, by then, we may need snow shovels."

"Now that you mention that, what do we have in the way of snow removal equipment?"

"Nothing but one grader machine with a blade, sir. I understand that when it snowed in the past the base just shut down until the runway and taxiway melted off."

My God! Here I was back to World War II again. No snow removal equipment! Who in the hell was thinking? General Joyce had a staff meeting scheduled for the next day and I was going to make this a major item for my presentation. It would probably be one more thing that would disturb the Wing Commander. I would be long gone from Kunsan Air Base by the time winter came to Korea but I knew that the time to think about winter was well before it arrived.

"How much snow accumulation do we get at Kunsan?" I asked.

In that neither Akers or Peterson knew, I asked Akers to get with Sergeant Butler and give me a report before the day was out.

*Winters in Korea were cold and miserable. At Kunsan Air Base, the moisture from the Yellow Sea added to the terrible environment. Shown above are crews of the 3rd Bombardment Wing stationed at Kunsan during the Korean War working during a snow storm to maintain their aircraft. (USAF)*

# DAYS FORTY-FIVE & FORTY-SIX
# A WEDNESDAY & A THURSDAY

I took the L-20 to Osan. Flying with me were a few passengers. I had ordered Akers to make a quick food run to Japan in order to be certain that we had supplies in hand before we were messed up by the in-coming typhoon.

When, at the Division staff meeting, my turn came to speak, I told General Joyce and the others that I had both good news and bad news.

"When it comes to good news, I can report that the runway at Kunsan has been repaired and the Fifth Air Force runway repair team should withdraw today. I've inspected the full length of the runway and the expansion joint rework looks good.

"Now to the bad news.

"With another typhoon apparently coming at us, I checked on the shovel situation and find that we still have received none from supply in Japan. Apparently, they have none and are now checking with Okinawa and the Philippines. My guess is that we have less than a week before this new typhoon may hit us -- assuming it follows the track of the last two typhoons. And the lack of shovels means that I am still in trouble -- I can't clean drainage ditches or fill sandbags by handfuls. I tried to talk the Fifth Air Force runway repair team out of their shovels but I failed. I've also examined local procurement as an option but, as you know, I have no money for that. That, however, is immaterial as nothing is available on the local market.

"And, moving ahead to another subject -- with the issue of winter hitting us in a few months, I find that, for all intent, there is no snow removal equipment at Kunsan. I don't know what you have at Osan or up at Kimpo but, based on the history of snow accumulation at Kunsan, and I have a chart here to show you average snow days and accumulations, we need equipment to stay in operation. I have checked my equipment authorization and none is authorized so I don't have a basis for requisition. I think someone needs to do some fast work on this or we are going to be in trouble in a few months."

Lt. Colonel Buck, the Kimpo Commander, immediately added his thoughts -- he had not one piece of snow removal equipment authorized and, obviously, none was on hand.

**As I expected, General Joyce assigned the task of sorting out the snow removal equipment problem to the Wing Commander. And, as I expected, the Wing Commander was unhappy at being told to do something that he ought to have initiated on his own.**

**Mid-way through the staff meeting, Jack Hubbard reported that he had obtained some goats to keep the grass down at the Osan Air Base. I thought he was pulling the Wing Commander's leg or just joking but it turned out that he was serious. I had to wonder how long it would take for the Koreans to steal the goats.**

**At the close of the Division staff meeting, General Joyce asked me to come to his office. I noted that the Wing Commander's eyebrows arched when he overheard the invitation.**

**When General Joyce and I were alone, he advised me that my replacement would arrive in about two weeks. He showed me a file covering my replacement and he was a good man -- experience, seniority and all.**

**I then told the General that in accordance with his instructions I had visited Kimpo and Kangnung and I briefed him on that which I had observed.**

**"Kimpo is going to be one of your big problems," he stated. "The pressure is on to get the land use sorted out and President Rhee's international terminal in operation. You may end up having to talk to Rhee himself. The Ambassador is not all that swift on the Kimpo subject -- he will accompany you to any meeting with the President but you have to carry the conversation. And, by the way, be prepared to talk loud as Rhee is getting more deaf with each passing day."**

**[*A later amusing event took place when President Rhee visited Kimpo to see how the USOM construction on "his international airport and terminal" was proceeding. It was a terribly hot day and I had been waiting for the President at a position near the terminal building. Chairs had been placed for the President, the American Ambassador and others. The Ambassador arrived in the President's limousine.***

***Trying to communicate to President Rhee, I soon found myself bending over and talking directly into his ear. Sweat was pouring off me and it had started to run into my eyes. Reaching to my back pocket for a handkerchief to wipe away the perspiration, I suddenly realized that the President's body guards had their guns out and trained on me. My hasty movement to my back pocket had been misinterpreted!*]**

Following the visit with General Joyce, I had lunch with Mike. She knew I was in and she was waiting for me at the Officers Club.

"That Lt. Colonel Buckner is a great guy -- we all enjoyed his visit. And how is it going with you?" she asked.

I did not mention the spy situation but did tell her about some of the other problems and some of the half-assed solutions I had managed to orchestrate. She was particularly amused at my account of the Mayor's reception.

"Those parties will kill you," she said. "They're brutal. Unfortunately, the enlisted men who learn of them think the officers are having fun and they do a lot of barracks gossiping about what happens. And the stories grow and grow. You'll find out. Eventually, the stories might come full circle back to you. Worse, an unhappy G.I. might write to your wife and recite the gossip. It just happened here and one officer is in the dog house with his wife back in the States. I don't think they'll be getting a divorce but things are bad. And the result is that the affected officer is hitting the bottle. As I told you before, Korea is hell."

Laughingly, I told Mike that I still had no shovels at Kunsan and I now faced Typhoon Number Three.

"You're not using your head," she replied. "You have shovels at Kunsan. I don't know how many but you can be certain that there are some down there."

"What the hell are you talking about? Where?"

"Your Corps of Engineers work force has got to have some."

"But they're Korean contractors and I have no contract money to hire them or acquire their tools."

"As I said, you're not thinking straight. The tools the Korean contractors have are most likely GFE -- furnished to the contractors by the Corps of Engineers. They will have their own A-Frames and such but not mixers, shovels and other tools. They come from old Uncle Sammy. And all you have to do to get them in your hands is put on a little pressure."

I felt like a total dummy. There had been no "shovel work" going on at any of the Corps of Engineers projects I had inspected but, obviously, there had to be shovels available. No doubt, the Corps of Engineers representative had them locked up somewhere. Why in hell had not I, or some of my staff, recognized this. I resolved immediately on my return to Kunsan to have a conversation with my Corps of Engineers representative.

**I was leaving the Officers Club to go to the flight line and head back to Kunsan when Colonel Kincaid, the Director of Materiel, called to me.**

**"You got some room on your aircraft?"**

**"I'm flying the L-20 and I have a couple seats open. How many passengers you got for me?"**

**"No passengers but I've located some shovels here in supply. A Wing Supply Sergeant was doing a little hoarding and they were not on the record. If you can take twenty, I'll have them at your aircraft in about thirty minutes."**

**"Believe me, if I have to kick off a passenger, I'll make room for them." I was not about to tell Kincaid about the possibility of obtaining shovels from the Corps of Engineers supervisor at Kunsan. Besides, I had long been convinced that "a bird in the hand was worth two in the bush."**

***The Corps of Engineers work done at Kunsan was, as above, accomplished by Korean contractors. This was all hand labor augmented with only small mixers and other minor mechanical support. In the above photo, the contractor is laying a concrete slab -- the aggregate and mix is transported by back packs or A-frame. My error in judgment was concluding that the shovels belonged to the contractor.***

Kincaid gave me a "thumbs up" and went to a telephone. By the time I got to the flight line, a truck had pulled up with the shovels. There was only one out-going passenger for Kunsan so I did not have to bump anyone from the loading list. I was in business but not by very much.

It was late in the evening when I landed back at Kunsan Air Base and I elected to leave the shovels on board the L-20 -- I would tell the staff about them at the morning meeting.

When the Thursday morning staff meeting came, Akers was not there -- a message was on my desk informing me that he had to RON in Japan and would not return until the afternoon of Thursday -- today.

Peterson, Polk and the others were pleased at just getting twenty shovels and I soon had agreement that ten would be allocated to the filling of sand bags and ten would be allocated to clean out work on the most critical drainage ditches. The shovels would be used on two shifts "until the rains come."

"There's going to be some blistered hands," Peterson suggested.

"If someone's hands get too blistered, pull him off the work and get a replacement."

Twenty shovels was not much but, with two shifts working, that was like forty shovels. Just so no one broke a handle. But, even if that happened, a replacement handle could be fashioned out of some lumber.

The bad news came from Sergeant Butler. The projected track of Typhoon Number Three was holding and it looked as if it would hit Korea on the coming Monday -- that was four days hence.

Following the staff meeting, I visited with the Corps of Engineers representative at Kunsan. I explained my need for shovels to do essential work to get ready for the on-coming typhoon. To a bottom line: Yes, he did have some shovels in his tool inventory but he alleged that the Army did not allow him to loan them out.

"How would you like to have the Officers Club and PX placed off limits to you?" I asked.

For a minute the Corps of Engineers representative just looked at me. I could appreciate what he was thinking -- that I did not have the guts to carry out my threat. On the other hand, he did not know what I might do. I held the cards and he was quick to recognize that.

"O.K. I'll loan you some shovels but I've got to get them back after your typhoon clears," the representative replied.

**"And you shall -- but loan me every one you have that is not in use. And," I added, "consider yourself a part of this organization -- not a tenant."**

**Later in the day, when Akers returned from the food run to Japan, I found that we had even more shovels for he had managed to scrounge some in Japan -- used ones, not new ones -- but, used or new, we were now in "shovel heaven."**

***An arrival scene at Kimpo International Airport taken after my assignment to Osan and during work on President Rhee's international airport project. The metal covered hangar in the background -- it looks better than it was -- is the one that was used by the Air Force as the military terminal. I usually used an L-20 commuting from Osan to Kimpo and the aircraft shown was my own. White gloved ROK Military Police are present in the above scene. Of historical interest, in the U.S. the ratio of persons coming to an airport to send off or meet friends is a small fraction of the number traveling. In Korea, at the time, the number of persons coming to the airport for each departing or arriving passenger was on the order of 200. And that had a terrific impact on the number of toilets and terminal support space that had to be provided. Obviously, there was no published statistical base for such design and engineering decisions.***

# DAYS FORTY-SEVEN INTO FIFTY FRIDAY INTO MONDAY

With the exception of a break on Saturday for a "grenade" throwing competition between my men and a team from Colonel Lee's unit -- this in lieu of a Saturday baseball game, the primary focus of attention for the next three days was on the "shovel brigades."

Major Akers had a group of men working steadily to sand bag roofs and accomplish other typhoon preparations to include building a reserve of filled sand bags. Captain Polk kept groups of his and other men working on the clean out and deepening of the drainage ditches. Several men did develop some serious hand blisters and they were pulled off the work details. The kidding among the men aimed at those who had "soft sissy hands" was heavy. Periodically, I would join a ditch clean out detail and work until my back and guts hurt. Challenges went back and forth as to who could dig the most the fastest. Never had I witnessed shovel men throwing dirt so fast. Here and there, men were fighting over the right to a shovel and the privilege of digging. Now and then a friendly dirt throwing exercise would erupt.

Noting the typhoon preparations and, especially, the sand bag operation, Colonel Lee asked if he could "borrow" some sand bags to help secure his structures and, I agreed. Lee didn't have regular shovels but his men did have some issue trenching tools and, while they were not the best of answers, they did a reasonable job.

The work would go on into Sunday but by Saturday night I decided to call in my two Chaplains, Captain Johnson and the new Catholic Chaplain, Captain Murphy, and suggest that, if they could bend to the mood of the situation, they address in their sermons the great work the men had done to get ready to counteract the on-coming typhoon. I suggested that the typhoon might be treated as the approach of the devil and how great a unified effort could be in counter-acting the evil influences with which we were all surrounded. I knew that I was on tender grounds to suggest a theme for the Sunday services but I had come around to a "what the hell" attitude.

Following church services, the digging went on again. Perhaps my suggested story had gotten through. I did not know as I had been so busy that I could not attend a church service.

**By Sunday evening, the advance elements of the typhoon were overhead and light rain was beginning to fall -- but most of the key drainage ditches had been significantly cleared. By then, Akers had moved the C-47 and L-20 to Kimpo and the ROKAF F-86s had deployed. To my surprise, Knight had stated that he wanted to fly the C-47 to Kimpo and that he wanted Jones to go with him "to get a few small things taken care of." The nuclear alert F-100s just tied down and waited for the storm to come -- and go.**

**On the Saturday, at what would otherwise have been the baseball game time, Wade had orchestrated a "grenade" throwing competition involving the ROKAF. For this competition, colored baseballs were used in lieu of grenades. As targets, Wade had set up a line of open end 55 gallon drums beginning with the first one at fifty feet from a throwing pit and then moving outward at fifty foot intervals. The drums were tilted at what was believed to be the expected angle of the arriving ball. The object was to get the ball in the drum "on the fly" -- a miss was judged "as good as a mile" off target. Each "thrower" was given six balls. Twelve men of the Kunsan baseball team made up the American side. I didn't know how Lee selected his team of twelve but they were good.**

**The Kunsan baseball team calculated that beating the ROKAF team would be "a piece of cake." But, on the first fifty foot throw, the Kunsan team was down by one ball. The spectators, which included a good number of ROKAF troops, were shouting and cheering on their men.**

**On the 100 foot throw, the score of balls in the can evened up and the excitement rose. Bets were being placed in a frenzied fashion.**

**At the 150 foot throw, the score still stood even and the Americans were going crazy.**

**And then came a 200 foot throw. The Kunsan baseball team was certain that they had an advantage due to their outfielders but, again, the number of balls that hit inside the drum was even.**

**Colonel Lee and I discussed the situation and we authorized a play off with the 200 foot target. The Kunsan team won by one ball.**

**By the time the competition was over, the American and Korean team players had surmounted the language barrier with mixed English and sign language. Everyone was happy. By pre-arrangement, each team won a dozen cases of Coca Cola -- one for each team participant. And, on their own, the Kunsan baseball team would decide to invite the ROKAF for a game of ball on the coming Saturday. We were becoming a U.S./ROK team. Wade asked me for some money for**

additional equipment and my response was to "Go get it!" I felt as if I was winning again.

Periodically during the Friday through Sunday, I had driven around the base to observe the on-going work. Everything appeared to be running smoothly. I was so pleased with what I saw and confident regarding the results, that, when I returned late Sunday to my office, I took the time to write a long letter to Mary. In the letter, I told her that my remaining time at Kunsan Air Base was short -- perhaps ten or fourteen days. Probably in about ten days I would inform my staff and begin packing for the move to Osan. As I wrote the words, a feeling of sadness came over me. The Kunsan experience had taken a lot out of me but, in the process, I had become attached to the base, the mission, the many challenges, the people and the community. I knew I would miss it but the indication was that I would have so much to do at Osan that I would have little time for missing anything.

On Saturday, Joe Pastiak advised me that he, Knight and Wild had met with the Mayor of Kunsan. After being shown the evidence, told the story and then my demands for restitution, the Mayor had pleaded for relief stating that he had no money and his city and its people were very poor. Joe said that the Mayor implied that there might be some other thing he could do "to please the American Colonel." It was obvious to Joe that the Mayor still viewed a "temporary wife for the American Colonel" as a way to solve all problems. When the Mayor was informed that the American Colonel was not interested in any special arrangement, the Mayor begged for some time to consider the situation. The meeting ended with a scheduled reconvening to be the coming Friday.

"I think the Mayor is going to come up with something," Joe forecast, "probably half of the quantity of fuel we estimate was siphoned off. If he does that, I think we should accept and let the matter die. Half a loaf is better than no loaf at all. And there will be a lesson in all this for the Mayor -- perhaps we will have no more of such activity and, if we agree to the compromise, we will get cooperation on many fronts in the future."

"How about the Sergeant who was involved?"

"He has confessed to everything. I have written up the case and sent it and the Sergeant to Osan. The Osan JAG will take care of the matter as we reached the conclusion it had to be within a general court jurisdiction."

So many matters seemed to be running smoothly that, for the moment, I had forgotten base security. And then I heard some distant machine gun fire! As usual, the Air Police had heard it but there was no information as to what was happening. I called the radar unit and learned that it was turning and that nothing special was on the scope. I decided to call Colonel Lee and invite him to a late Sunday lunch.

Lee had heard the shooting but he professed to hold no information on the event.

"I think it's just one of those many attempts by North Korea to land some agents," he said. "Most likely, the attempt was spotted by our people and no agents were landed -- or, if landed, they were taken care of. Our coastal watch is pretty good."

"But we don't have a coastal watch operating around here -- do we?"

"No. In this immediate area, my Government depends very much on the fisherman for intelligence. It has worked out pretty good but I still worry about that person who cut your electrical line. I have not received any definitive information from our intelligence people. However, I have learned that several newly-used North Korean ration containers have been found on the islands offshore from Kunsan. Whether there is a connection, we do not know. Still, our government is considering placing some military personnel on those islands. This is all most distressing and I apologize to you for what has taken place. It should not be so. You should not have to worry about infiltration here at Kunsan -- that should be taken care of by my country."

"I appreciate your thought but we still have to face reality and I believe you know how much I am concerned about the defense situation here at Kunsan Air Base?"

"Yes. And I commend you on the machine gun team you have organized. I think it is very impressive. I have given thought to doing something along the same lines but I cannot obtain a gun and ammunition. Could it be that you could obtain these things for me?"

"I don't know. They would have to come through Military Assistance Program channels. My guess is that you would be told to acquire them from the ROK Army."

"That would be most difficult," Lee observed.

"What about the ROK Army unit that handles the anti-aircraft guns around the base? Cannot they help you out?"

"I doubt it. They operate on what you call a *shoestring* already."

"Have you talked to the commanding officer of the unit?"

"No. He and his men live in a village on the road to Kunsan."

"How do you contact him?"

"I think his men have a field land line that runs to his house."

"Do you think we could contact him and you and I visit his gun installations -- perhaps tonight or tomorrow?"

"Let me try."

Late that evening, Colonel Lee informed me that he had talked to the commander of the anti-aircraft guns, a Lieutenant Shik, and that a tour of the gun positions was laid on for 1000 hours the next morning -- Monday -- and that would mean "in the rain." Perhaps this was a good, but unplanned, idea. An attack did not need good weather -- in fact, bad weather could favor the attack.

I regretted that I had not had the time to visit the gun positions before this date. For protocol, I obtained a bottle of cognac to present to Lieutenant Shik when we met. I told Sergeant Young to accompany me and, at the appropriate time, pass it to me for presentation. I advised Young to carry a side arm "for appearance sake." Colonel Lee indicated that the tour would start at one of the gun positions -- we would have to travel by jeep. I anticipated that Lieutenant Shik would have his men at their best. I did not tell Wild of the planned event as I concluded that, if he knew, he would want to set up some security that would make the whole operation cumbersome.

From Lieutenant Shik, who spoke reasonable English, I would learn that no American had visited his guns. In an emergency, at best he could place no more than three to, at most, four men at each gun installation. They were all dug-in, single barrel, forty millimeter, visually aimed guns -- and, due to revetting, none of them could depress sufficiently to counter ground movement. The Lieutenant had not fired any of the guns since the Korean War -- the sites he occupied had all been placed in position during that conflict when a B-26 Invader unit had occupied Kunsan Air Base.

I examined several of the guns and, in spite of their age, they were in good condition. To protect them from the elements, well worn but still effective tarps covered each gun -- now, although water was falling, they were uncovered for my inspection. At each gun position, there were covered boxes of ammunition. I suspected that they had been moved into proximity of the guns for my benefit.

Lieutenant Shik stated that he had no reserve of ammunition -- what he had was all at the gun sites. I estimated that there was not more than 100 rounds at any site.

Because he was very limited in manpower, Lieutenant Shik stated that, normally, he only kept a full gun team on one or two guns. On the other gun sites he had a single man positioned. "One man can

**fire the gun but he must stop to reload the clip. Because the guns must be visually aimed, we do not keep a full team on any gun during the night."**

**There was a telephone at each gun site -- one of the old field telephones. Each gun site had been sand-bagged many years ago and many of the bags had become holed and were leaking sand -- with the current increase in the fall of rain, the situation was most depressing -- the surface around the guns had been layered with a few boards and some PSP sections but, with the rain, it was a mess.**

**At most of the sites, the men had constructed shallow, dug-in shelters with the walls made of a row of sand-filled 55 gallon drums. The roofs of the shelters were timbers covered with corrugated metal and then covered with sand. Grass and weeds grew from the shelter roofs. I could see that, for winter warmth, the men had constructed small stoves in the shelters and some sleeping capability existed. For fuel, each site had bundles of grass and some branch wood piled next to the shelters. Apparently, the stoves also served for cooking.**

**The ROK Army men at the gun sites were armed with old, worn carbines. I had to wonder if any of them were still in working order.**

**I was terribly depressed at what I observed. The anti-aircraft guns, everything I viewed, was not only old but, by current standards, virtually primitive. Yet, these men were standing alert as if they had the best of equipment and support.**

**The time, I thought, had arrived when a troubling question had to be asked.**

**"What are your rules of engagement?"**

**It was apparent that Lieutenant Shik did not understand the question so I rephrased it.**

**"In case of attack, do you have to get authority to fire your guns and, if so, from whom?"**

**"I am not authorized to fire my guns unless I receive a *guns free* order from my commander in Seoul. If such an order is given, they will probably tell me what the attack is and the direction of approach."**

**"And in a *guns free* status, how do you know what to shoot at?**

**"Through visual recognition."**

**"Is there any other time you can fire?"**

**"Only if fired upon."**

**With all the other worries I had, I now had a new one. Obviously, an enemy aircraft could approach Kunsan Air Base from the Yellow Sea area, either below the radar coverage or at a time when**

the Kunsan radar was down for maintenance, and wipe out the alert aircraft and more without a reaction coming from the ROK anti-aircraft guns.

"How do you operate when you have no communications with your senior command? Suppose an enemy aircraft attacked this base at such time -- what would you do?"

"If we were fired upon, we would return the fire. But more than that I could not do."

"And so," I thought, "one would have to be dead in order to be authorized to fire."

"Would you take a fire order from me?" I asked.

"That I could not do," Lieutenant Shik replied.

"Could you take a fire order from Colonel Lee?"

"No sir. I can only take a fire order from my senior commander in Seoul."

There was no point in pursuing the question. Lieutenant Shik had his orders and I was faced with still another example of the fractured command situation that governed everything. I wondered if our enemies knew how tangled and disjointed our system was?

When the tour of the gun sites was over, I asked Lieutenant Shik if he could not use some sand bags to replace the old and torn bags I had observed. I told him that I did not have a lot of sand bags but that I might be able to give him a few hundred. The Lieutenant beamed. "We have had no new sand bags since the Korea War," he stated. "If you can give us some, they will be well used and my men will be much in debt to you."

"How long have you been assigned here?" I asked.

"Since before there was the armistice," he replied. "My family, it has grown up here at Kunsan."

I was overwhelmed at the situation. For now, years upon years, this Lieutenant and, presumably, his men had manned a ring of anti-aircraft guns, now much out-dated guns, around the perimeter of Kunsan Air Base -- day after day, year after year, with no let up. Perhaps the ROK Army viewed them as much on the forgotten frontier as I found myself. I had already observed the scarce food, mostly kimchi, that kept these men alive -- men on whom all of us at the main base, supposedly a major nuclear base of the United States, depended. Alongside many of the gun sites, I noted that the ROK men had planted small vegetable gardens.

Well soaked by the rain, I returned to the Waldorf Astoria thoroughly troubled. Mentally, I imagined myself addressing a joint

**session of the Congress as I had done in my dream of some days past. But I was no Douglas MacArthur. And my time was running out -- only days were left until I would transfer to Osan.**

**Still, I had to do something -- something before I departed to Osan -- something to emphasize the local situation and what had been done to make it better -- and it had to be something to make the outside world of enemies and higher echelons pay attention.**

**As I examined various scenarios, I decided that the best thing I could do was call a base alert and show everyone that we knew how to defend ourselves. But that call would have to wait until the current typhoon had passed -- and I had a sensible plan. While I knew that the time was terribly short, tentatively, I set the coming Saturday for the event.**

**As I examined the situation that would be existing on a Saturday, the logic of that date was reinforced. My idea was to call the alert in the middle of a baseball game. Many persons would be present and the impact of men rushing to the defense of the base could be significant. Mentally, I could see the baseball team assemble and proceed to a defense position with one of the fifties. But there would be a negative reaction to the interruption of the baseball game. I could already hear the words: The S.O.B. has done it to us again!**

**The answer, I concluded, was to have the exercise kick off at the "seventh inning stretch," and then return and continue the baseball game with a following "beer bust."**

**But, to make this defense action realistic, I knew that some firing of guns was important. So I decided to find a way to get not only "the fifty" of the baseball team in operation but an anti-aircraft gun of the ROK Army. I also considered setting up some silhouette targets off the sea wall to simulate an invasion party and allow the "defenders of Kunsan Air Base" to blast away. Setting up such off-shore targets would not be easy as we did not have so much as a row boat and to walk out on the mud flats, although the Koreans did it, was most treacherous. I had tried it once and almost got mired down in black, ugly goo.**

**As I reviewed this scenario, I knew I had but one organizer and that was Jones -- my now "Executive Officer." But he was off to Kimpo with Knight. Hopefully, there would be no delay in his return to Kunsan.**

**After several days during which I had been in the depths of depression, my adrenaline was again beginning to flow.**

# DAY FIFTY-ONE
# TUESDAY
# TYPHOON NUMBER THREE

**Heavy rain had started on the Sunday evening and, for a while, it seemed that the world would wash away. The heaviest water fell on the Monday but we were spared the high winds of a typhoon. For a while, it appeared that the typhoon simply sat on top of us -- never to move -- then it tracked toward the Sea of Japan. Once again, except for MARS, all communication with the outside world was lost.**

**Before communications with Osan were lost, a message did arrive from the Wing Commander which chastised me for having the worst Air Force vehicle accident rate in Korea and he demanded that I do something about it. I knew that we had a number of vehicle accidents but most seemed to be the result of the lack of parts support and resultant maintenance shortfall coupled with the sorry road conditions in the area. And I had no way of knowing how the Kunsan Air Base vehicle accident situation stacked up against such accident prone organizations as the 5th Motor Transportation Squadron in Seoul -- an organization that would ultimately be disbanded due to vehicle accident rates. Obviously, the Wing Commander had discovered a hole in my armor and he was going to make the most of it. But I knew that, in the few days I had remaining at Kunsan Air Base, I would be able to do virtually nothing about the situation.**

**[*Following my departure from Kunsan Air Base, a top notch Ground Safety NCO was brought in to assist in personnel training and, in the ensuing twelve months, there was not a single reportable motor vehicle accident -- a record that could not be matched by the Wing Commander's operation at Osan Air Base.*]**

**Although we had solved much of the shovel problem, we never did get the requisitioned items. Peterson had ordered round point shovels and we eventually got a "not in stock." I was to learn that there were adequate numbers of square point shovels in stock in Japan but the technicalities of the system had outwitted us. The next**

**requisition for shovels listed either round point or square point but I would be long gone from Kunsan Air Base before they arrived.**

**With rain keeping everyone inside and with no external communications to bother me, I used the time to work with the staff to refine the base defense plan. The object was to keep it simple and yet effective. The major obstacle was the absence of radios. To offset that deficiency, it was agreed that some land line field telephones would be set up to key points -- the old crank field telephones of which a number of Korean War leftovers were found in the war reserve pool. And discovered in the war reserve pool was a large amount of wire also left over from the Korean War. Major Benson and Lieutenant Short reviewed with me what they could do through the use of the available field telephone equipment.**

**To overcome the language barrier, a plan was established to, in an emergency, deploy Americans in key spots such as the lead ROK Army gun position and the ROKAF headquarters. In turn, Lee would place bi-lingual ROKAF persons in the Air Police Command Center and some other key spots. All command locations, to include the key ROK Army gun position, would be linked by direct line field telephone.**

**The Air Police Command Center was established as the central command post with the back-up being my headquarters. Each of the central posts was set up with a large plotting map of the base for wall use -- the base was divided into sections so that locations could be called out by number. Smaller maps were made for use by persons in defense assignments.**

**The objective of the plan was, on the signal of the sirens, to get men armed and into pre-determined locations. Movement of flights (we termed them *platoons*) or other elements from pre-determined locations to meet known threats would be orchestrated from the central command posts. For each pre-determined location, a platoon number was assigned and each platoon unit had a designated commander and deputy commander. The Air Police and the other two fifty caliber gun units were each designated by a color.**

**One of the major concerns was centered on keeping units from viewing each other as the enemy and a committee was established to work on identification and signaling methods.**

**The threat to the base was described as three-fold: (1) coming from the air in the sense of landed troops, (2) coming from the sea, (3) coming from the land approaches. A typical threat was described as from 50 to 100 armed men but with individual armament that exceeded our standard issue. A subordinate threat placed in the plan, and one**

requiring more riot control tactics than combat, was an outgrowth of the recent Kunsan Air Base "invasion" by indigenous Koreans.

Each unit and section commander was, by inspection, to insure that the men in his organization had assigned all combat gear except weapons -- weapons were to be issued at the time of the emergency and returned on the all-clear signal. To speed weapon issue to my men, three weapon issue points were established -- one was the Air Police Command Center.

Armament of our own men was to be the standard forty-fives and carbines with an initial allocation of two clips with each weapon. One Thompson sub-machine gun and one shotgun, along with ammunition, was allocated for each platoon. In addition, each platoon was to be issued a dozen fragmentation and a dozen tear gas grenades. As soon as possible, a limited number of men in each platoon would be instructed on the handling and use of these grenades.

The three fifty caliber guns were allocated: (1) to the Air Police reaction team, (2) to the baseball "fifty" team and (3) to a special volunteer team.

Considering the possibility of opposition to action by the fire fighters manning the foam truck and the water pumper, two support platoons were established to provide protection and to assist as needed.

Lieutenant Short agreed to head one platoon to maintain communications and lay additional wire on call. One jeep was to be modified to carry a rear mounted wire roll for laying wire on the run. Units not serviced by telephone were to rely on runners for communications.

Priority defense areas were established as: (1) the nuclear alert and storage area, (2) the fuel dump, (3) the bomb dump, (4) the central communications and other facilities to include the radar installation, (5) parked aircraft and (6) the main runway.

The ROKAF was assigned one segment of the perimeter in addition to their own aircraft, supply and administrative areas. If augmentation of the ROK Army anti-aircraft guns was needed, the ROKAF would supply it. Mutual support from or to the ROKAF would be coordinated by way of the Air Police or alternate command center but, to avoid confusion, and certainly to avoid any "friendly fire," the U.S. and ROKAF elements would be kept apart as much as possible.

If the operation took place in daylight hours, the C-47 and L-20 would be launched to assist in observation. To expedite the launch of these aircraft, the unused macadam runway on the field was authorized for emergency takeoff. Akers was to have a primary and alternate crew assigned to each aircraft. Communications to and from the aircraft would be via the tower but a system of flares and light signals would be established for emergency communications. Unresolved were the circumstances that would call for a safety launch of the F-86s and the F-100s -- this, I knew, had to be something to discuss with the Division at Osan -- but at a later time.

One of the defense problems that consumed a lot of discussion time was the matter of how to deal with the Korean population on the base at the time of the exercise. Eventually, it was decided that the platoon in each sector would be responsible for insuring that the Korean civilians in that sector were monitored and not allowed to move to adjacent sectors. In an actual situation, the Korean civilians would be "bunched" in each sector and isolated -- probably in one of the buildings.

By the time the rains let up on Tuesday, we had the skeleton of a base defense plan in which most of the key persons had participated in the formalization process -- and it was understood. Lee and Lieutenant Shik had been brought into the planning process and both were complimented and pleased. Both assured me that, when the sirens sounded, their men would do a good job. For the sub-plan, Lee suggested that his men might be more effective in that he did not operate under the constraints of the American system. I liked the idea and told him that I would call on him for assistance as needed.

Of interest, during a search of the war reserve materiel yard for items that could be used to support the base defense plan, a large box was discovered to contain trenching tools. Apparently the tools had been collected at the end of the Korean War with the container in which they had been placed not labeled in accordance with the contents. The discovery was made when one of the boards, the nails having rusted through, fell away from the box. Had the existence of these trenching tools been known, they could have been used in the filling of sand bags. Now, however, they could be useful in the event of a real fire fight and they were distributed to the men as standard equipment.

With the plan formulated, the next task was to brief the men and, on the coming Saturday, to exercise the system. I would liked to have told all those present of the North Korean spy ring on the base but I could not. Secretly, I knew that, by Saturday night, some messages would probably be out-going to North Korea advising of the increased defense preparations at Kunsan Air Base and, if there was an enemy plan afoot to do harm to Kunsan, the odds were that the planners would be sent back to the planning table.

Tuesday afternoon, the tower called me and said that our C-47 was in-bound from Kimpo and that Knight had asked that I meet them on arrival. All I could think of was another problem that had to be dealt with and I was in a sour mood as I waited at the Operations ramp for the C-47 to taxi up. When the cabin door of the C-47 swung open and the steps were lowered, Knight waved to me to come aboard -- and I had the shock of my life.

The cabin of the Gooney Bird was stocked to the ceiling with crates of food and, of all things, sides of beef.

"How the hell did you get all this stuff?" I asked.

Knight and Jones could not suppress their smiles.

"A call came in from your Marine friend up at UNC -- a Lt. Colonel Buckner," Knight answered. "I took it. Apparently, you and he had discussed food problems and how the Army seemed to be getting better stuff than we got. Anyhow, Buckner told me that a reefer ship had docked at Inchon and that, if we wanted to get to the head instead of the tail of the line, we needed to get our butts up there and do a little demanding. He said that the news of the docking of the reefer ship had already been passed out to the Army units and that they were beginning to move trucks to the port. With the typhoon on us and the need to get the C-47 out of the area, I decided to use the occasion to try to stock up on food while at Kimpo. Everything worked out great. And, in the process, I got more than normal as I found out that we were getting our rations based on a permanent party count provided to the depot by the Osan Wing -- no allowance was made for the large transient population at Kunsan. I upped the count to take care of our transients -- actually, I over-stated the transient numbers and no one questioned it."

"I'll be damned. That means that we have been living on partial rations. Do you think it was Wing stupidity or on purpose?"

"I think it was just stupidity."

"Well, now we have the answer to another of our problems. I'm just pissed that I didn't catch that problem myself. Damn good thing you came along. And is that orange crates I see?"

"And that ain't all," Jones stated. "But the good things are the sides of beef. We have enough that all the messes and clubs can serve steamship rounds as soon as we can get these sides butchered."

"Lt. Colonel Buck, the Kimpo Commander, helped us with trucks" Knight added, "and we made sure that he participated in the haul. He was pleased to beat all hell and he sent you his best regards."

"Frankly, Bob, I don't know what to say. I guess Tommy has learned the trade. And, appointing you as my food service officer was probably the best thing I ever did. Congratulations to both of you. There will not be a person here at Kunsan who will not be grateful for what you achieved. Now let me get out of the way and so you can get that frozen stuff you're carrying off the aircraft and into the reefers before we have a melt down."

That evening, I had a private meeting with Colonel Lee, Knight, Akers and Jones. Prior to the meeting, I gave Knight and Jones a hasty run down on the defense planning that had been accomplished.

To make the Saturday exercise realistic, I told Lee and the others that I would authorize a half dozen bursts of fifty caliber ammunition directed out to sea at about a fifteen degree angle. To insure that the sea area was clear, Akers was to fly the L-20 over the sea area and, on return to base, fire a green flare if there was no boat in range -- a red flare if there was a boat in the vicinity. If a red flare was observed, there would be no firing. And then I asked Lee if one of the ROK Army anti-aircraft guns could be cleared to fire a half dozen rounds seaward at an angle of fifteen degrees above the horizon -- this firing to coincide with our firing of the fifty bursts. He thought it could be arranged and he would talk further with Lieutenant Shik. Lee was enthused at the possibility. "It will do my men good to hear this fire," he said.

I then discussed the idea of having off the beach in range of carbine fire some silhouettes of North Korean invaders. Jones thought he could get them in place. If they were in place and if there were no Koreans seaward, I thought that the show might end with a volley of fire from those who manned the sea wall. The idea was accepted but it was further proposed that, if the ricochet area was clear, a burst or two from the fifties aimed at these targets be authorized.

Finally, someone suggested that we could add a real fire to the exercise -- something in which the Air Force and ROKAF fire units could participate in jointly. Frankly, I had not thought of that but the idea seemed to have merit.

Turning to Knight, I asked: "Are any of those on-base hootches still standing or have they all been dismantled and moved?"

"Most of them are gone -- two skeletons are still out there -- minus the metal roofing. It seems that what is left is worthless."

"Good. As a part of the exercise, plan to douse one of those skeletons with fuel oil -- not gasoline or JP-4 -- fuel oil. A few minutes after the sirens sound, set the structure afire and have the ROKAF and our own water unit respond. Hold the foam truck in position."

"This will be one great event," Lee commented.

Then, with Lee's agreement, I drafted a message.

TO:
314 AIR DIVISION
FIFTH AIR FORCE
ROKAF
ROK ARMY

THIS IS TO ADVISE THAT ON SATURDAY THE (DATE), AT APPROXIMATELY 1500 HOURS, A JOINT BASE DEFENSE EXERCISE WILL BE IMPLEMENTED. FROM 1300 HOURS TO 1700 HOURS, KUNSAN AIR BASE WILL BE CLOSED TO ALL TRAFFIC OTHER THAN EMERGENCY, AIR DEFENSE LAUNCHES AND RECOVERY, AND PRE-PLANNED OPERATIONS. DURING THE CITED TIME PERIOD, THE AIR SPACE WITHIN TEN (10) MILES OF KUNSAN AIR BASE IS DECLARED RESTRICTED TO 9,000 FEET. A NOTAM WILL BE ISSUED. DISTRIBUTE AS NECESSARY.

ORDERED JOINTLY BY COLONEL MOENCH (USAF) AND COLONEL LEE (ROKAF)

"Should this message not be classified," Lee asked.

"I think not," I answered. "Let us allow the world, and particularly our enemies, to know that we are prepared."

Lee smiled. I knew he understood. I wondered if he also knew that there was a North Korean spy ring on the base. I thought not.

Lee was about to depart when he came up with a suggestion.

"Would it be possible during this exercise for me to launch a formation of four of my F-86s and at the close of the exercise put on a demonstration over the base -- some low passes and some acrobatics?"

I thought a while. There were safety problems involved and I wanted no accidents to mar the event.

"I think it can be done but we need a plan and some ground rules. Have your Operations Officer meet with Major Akers and work

**out the details. If it can be arranged without endangering the exercise or the people on the ground, I think it is a good idea."**

**"If it is agreed that we can do it," Lee answered, "I will personally lead the flight."**

**After Lee had departed, I placed a call to Jack Hubbard at Osan. I anticipated that the transmission of the exercise message would cause some reaction, especially at Wing -- possibly at Fifth Air Force, and I wanted to build a fire break. I took pains to explain to Jack the nature of the exercise and read him the message. He agreed with the concept and that was all I needed to press on. He asked me to send him a "how did it go" report when the exercise was completed.**

**Capping the evening, I decided to write a letter to Paul Buckner, my Marine friend at UNC, especially to thank him for the assistance on the food acquisition but also to lay out the defense plan we had developed. I asked him for a quick comment. With communications back on line, the next morning, I would call him to explain my need for fast response to my letter -- my projected reassignment. He would suggest visiting Kunsan Air Base on the day of the practice alert and I would agree.**

**That night, at the Officers Club and for the first time since my arrival at Kunsan Air Base, there was singing.**

KUNSAN AIR BASE

**To the tune of:**
*Sweet Betsy From Pike*

***Here's to old Kunsan, it's a hell of a place.***
***The way things are run is a frigging disgrace***
***There's Captains, and Majors and a Light Colonel too,***
***With their thumbs up their asses and nothing to do.***

***They stand on the flight line and they scream and they shout.***
***They scream about things they know nothing about.***
***For all of the good they do, they might as well be***
***Shoveling shit on the Isle of Capri.***

***Yes, there were more verses!***

# A CONCLUSION

The days that followed formed a kaleidoscope into which so many things were squeezed in so short a time that sorting out what happened at what point is impossible.

The base defense plan went off splendidly. Somehow, the Korean community learned of the exercise and part of the Air Police problem was to control those who gathered in the vicinity of the sea wall to watch it. The crack and crackle of the guns in the final phase of the exercise was most impressive. When the ROK Army anti-aircraft boomed, instinctively most persons ducked. But the coup de grâce came when, after a show of acrobatics, Lee's formation made a low pass over the base from east to west and, when clear of the base, strafed the mud flats. I had not been advised of this finale and, for a moment, was pissed. Later, I would learn that my staff had set it up with Lee as a surprise for me.

The base defense exercise over, I felt certain that some messages would flow to North Korea -- if not in other directions. Whether there was or was not a connection, the Korean PX manager disappeared from the scene. Jones reported that, after an absence at work for two days, he and Wild had gone to the off-base house of the Korean manager and found it occupied by other Koreans. We would never learn what happened to the Korean PX manager. I wondered what now would happen to the North Korean spy ring -- would there be a new leader assigned to Kunsan Air Base?

When detail of the Kunsan base defense exercise reached the Wing Commander, he was furious -- especially regarding the fire to seaward. The result was a new regulation prohibiting such action.

Following the base defense exercise, I called my key staff together and told them that I would be leaving for a job at Osan -- that a new Commander for the base would be on hand by the time I departed. I then called Colonel Lee and told him I was leaving. He insisted on an immediate party in my honor. Lee assured me that I would not have to sing at my own party.

Packing up for the move to Osan was an emotional chore. It seemed as if I had just unpacked. Frankly, I did not want to leave Kunsan Air Base -- in the two months I had served as its Commander, it had become "my" air base. And there was so much still to be done.

**But I knew I could not worry about that. One thing about the military system was that reassignment, the equivalent of periodic divorce, was to be expected. That, from this constant changeover, good would come was to be expected as, normally, each new person tried to do better than the person he replaced.**

**When the time came for me to depart, a six-by pulled up to the Waldorf Astoria and loaded my footlockers to be taken to the flight line for the trip north. Akers and Peterson were to do the flying of the Gooney Bird. Knight brought the staff car to the Waldorf Astoria and he and I took one last drive around the base. I felt as if I was saying goodbye to an old friend.**

**Then we pulled up in front of Operations and, to my surprise, there was a large formation of men -- not a handful as when I arrived -- a real military formation of some size -- and one element was ROKAF with Colonel Lee in the command position. Unlike the rag tag of the first formation that greeted me at Kunsan Air Base, this formation "measured up."**

**As Knight maneuvered the staff car in front of the formations, someone called attention and all ranks "came to."**

**There was a lump in my throat. I saluted and suddenly I realized that a senior Air Force Sergeant, the Sergeant who had run the blade to cut the water path to the sea during the flood of Typhoon Number Two, had come forward. Resting in his hands was the first flag that had flown over the base after my arrival. He passed it to me with "best wishes" and then, grasping my hand, he said: *Colonel we needed you.***

**I could have received no greater reward.**

**I saluted the formations and then proceeded to the Gooney Bird. En route to the C-47, I shook hands with Knight and Colonel Lee. Then I passed between a double line of Air Police presenting arms -- one side was Air Force and one side was ROKAF. I was losing my base but I felt that I had won! Yet, there was moisture in my eyes.**

**In minutes, the Gooney Bird was airborne and heading for Osan. As I looked back at the base there were many conflicting thoughts -- the North Korean spy ring, the security situation, relations with the ROKAF and the Korean population, the housing and other facilities, recreational items, education programs, . . . . But, of all the thoughts that ran through my mind, foremost, I still wondered if the alleged nuclear weapons were really nuclear weapons or just Silver Bullets?**

# EPILOGUE

**The events illustrated in this story took place three and a half decades ago. In the intervening years, the U.S. military basing options in the Far East dwindled as accessibility to Okinawa, the Philippines and other areas, to include Japan, was lost or greatly diminished. The result was that Kunsan Air Base, identified as "K-8" and now known as "The Kun," became increasingly important as a fixture of U.S. and Korean strategy.**

**In the years between the events illustrated in this story and today, scores of base commanders and thousands of supporting staff and other personnel struggled to make Kunsan a better place.* Fighting always a military budget that often did not even allow for basics, step by step the facilities at Kunsan Air Base were improved. No single person can take credit for what transpired and the names of most of those who contributed have long been lost from the record.**

**Today the ROKAF is still at K-8 but now equipped with F-5 aircraft. Typically, the Air Force units operating out of K-8 are now flying F-16s and are on permanent assignment rather than simply rotating through the base. As this book goes to press, Kunsan Air Base is the home of the 8th Fighter Wing, *The Wolf Pack*.**

**Nuclear weapons, if there were any ever there, allegedly were removed some years ago. Nonetheless, war always seems somewhere in the near future. Now, however, K-8 is no longer dependent for defense on a handful of poorly equipped men -- instead, well-equipped ROK**

---

* Immediately following my departure from Kunsan Air Base, a major step forward in base improvement began with the deployment of Company "C" of the 802nd Engineer Battalion (Heavy Construction) to open a quarry at the base to obtain fill for road, runway and other improvements. A total of 18,000 cubic yards was removed during the following year. But this was only a start in the way of needed improvements at Kunsan Air Base. The major step forward was later triggered by the overt actions of North Korea during the 1966-1969 time frame when Kim Il-sung undertook a series of military actions across the DMZ, increased infiltration into the ROK, seized the USS Pueblo, and shot down a U.S. Navy EC-121-M. Countering these action by North Korea, the Fifth Air Force, tied politically to Japan and unable to employ directly the U.S. Air Forces stationed in that country, sent tactical air and support units to Kunsan and other ROK bases. Concurrently, the USAF realized that Kunsan Air Base was the only facility capable of serving as an alternate headquarters to Osan Air Base. The result was a flow of long-needed improvements to Kunsan Air Base -- improvements that have been steadily built upon as the tactical and strategic situation in the Pacific area altered.

Army troops provide a ring of security around The Kun and there are fences, pill boxes, radios, effective armaments and more. The old 40 millimeter guns of the Korean War time frame have been replaced with Gatling guns and missiles. Today, air defense units of the U.S. Army augment the Kunsan defenses. And now the radar and other support accouterments are high tech. No longer is communications dependent on vulnerable land lines or signaling by gun fire and runners. And, while MARS still exists but now termed the "Military Affiliate Radio System," today one can dial Kunsan Air Base from any telephone in the world.

*An 8th Fighter Wing F-16 aircraft in front of a concrete shelter -- Kunsan Air Base. 1995 (8FW)*

Many of the persons who now serve at The Kun were not born in the time frame of this story and all too many who were living at the time of this account are now dead. The world has changed, Korea has changed and Kunsan Air Base has changed.

At the time of this account, there was still the philosophy of the commander moving out on his own armed with a simple order and with initiative and responsibility residing mostly in himself. Today, all too many things are orchestrated and controlled in minute detail from central points to include the burgeoning establishment in Washington, D.C.

War planning, which in the time of this account was largely a few select brains working with pen and paper, is now a highly computerized undertaking. Logistics is mostly computer controlled. Surveillance emerges even from far away space. Spies and agents, however, still exist and perform essential roles for all parties. Security clearances, which had become an operational albatross at the time of this illustrative account, have managed to grow to phenomenal dimensions and only those who know of the problem can comment -- meaningful public comment, however, would be precluded by the system itself.

Kunsan City, which at the time of this account had a population of about 80,000, is now a city of over 200,000 but it still does not provide a "comfortable place to go." Lacking a first rate hotel, the second rate Kunsan Tourist Hotel of 113 rooms, while affording many accouterments, does not accept credit cards.

Seoul, which at the time of this account was a city of poverty and A-frames, is now a modern city with high rise buildings, traffic jams and all the dubious benefits of industry and a crowded population.

And no longer is the Republic of Korea a country oriented to primitive farming and a manufacturing base keyed to scrap metal. Today, South Korea is a major producer and exporter of high quality goods, agriculture has become modernized and the education of the population has moved into the 20th century.

The United Nations Command remains in place but the force at its disposal are those of the ROK and the U.S. Ground forces of these two countries remain entrenched along the DMZ and Osan continues as the center of air operations in Korea but its facilities have expanded and improved significantly. At the time of this account, the senior USAF officer at Osan was a Brigadier General -- today it is a Lieutenant General.

In the support area, the Koon-Ni range is still operational but now old car bodies form targets -- old car bodies that at the time of this account, if they existed, would have been quickly salvaged for metal and other elements.

At The Kun, the white chapel, the only new building at K-8 at the time of this account, has been twice replaced. Base recreational facilities, which were nil, now include a sports and fitness center with basketball, racquetball, exercise and weight room, sauna and more. In addition, there is a golf course, swimming pool, two softball diamonds, a 220-yard track, four lighted tennis courts and several picnic areas to include one overlooking the Yellow Sea.

Educational facilities, which were virtually non-existent, now include a center, a well-stocked library and courses provided by the University of Maryland and the Central Texas College. Associate degrees are offered through the Community College of the Air Force. Extension courses through the Extension Course Institute, the Air Command and Staff College, the Air War College, the Noncommissioned Officer Academy and other facilities are readily available.

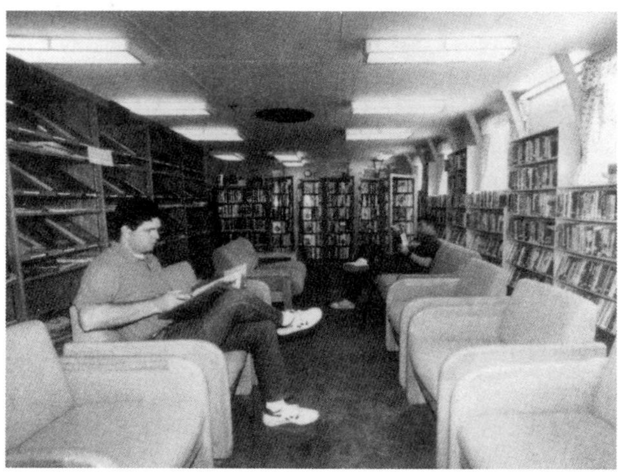

*Kunsan Air Base library. (8FW)*

Except for the old, single unit officer quarters, the living facilities at The Kun have all been replaced with modern multi-storied buildings *and the grass is neatly trimmed* -- while, in outward configuration, these old officer units still look about the same, they have been completely modernized and are serviced by paved roads with parking spaces for

*Kunsan Air Base swimming pool. (8FW)*

**occupant vehicles. For the enlisted men, no longer are there ramshackle, open, flood prone barracks -- now among the worst of lower grade situations is a shared bathroom. Master Sergeants get a private room and bath; Senior Master Sergeants and Chiefs get a private room, bath and bedroom.**

***One of the few remnants of Kunsan Air Base at the time of this account is the old officer quarters now modernized and serviced by paved roads. 1995 (8FW)***

***Multi-storied buildings and neatly trimmed grass -- today's K-8. (8FW***

Supporting both the military and civilian population of vehicles in Korea, good highways now criss-cross the country. Osan, which in the time frame of this account was a difficult full day's journey away by road, is now a comfortable three-hour drive from Kunsan. The highway from Kunsan Air Base to Kunsan City is, however, one of the most dangerous in Korea and nighttime driving by military personnel is restricted.

The main gate to Kunsan Air Base, which at the time of this account was a small roadside shack, is now an entrance marked by a substantial Korean style structure through which pass two lanes of vehicular traffic.

*The main gate entrance to Kunsan Air Base. Korean and American personnel man the gate. 1995 (8FW)*

The ROKAF, which at the time of this account was just being integrated into the whole of the base operation and defense scheme, now participates fully in base security. The ROK Army, which was only a distant resource to the defense of Kunsan Air Base, is now an integral partner. Vague and previously unfenced property lines are now clearly established and the absence of fencing no longer plagues the base. But defense in depth still requires the training and

**commitment of the greater base population as both the ROK and U.S. commanders recognize the importance of the base and the every day threat from North Korea and other sources.**

***A Kunsan Air Base property line protected by chain link fence with climb-over razor wire and backed up by razor wire concertina. Sensors add to the defense array. (8FW)***

**Unlike the situation set forth in this story, a time when there was insufficient money for a flag, adequate food, vehicle tires or even toilet paper, the "Can Do" Supply Squadron of the 8th Fighter Wing manages over 50,000 line items with a value of over $100 million. No longer is Kunsan Air Base driven by the need to make do with virtually nothing. And the Base Exchange that in the time frame of this account was a hand-to-mouth, shoestring affair operating out of a small wartime building is now equal to or better than most Stateside Exchanges.**

**For U.S. service personnel, Kunsan Air Base is still a one-year unaccompanied assignment which means that new faces are always arriving while the older, experienced personnel are forever departing. For many of the newly arriving persons, while Korea is now one of the more advanced countries in the world, it remains a cultural shock -- the**

language is strange, the customs are different and American schools, mostly oriented to Europe, provide to the typical arriving person little of the rich historical background of Korea.

But The Kun is still where K-8 was at the time of this account -- on a peninsula jutting out into the Yellow Sea with China to the West, Port Arthur at the north end of the Yellow Sea and North Korea about 120 miles north of The Kun and dominating the problem. Offshore, South and North Korean fishing boats still operate but now, instead of sails, they are larger and motorized. And, as always, the massive tide flows in and out.

World War II and then the Korean War brought the United States and the Republic of Korea together but it was only a first step. In culture and more, there was then and there still remains a vast difference between these two countries. But there is now a significant Korean population in the United States with many of the students of those who came to America challenging the proficiency of those who have long lived in this country. And, in Korea there is an ever-growing, highly educated, English-speaking element of the population. Day-by-day, the focus of both countries emerges stronger on common points and day-by-day the cultural and other differences of the past moderate.

Life changes while much of it remains the same. Today, persons stationed at The Kun still worry that their housekeepers, laborers and others might be North Korean agents. Adding to the dimension of worry and alertness of the Kunsan Air Base residents is the continued infiltration of the ROK by North Korea -- infiltration countered effectively by the forces of the ROK.

More significant, the overt and covert military threat to The Kun persists as in this account -- only now modernized and more substantial. Those whose job it is to worry about the threat from North Korea, from infiltration and for base and air defense, share the same worries today that were present at the time of this account. One advantage these "new kids on the block" have is that there is more understanding of the problem, more commitment and more in the way of resources with which to work. No longer is the Air Force Commander virtually on his own in acquiring the resources necessary to do the job. No longer is the quality of U.S. personnel so suspect. No longer are kitchens dependent on converted 55 gallon drums. No longer is food for the military population dependent on now-and-then supply flights to Japan, ice cream flown from Kimpo, convoys that get lost on treacherous and unmarked roads or the inventiveness and connivance of a few. At The Kun it is no longer necessary to search out

**an unused barracks bed for transients for now good transient facilities exist -- and senior persons actually do spend more than a few short hours at the base.**

**Bringing order out of the uncertainties of decades ago, there is a meaningful Status of Forces Agreement between the Republic of Korea and the Unites States -- an understanding that came into being during the time of President Park Chung Hee and which has since been expanded upon. Further, there has developed detailed host-tenant agreements that prescribe unit and individual relations on Kunsan Air Base and beyond. But that has meant that the hip-shooting, "do it as you like" rules of the past have been replaced by organizational and operational order.**

**Many of the "new kids on the block" now assigned to The Kun, be they American or ROK, may view the place as terrible but, from the perspective of three and a half decades ago, The Kun really has become "The Riviera of Korea" it has long been proclaimed to be.**

**Kunsan Air Base, K-8, The Kun has a great history -- a history dating back for over a half century. Someday, someone will write it.**

***The 8th Fighter Wing began its career as the 8th Pursuit Group in 1918, flew in WW I, later flew air mail across the U.S. In WW II, as the 8th Fighter Group, it operated in the Pacific and, as the 8th Fighter Wing, it was the first air unit committed to the Korean War. In the Vietnam war, the unit picked up the name "Wolf Pack." In 1974, the Wing took up residence at Kunsan Air Base. (8FW)***

# KUNSAN AIR BASE

# K-8

# THE KUN

# WELCOME TO THE RIVIERA OF KOREA

## APPENDIX A

# ABBREVIATIONS, ACRONYMS AND MILITARY SLANG

**8FW = 8th Fighter Wing**
**201 File = Personal records file**
**A-26 = aircraft designation (Invader)-- attack aircraft later designated B-26**
**AB = Air Base**
**ABS = Air Base Squadron**
**AC&W = Aircraft Control and Warning**
**ACLU = American Civil Liberties Union**
**AD = Air Division**
**AFAG = Air Force Advisory Group**
**AFB = Air Force Base**
**AFKN = Air Forces Korean Network**
**Annyong hasipnika = Korean greeting -- "on your horse amigo" (slang)**
**ASAP = as soon as possible**
**AWC = Air War College**
**B-26 = aircraft designation -- medium bomber (Marauder or Invader)**
**B-4 bag = a military traveling bag**
**BOQ = bachelor officer's quarters**
**Broken Arrow = a nuclear accident report**
**Buddy system = the pairing of guards and other persons to prevent individual action -- not to be confused with the same term used to stipulate the pairing off of Americans with Koreans for on-the-job soldier training**
**Bug Out = hasty retreat (military slang)**
**C-45 = aircraft designation -- transport**
**C-46 = aircraft designation -- transport**
**C-47 = aircraft designation -- transport**
**C-54 = aircraft designation -- transport**
**CG = Commanding General**
**Chicom = Chinese Communists or Communist China**
**Chink = Chinese person (slang)**
**CIA = Central Intelligence Agency**
**CINC = Commander in Chief**
**CINCUNC = Commander in Chief, United Nations Command**
**CINCPACAF = Commander in Chief, Pacific Air Forces**
**CINCUSAFE = Commander in Chief, United States Air Forces, Europe**
**C.O. = Commanding Officer**
**COMAFK = Commander, Air Froces Korea**
**COMINT = Communications Intelligence**
**COMUSFK = COMUSKOREA**
**COMUSKOREA = Commander, United States Forces, Korea**
**CON = control, e.g. ground control (GND CON)**
**CYA = cover your ass**
**Daddy Rabbit = someone in charge; someone running things; often CIA**
**DCS = Deputy Chief of Staff**

**DMZ = Demilitarized Zone separating North and South Korea**
**Doc = Doctor (slang)**
**DOD = Department of Defense**
**DV = Distinguished Visitor**
**EC-121M = aircraft designation -- electronic intelligence gathering**
**ELEV = elevation**
**ELINT = Electronic Intelligence**
**EM = enlisted man (or men)**
**EMT = electrical metal tubing**
**ER = Efficiency Rating also Efficiency Report**
**F-5 = aircraft designation -- fighter**
**F-16 = aircraft designation -- fighter**
**F-86 = aircraft designation -- fighter**
**F-100 = aircraft designation -- fighter**
**FBI = Federal Bureau of Investigation**
**FEAF = Far East Air Force**
**Feather Merchant = a civilian; a civil servant**
**FIGMO = "Fuck you Joe, I got my orders."**
**File 13 = a theoretical trash can**
**Form 5 = flight record**
**G = gravity unit**
**GCA = Ground Controlled Approach**
**GFE = Government Furnished Equipment**
**G.I. = Government Issue -- anything military -- also an enlisted person**
**G.I.s = diarrhea (military slang)**
**GND = ground (see CON)**
**Gooney Bird = C-47**
**Grunt = a ground soldier, usually infantry**
**HEAT = high explosive anti-tank (warhead or weapon)**
**Hootch = also spelled as *hooch* -- as used here it is any front line place where Americans live -- also the dwelling of a prostitute -- it comes from the Japanese *uchi* (house) -- the spelling as *hootch* was selected to differentiate this term from *hooch* meaning homemade liquor -- the latter derived from the Chinook *hoochenoo***
**Hq. = Headquarters**
**HRA = Historical Research Agency, Maxwell AFB, Alabama**
**ID = identification (normally a card)**
**IFR = Instrument Flight Rules**
**IG = Inspector General**
**Instant Cement = Lomotil (military slang)**
**J-5 = Plans and Policy in a joint staff**
**J-51 = a unit in J-5**
**JAG = Judge Advocate General**
**JCS = Joint Chiefs of Staff**
**Josan = a girl; a woman; a prostitute -- now offensive language**
**JP-4 = a jet fuel designation**
**KATUSA = Korean Augmentation to the U.S. Army -- Koreans used as "fillers" to U.S. Army units (normally untrained)**
**KMAG = Korean Military Advisory Group -- also "Kiss My Ass Goodbye"**
**L-4 = aircraft designation -- liaison**

L-5 = aircraft designation -- liaison
L-20 = aircraft designation -- liaison
Lt. = Lieutenant
MAAG = Military Assistance Advisory Group
MARS = Military Amateur Radio Station -- now Military Affiliate Radio System
MATS = Military Air Transport Service
Mickey Mouse = covert or intelligence operations; something secret
MIG -- Soviet fighter aircraft
Moose Call = a wide-open combat unit party with hostesses -- "moose" is a corruption of the Japanese word for woman -- now offensive language
NATO = North Atlantic Treaty Organization
NCO = non-commissioned officer
NE/SW = northeast/southwest alignment -- usually a runway
No sweat = no trouble; I can handle it
No sweat pills = an antibiotic taken as a preventative
NOFORN = Not for Foreign Nationals
NOTAM = Notice to Airmen
Nukes = nuclear weapons
Number 1 = the best (Number 10 translates to the worst) -- this is opposite of some numerical values of worth
Ops = Operations
P-51 = fighter aircraft later termed F-51
PACAF = Pacific Air Forces
PSP = pierced steel plank
PT boat = fast, light patrol craft
PX = Post Exchange -- equivalent to BX or Base Exchange
R & R = rest and recreation (sometimes "rest and recuperation" or "rest and relaxation")
RAF = Royal Air Force
Ration = one day's food for one person -- typically three meals
Rehab = rehabilitation (also repair)
Ret = Retired
RHIP = rank has its privileges
ROK = Republic of Korea
ROKAF = Republic of Korea Air Force
RON = remain over night
RWY = runway
SAC = Strategic Air Command
SCARWAF = Special Category Army personnel with Air Force
Siberia = the worst possible assignment
Silver Bullet = an inert nuclear weapon
Slicky = a thief
Slickied = stealing
S.O.B. = son-of-a-bitch
SOG = Special Operations Group
SOP = Standard Operating Procedure
T-6 = trainer aircraft
TB = tuberculosis
TELEX = telegraphic message
TV = television

**UC-64 = aircraft designation -- utility cargo aircraft**
**UN = United Nations**
**UNC = United Nations Command**
**U.S. = United States**
**USAF = United States Air Force**
**USAFE = United States Air Forces in Europe**
**U.S. EUCOM = United States European Command**
**USFK = United States Forces Korea**
**U.S.M.C. = United States Marine Corps**
**USN = United States Navy**
**USO = United Services Organization**
**USOM = United States Operations Mission**
**VD = venereal disease**
**VIP = Very Important Person**
**VFR = Visual Flight Rules**
**VOQ = Visiting Officers Quarters**
**WW II = World War II**

## APPENDIX B

# THE CHARACTERS

**The named parties cited in this illustrative account are fictitious unless printed below in *italics*.**

**The following are in the general order as they emerge in the foreword, footnote and text.**
**Military grade is as of the time of the event.**
**Photo credits are not here listed.**
**The term Kunsan as used here or in text may relate to Kunsan Air Base (K-8), Kunsan City or the general area of Kunsan -- below, Kunsan Air Base is cited as *Kunsan AB*.**

***Moench, John O., Colonel, USAF, author and Commander of KunsanAB***
***Smith, Charles B., Lt. Colonel, U.S. Army (Task Force Smith), Korean War***
***Eisenhower, Dwight D., General of the Armies, U.S. Army***
***Washington, George, General, first President of the United States***
***Schwartzkopf, Norman, General, U.S. Army, Desert Storm***
***Wainright, Jonathan, General, U.S. Army, WW II, Philippines***
***Mike, a Secretary @ Osan AB***
***Annie, a Korean waitress @ Kunsan AB***
***Moench, Mary C., (wife of John O. Moench)***
***Peterson, Chesley G., Colonel, USAF, President of AWC Class and the youngest Colonel in the Air Force***
***Emrick, Paul S., "Stan," Major General, USAF***
***Todd, Walter E., Lt. General, USAF***
***Tate, Robert E., Major General, USAF***
***Smith, Frederick H., Jr, Major General, USAF***
***Norstad, Lauris, General, USAF***
***Truman, Harry S., President of the United States***
***Johnson, Louis A., Secretary of Defense***
***Forrestal, James V., Secretary of Defense***
***Vandenberg, Hoyt S., General, USAF***
***Bradley, Omar N., General of the Army, U.S. Army.***
***Collins, Joseph Lawton, General, U.S. Army***
***Chiang Kai-shek, Generalissimo and President of China***
***MacArthur, Douglas, General of the Army, U.S. Army***
***Hodge, John R., Major General, U.S. Army***
***Rhee, Syngman, President of The Republic of Korea***
***Roberts, Lynn W., Major General, U.S. Army***
***Farthing, William E., Major General, USAF***
**Bill, friend in Director of Transportation, Hq, USAF**
***Asahina, Goro, AKA "Smiley" -- bandleader at Tachikawa Officers Club***
***Miller, Glen, WW II band leader***
***Rhee, Mrs. -- wife of President Rhee***
***Pal, Radnabinod, Justice, India***
**Davidson, Walter, Lt. Colonel, USAF -- first Deputy Base Commander @ Kunsan AB**
**Pastiak, Joseph "Joe," Captain, USAF -- JAG @ Kunsan AB**

*Smith, Margaret Chase, U.S. Senator*
*O'Donnell, Rosie, General, USAF, CINCPACAF*
**Musgrave, Colonel, USAF -- Wing Commander @ Osan AB Base**
**Young, Paul, Master Sergeant -- First Sergeant @ Kunsan AB**
**Lee, Miss -- Korean Secretary to Commander @ Kunsan AB**
**Akers, Thomas "Tom," Major, USAF -- Operations Officer @ Kunsan AB**
**Peterson, Steve, Major, USAF -- Supply and Transportation Officer @ Kunsan AB**
**Benson, Paul, Major, USAF -- Communications and Electronics Officer @ Kunsan AB**
**Wild, Peter, Captain, USAF -- Head of Air Police Section @ Kunsan AB**
**Polk, Jesse, Captain, USAF -- Engineering Officer @ Kunsan AB**
**Grossman, Able, Lieutenant, USAF -- Dentist @ Kunsan AB**
**Jones, Thomas "Tommy," Second Lieutenant -- Administrative Officer, later Executive Officer @ Kunsan AB**
**Joyce, James, Brig. General, USAF -- Commander, 314th AD @ Osan AB**
*Samuel, John S. Colonel, USAF -- Commander, 322nd Bombardment Group (M) in WW II*
**Kim, Mister, Head of Korean guards @ Kunsan AB officers area**
**Johnson, George, Colonel, USAF -- serving in DCS/Materiel, Headquarters, USAF**
*Michele and Jeff -- daughter and son of John and Mary Moench*
**Collins, Father -- Catholic Chaplain @ Kunsan AB**
**Anderson, Amos, Sergeant, USAF -- Airman @ Kunsan AB**
*Patton, George S., General, U.S. Army*
**Butler, Paul, Sergeant, USAF -- Weather Officer @ Kunsan AB**
**Turnbull, John, Major, USAF -- Initial Senior Officer, Nuclear Alert Aircraft @ Kunsan AB**
**Phillips, Alexander, "Alex," -- Engineer and Crew Chief @ Kunsan AB**
*Lovejoy, Josephine F. -- Secretary @ Kunsan AB during Korean War*
*Chase, George H. Lt., U.S. Army @ Kunsan AB during Korean War*
*Eisenhower, Dwight D., General of the Army, U.S. Army*
**Willis, Stan, Sergeant, USAF -- Fire and Rescue Chief @ Kunsan AB**
**Barbara -- Secretary to General Joyce, 314AD @ Osan AB**
**Kincaid, Walter, Colonel, USAF -- Director of Materiel, 314AD @ Osan AB**
**Hubbard, Jack, Colonel, USAF -- Director of Operations, 314AD @ Osan AB**
*Bolger, Daniel P, Major, U.S. Army, author*
*Bonesteel, Charles H., III, General, USA -- CINCUNC plus COMUS Forces Korea and CG Eighth Army*
*Hetherington, Mary -- Secretary @ Kunsan AB during Korean War*
*Tae-won-goon, father of the last king of the Lee Dynasty*
*Pyle, Ernie, WW II journalist*
**Wright, Mr. -- an Australian -- PX Manager @ Kunsan AB**
**Baker, Charles, Captain, USAF -- Flight Surgeon @ Kunsan AB**
**Smith, Reginald, Airman @ Kunsan AB**
**Short, William, Lieutenant, USAF -- Deputy to Major Paul Benson, Communications and Electronics @ Kunsan AB**
**Jake -- a friend in Japan**
**Preston, Lieutenant, USAF -- pilot assigned to staff of Major Akers @ Kunsan AB**
**Buck, George, Lt. Colonel, USAF -- Commander @ Kimpo AB**
**Jenkins, Albert "Al," Colonel, USAF -- Chief, ROKAF Military Advisory Group, Seoul, Korea**
**Olson, Mr. -- Counter Intelligence**

**Buckner, Paul, Lt. Colonel, USMC -- CINCUNC staff planner**
***Nazzaro, Joseph J., General, USAF -- CINCPACAF***
**Newcomb, Charles, Major, USAF -- Commander @ Taegu AB**
**Pepperman, William, Mr. -- civilian inspector, 314 AD @ Osan AB**
**Wilcox, Stanley, Sergeant, USAF -- senior baseball person @ Kunsan AB**
**Shingleton, Raymond "Ray," -- JAG @ Osan AB**
***Yoon Chun Kun, Major General, ROK Army, First Military District Command***
**Kim, Mr. and Mrs., Korean father and mother of deceased boy**
**Lee, Colonel, ROKAF -- ROKAF Commander @ Kunsan AB**
**Wade, John, 2nd Lieutenant, USAF -- Deputy to Captain Wild, Air Police @ Kunsan AB**
**Knight, Robert "Bob," Lt. Colonel, second Deputy Commander @ Kunsan AB**
**Joe, Bartender @ Kunsan AB**
**Berkowitz, Staff Sergeant, USAF -- Air Policeman @ Kunsan AB**
**Dupont, Sergeant, USAF -- Air Policeman @ Kunsan AB**
**Kitchens, Major, USAF -- New Senior Officer, Nuclear Alert Aircraft @ Kunsan AB**
***MacArthur, U.S. Ambassador to Japan***
**Murphy, Captain -- new Catholic Chaplain @ Kunsan AB**
**Lieutenant Shik, ROK Army -- anti-aircraft Commander @ Kunsan AB**
***MacArthur, Douglas, General of the Armies, U.S. Army***
***Park Chung Hee, President of the Republic of Korea***